THE CITY & GUILDS TEXTBOOK
LEVEL 2 VRQ DIPLOMA IN
HAIRDRESSING

About City & Guilds

City & Guilds is the UK's leading provider of vocational qualifications, offering over 500 awards across a wide range of industries, and progressing from entry level to the highest levels of professional achievement. With over 8500 centres in 100 countries, City & Guilds is recognised by employers worldwide for providing qualifications that offer proof of the skills they need to get the job done.

Equal opportunities

City & Guilds fully supports the principle of equal opportunities and we are committed to satisfying this principle in all our activities and published material. A copy of our equal opportunities policy statement is available on the City & Guilds website.

First edition 2012
Reprinted 2013

ISBN 978 0 85193 207 1

Edited by Tom Guy
Text design by Purpose
Cover design by Select Typesetters Ltd
Typeset by GreenGate Publishing Services
Printed in Croatia by Zrinski

British Library Cataloguing in Publication Data

A catalogue record for this book is available from the British Library.

Publications

For information about or to order City & Guilds support materials, contact 0844 534 0000 or centresupport@cityandguilds.com. You can find more information about the materials we have available at www.cityandguilds.com/publications.

Every effort has been made to ensure that the information contained in this publication is true and correct at the time of going to press. However, City & Guilds' products and services are subject to continuous development and improvement and the right is reserved to change products and services from time to time. City & Guilds cannot accept liability for loss or damage arising from the use of information in this publication.

City & Guilds
1 Giltspur Street
London EC1A 9DD

T 0844 543 0033
www.cityandguilds.com
publishingfeedback@cityandguilds.com

CONTENTS

ACKNOWLEDGEMENTS

City & Guilds would like to sincerely thank the following:

For invaluable hairdressing expertise
Diane Mitchell, Lou Hockings, Gail Brown and Alison Atkinson

For their help with the cover photoshoot
Andrew Buckle (photography); Kate MacLellan (hairdressing);
Kym Menzies-Foster (make-up); Natalie Mockett (model)

For their help with taking pictures
Hugh Baird College: Denise Johnson, Stephen Beckley, Susan Billington,
Diane Flanagan, Jane Clappison, Siobhan Parr, Karen Critchley, Joanne
Walsh, Eilidh Sanders, Tim Bolton, Sarah Gannon, Becky Thow, Toni
Cansfield, Hayley Cater, Cara Wall, Stephanie Connolly, Chloe Lynch,
Lizzy Woodward, Michael D. A. Johnson, Amy Sheridan, Stevie O'Toole,
Ray Wright, Lewis Mahei

For contributing their photographs
American Crew, Beauty Express, Bed Head, Goldwell, Lynne Webbster,
Wella

Picture credits
Every effort has been made to acknowledge all copyright holders as
below and the publishers will, if notified, correct any errors in future
editions.

The Academy Enfield Training Services: pp9, 10, 19, 37, 66–67, 103, 126, 143,
146–147, 150, 151, 152, 160, 169, 197, 198, 203, 221, 240, 242, 276, 280, 281, 282,
283, 284, 291, 301, 321, 332, 371, 459, 416, 464; **Acclaim:** p233; **Alamy:** © Alex Hinds
pXIII; © BlueMoon Stock p366; © Caro p390; © Catchlight Visual Services p261; ©
EIGHTFISH p222; © Greg Balfour Evans p261; © Henry Westheim Photography p222; ©
Jeffrey Blackler p6; © Kathy deWitt 261; © Keith Morris p221; © Lisa F. Young p333; ©
Maximilian Weinzierl p369; © mmadpic p261; © Paul Broadbent p397; © Paul Hakimata
p105; © Paul Maguire p332; © picturesbyrob p6; © PYMCA p6; © Simon Dack Archive
p14; © Stock Connection Blue p105; **American Crew:** p356; **Aroma Truth:** p438;
BeautyExpress.co.uk: pp437, 438; **Bed Head:** p421; **Blushes:** pp14, 411, 415, 419,
420, 422, **Cambridge Regional College:** pp5, 10, 64, 91, 92, 122, 124, 129, 190, 219,
241, 254, 315, 316, 327, 328, 329, 331, 338, 339, 340, 341, 343, 344, 345, 346, 347,
348, 349, 350, 351, 352, 353, 354, 355, 357, 361, 362, 363, 364, 365, 372, 373, 375,
376, 377, 381, 411, 412, 414, 415, 417, 419, 423, 424, 432, 438, 449, 450, 454; **Camera
Press:** © Benainous Alain pp289–290; © Chris Ashford pp289–290; © James Murphy/
LNC pp289–290; © James Veysey pp289–290; **Central Training Group:** pp19, 51, 66,
141, 142, 144, 146–147, 197, 198, 199, 213, 215, 216, 296, 268, 269, 286, 306, 307,
308, 310, 311; **Cheynes Training:** ppXIV, XV, 16, 77, 153, 154, 155-156, 157, 158, 159,
160, 162, 163, 164, 165, 167, 169, 214, 228, 285, 288, 304, 318, 396, 414, 495;
Concerca: pp71, 334; **Ellisons:** p269; **Epping Forest College:** ppXIV, XVI, 4, 20, 22,
24, 35, 42, 20, 21, 52, 53, 56, 63, 65, 93, 94, 99, 103, 115, 120, 127, 157, 174, 260,
277-8, 279, 281, 282, 305, 306, 307, 364; **Fotolia:** © Alan Stockdale pp54–55; © Hart
photography pp54–55; © Jenny Thompson pp54–55; **Fellowship for British
Hairdressing, National Hairdresser's Federation, The Hairdressing Council:** p7;
**The Freelance Hair and Beauty Federation, Hair and Beauty Benevolent, Hair
and Beauty Industry Authority:** p8; **Getty Images:** pp146–147, 276, 473; **Glow
Images:** p243; **Goldwell:** pp2, 20, 52, 104, 115, 123, 174, 179, 122, 238, 277–278,
422, 436, 497; **Hair Tools:** p45; **Havering College:** pp10, 19, 21, 37, 43, 45, 49, 51, 52,
61, 63, 102, 103, 105, 107, 108, 109, 114, 116, 120, 126, 130, 131, 133, 137, 168, 212,
217, 224, 269, 270, 321, 421, 465, 466, 467, 469, 473, 478, 480; **Head Gear:** p5;

ABOUT THE AUTHOR

My mum is a hairdresser and I grew up wanting to be a hairdresser too. I started working in a salon the day after I left school, 23 years ago, and completed the youth training scheme (YTS). I then travelled to London, struggling on £65 a week and paying £48 for fares – but when you want something badly enough, you are prepared to work hard for it and I now have a career to be proud of.

I started teaching and assessing 15 years ago, where my love of hairdressing and training has gone from strength to strength. I have taught both full-time and part-time students, from NVQ Levels 1, 2 and 3 and VRQ Levels 1 and 2. In my current role as a Senior Manager and Group Head of Curriculum, I train new assessors, carry out teaching observations and develop the curriculum across all the centres at Central Training Group.

Sharing my skills and knowledge with new learners throughout my teaching career has been a highlight. Watching someone master the art of hairdressing or achieving summative assessments is what training is all about, and I love it.

Keryl Titmus

I've worked in this fascinating industry for 35 years, beginning my career as an apprentice and working my way through to salon management before moving into education. My career has been both varied and exciting, and I've had the privilege of working with and meeting some incredibly talented people.

The hairdressing and beauty industry is a major employer in the UK, supporting 35,000 salons, and providing employment for 250,000 professionals and trainees. City & Guilds embraces the passion of the industry and strives to provide support and learning resources to help you achieve your goals in life. This textbook is a perfect accompaniment to your City & Guilds Level 2 Hairdressing or Barbering qualification.

Keryl Titmus, the author of this textbook, is one of the industry's experts; she has drawn on her experience as a tutor by sharing learning methods through handy hints, activities and revision exercises to help you build an in-depth knowledge of the subject. Keryl has also included detailed step-by-step guides, which walk you through a wide range of practical skills. You will find everything you need and more in this textbook, so use it as a reference and a guide, enjoy the creativity of being a hairdresser, and embrace every opportunity that comes your way. Good luck!

Diane Mitchell
Hairdressing Portfolio Manager, City & Guilds

HOW TO USE THIS TEXTBOOK

You will find that your City & Guilds VRQ Level 2 Hairdressing textbook is laid out in the same way as your City & Guilds VRQ Level 2 Hairdressing logbook to aid your navigation and understanding of both.

Each chapter in your textbook covers everything you will need to understand in order to complete your assignments or online tests and practical assessments.

Throughout this textbook you will see the following features:

HANDY HINTS

Revisit Unit 203 for more in-depth information on consulting with your client.

Handy hints are particularly useful tips that can assist you in your revision or help you remember something important.

INDUSTRY TIP

It is your duty to maintain the health and safety of yourself and others who may be affected by your actions.

Industry tips are designed to smooth your passage into the workplace by increasing your awareness.

Adverse

Unfavourable, poor or difficult, not suitable

Words in bold in the text are explained in the margin to aid your understanding.

WHY DON'T YOU...

Why don't you – These hints suggest activities for you to try to help you practise and learn.

ACTIVITY

Activities – The activities help to test your understanding and learn from your colleagues' experiences.

 SmartScreen 210 handout 2

SmartScreen – These icons refer to the City & Guilds SmartScreen resources and activities. Ask your tutor for your log-in details.

At the end of each unit are some 'Test your knowledge' questions. These are mostly multiple choice questions, designed to prepare you for your assignments or online tests and to identify any areas where you might need further training or revision.

Some units are followed by a case study on an industry expert, who explains the background to their career, and offers helpful advice in their specialist area.

ARE YOU READY FOR WORK?

If you are not yet working in a salon, you may decide you want to, either during your training or once you have achieved your qualification. Preparing for an interview is as important as the interview itself and you need to promote your strengths, without drawing attention to your weaker areas.

The potential employer's first impression of you will be your CV and your covering letter – you want to ensure your potential employer reads these and places you at the top of the pile for interviews, and not at the top of the waste paper bin.

Mark and Jo Bidston are the salon owners of 'FX Hair and Colour Studio', in Leigh-on-Sea, Essex. Mark is the hairstylist director, whilst Jo manages the salon, organises the staff training and interviews prospective employees. Together they make a great team, focusing on the needs of the client and also the training needs of their team.

Mark and Jo Bidston

Both Mark and Jo work closely with local schools and hairdressing training providers/colleges. They offer work experience placements in their salon for 14–16 year olds completing their VRQ Level 2 Diploma in Hair Services (as well as post-16 year olds completing their apprenticeship), and they visit training providers giving advice to learners.

Mark offers advice on:

- what you can expect from the industry/employers
- what the industry/employers expect from you.

Working in a salon

Jo offers advice on:

- how to write a cover letter
- how to write a CV; including what not to write
- preparing for the interview and what to expect
- mock interviews and interview techniques.

JO'S COVER LETTER AND EMAIL TIPS

If you send a CV through the post to salons or attach a CV to an email, you must make sure that your covering letter or email is written well. It should be brief but to the point, including only what a potential employer may want to read about you.

Follow Jo's simple tips:

- Make sure you proofread what you've written, ideally asking another person to read it through; checking for punctuation, spelling and grammar. It is not acceptable to use lower case 'i' instead of 'I' just because you're sending your CV via email.
- Explain the salon position you are applying for and why you would like the job.

Applicant writing a CV

- Briefly describe why you would 'love' to work at the salon and join their team, but do not go over the top! You could drop in a factual comment about the salon, demonstrating to the employer that you know about or have researched their business.
- Briefly list some of your skills that show you would make a suitable candidate for the job role and employee for their business.
- Briefly state your most recent qualifications or relevant training that could pitch you above the rest of the applicants.
- Avoid mentioning too much personal information that is not relevant to the job role.
- Don't forget to attach your CV.

> **HANDY HINTS**
>
> You may find the following websites useful for further hints and tips, or for CV templates:
>
> **www.direct.gov.uk**
>
> **www.jobsearch.co.uk**
>
> **www.cvtips.com**
>
> **www.careersandjobsuk.com**

Advert for a salon assistant

JO'S CURRICULUM VITAE TIPS

When writing your CV, the layout is extremely important. Make sure the presentation is balanced and the contents are clear and clean; ideally all on one page. Many applicants list their experience in date order, oldest to most recent; whereas most employers will want to know the most recent qualifications, training and job roles first, as these are the most crucial and important for the current application.

> **HANDY HINTS**
>
> Do not rely on your PC's spell checker – ask someone else to read it through for you (ideally your college tutor), or re-read it a day or two later, when the contents are not fresh in your mind.

Follow Jo's steps to successful CV writing:

1 **Contact details:** Name, address and telephone number. Only list your email address if it reads professionally and you regularly check your emails. Do not use an email address if it is something like: hotbabe@hotmail.com – save this email for your friends only! Remember, adding your age or date of birth is not mandatory; this is due to 'age discrimination' so you can choose whether or not you want to put your date of birth on your CV.

2 **Job roles:** If you are already employed or have worked in a salon, list your most recent job first. Describe the duties you carried out, demonstrating your knowledge of the industry – especially if this highlights your capabilities and matches your skills and experience with the employer's needs. State the start and end date of each job role. If the reason for leaving this job is positive and you are looking to move on for career progression, you should write your reason for leaving. If you have been dismissed or 'hated' your line manager, you'd be best leaving these details off your CV.

3 **Qualifications:** Start with your most recent qualifications or predicted grades. Then give details of the school/college you attended, listing your leave date. You should include any other qualifications or attributes that could be relevant to the job position you are applying for, such as: first aid qualifications, computer courses, being a head girl/boy, etc.

Make a good impression – hand deliver your CV to the salon.

4 Additional personal information: Add some personal details about you, such as hobbies, clubs you attend/are a member of, achievements and anything else that may show commitment and trustworthiness. You should avoid listing your interests as 'clubbing or partying'; instead state that you enjoy socialising with family and friends. Social skills are important within the hairdressing industry – clubbing and partying could imply you may have time off work on Saturdays due to tiredness, or worse still, a hangover.

5 References: Finally you need to add two names and addresses for references: one professional reference – from an employer/work experience provider, or school/college tutor. The second reference can be an additional professional reference or a personal reference. Under no circumstances should your personal reference be a family member – they are likely to be biased, and potential employers are very unlikely to take the reference seriously.

Training opportunities – product knowledge training

JO'S INTERVIEW TIPS

Follow Jo's simple steps to preparing for that all important interview:

- Double check the interview date and time.
- Research the company before the interview – aim to know everything there is to know about the salon – the services they offer, the size of the business or how long they have been trading for.
- Think about why you would like to work for the company – you may get asked this question.
- Prepare a few questions to ask the interviewer, such as: why the position is vacant, what your key responsibilities will be, what training opportunities you will be given, what the expected time length of your training is, what the company's growth plans are, how would they describe the culture and atmosphere of the salon and the team and, once qualified, what will the financial opportunities be and what career paths will be available to you.

- Know how to get to the interview via public transport (if relevant) to ensure you arrive in good time.
- Work out what time you need to leave home, in order to arrive 10–15 minutes before the time of your interview.
- Tell someone where you are going and roughly when you expect to return.
- Be well-presented – especially your clothes and hair.
- Turn off your mobile phone prior to walking into the salon.
- Resist the temptation of smoking a cigarette before your interview and ensure your breath is fresh.
- During the interview listen to the questions, and if you do not understand what is being asked, say so.
- Be honest with your answers and your expected exam grades.
- If you are still at school/college, let the interviewer know if you can work weekends, school holidays or evenings.
- If you are keen to work for the company – show it.
- After the interview, write down any questions that you felt you could have answered better and work on these answers.

A trial day helps you to demonstrate your skills.

HANDY HINT

Ask if there is an opportunity for a trial day, where you can prove how you work in a team environment.

JO'S INTERVIEW QUESTIONS

Listed below are some examples of the sort of questions that Jo asks her interviewees, and what other employers may ask you during an interview:

Beginning of the interview – The calming questions; employers are aware that people get nervous when being interviewed. A good interviewer will try to put you at ease, in order the get the most from you during an interview.

A well-presented interviewee

- How was your journey here?
- Tell me about yourself.

Past questions – The interviewer is now trying to get to know you – sell yourself, but be honest.

- What achievements are you most proud of?
- How IT literate are you?
- What changes would you make if you could go back in time?

Future opportunity questions – The employer is now trying to decide if you are suitable for their business.

- What do you know about us?
- Why have you applied for this position?
- What can you bring to this job/company?
- What are your long-term career plans?
- What exactly are your career goals?

Personality questions – The employer is still trying to decide how well you will fit into the company.

- What is your attitude to authority?
- How would you deal with a difficult client?
- What do you do with your spare time?
- What motivates you?
- What would you do if you won the lottery?
- What is your definition of success?
- How well can you handle stress?

Finishing questions – Your final chance to make a good impression.

- What questions do you have for me?
- Why should I choose you?

Employer and applicant – interview in progress

Now off you go and prepare for your interview – Good luck and be positive!

201
WORKING IN THE HAIR INDUSTRY

Working in the hairdressing industry is a great career choice, with endless opportunities for development and variety within the job role. Hairdressing offers a lifelong career that will adapt to suit lifestyle changes and present numerous opportunities to develop your skills with the flexibility to change your career path. As long as you have excellent customer service and communication skills, continue to update your skills and maintain a good professional image, the world is your 'oyster'. Enjoy!

There are two learning outcomes in this unit. The learner will be able to describe:

- the key characteristics of the hair industry
- working practices in the hair industry.

THE KEY CHARACTERISTICS OF THE HAIR INDUSTRY

During this part of the unit you will learn about:

- types of organisations
- main services offered
- occupational roles
- employment characteristics
- career patterns
- education and training
- opportunities to transfer to other sectors.

TYPES OF ORGANISATIONS

Within the hairdressing industry there are many types of different organisations that you might communicate and liaise with or work for. These could be manufacturers and suppliers of hairdressing products, other salons, professional membership organisations and industry leading bodies.

MANUFACTURERS OF HAIRDRESSING PRODUCTS

There are too many to mention, but some of the leading professional hairdressing product manufacturers are companies such as: Wella Professional, L'Oréal Professional, Paul Mitchell, Clynol, Schwarzkopf, Aveda, Keratase, Goldwell and KMS, Matrix, Redken and TIGI.

Choosing the right manufacturer for the salon can have a huge impact on the salon's business and its development. When salon owners are deciding which manufacturer is the most suitable for the salon, they will need to consider many things. They will consider the salon's client group, retail opportunities, the salon's profit and turnover; also what the salon can afford and the benefits that the manufacturer can offer.

Manufacturer benefits

Manufacturers can offer salons all or a combination of the following benefits:

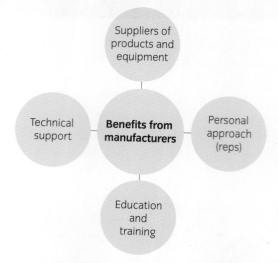

Suppliers of products and equipment

Manufacturers can supply retail products, equipment and salon fixtures and fittings.

- Products range from shampoos, conditioners and hair treatments, styling and finishing products, to chemicals for colouring and perming services.
- Equipment ranges from styling (hairdryers, straightening irons, etc) to tools such as tint bowls and brushes, to scissors and combs, etc.
- Fixtures and fittings for the salon range from shampoo basins to mirrors and styling stations.

Personal approach (reps)

Manufacturers can offer salon packages with a more personal approach by supplying the salon with their own representative (rep). The rep supplies the salon with their products and offers a good salon discount with suitable payment terms to suit each individual salon. They can also offer product knowledge and display ideas.

The discount will vary from salon to salon, depending on how good the business is for the manufacturer, for example, the salon's retail sales, their monthly/yearly spends with the manufacturer and how much promotion the manufacturer gets within the salon itself.

Loyalty schemes are often offered to salons. If they reach an agreed monthly spend, they acquire a better discount and can sometimes accumulate reward points. These points can then be 'cashed' in for tools, equipment or training depending on the salon's needs.

Education and training

Some manufacturers provide free/discounted education and training to the salon and its staff when new product ranges become available, changes are made to current products or to promote new services, such as '**Brazilian Blow-dries**' or hair extensions. This might take place in the salon or at one of the manufacturer's professional training centres.

Brazilian Blow-dries
A hair-straightening service

Education and training might be available from manufacturers

3

Technical support

Sometimes hairdressing services do not go to plan and technical support or advice is required. Most manufacturers offer technical advice to the salons; this allows the salon to telephone and ask about technical services, make enquiries about products and even ask 'What do I do?' if something has gone wrong.

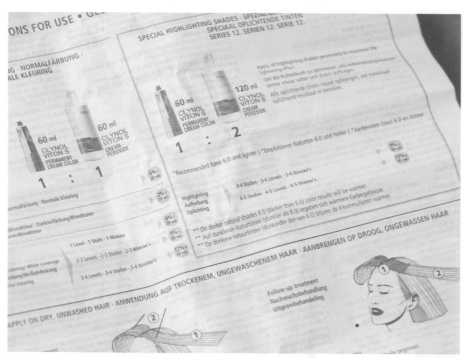

ACTIVITY

Search for manufacturers using the Internet.

- How many you can find?
- Choose three and research what benefit they offer to salons.
- Describe which manufacturer you would choose if you were a salon owner and why you would choose them.

SUPPLIERS

Across the country there are hundreds of hairdressing suppliers/**wholesalers**. These can range from **corporations**, **franchises** or individual companies. Some offer in-store, telephone and online purchasing facilities; others only online or in-store orders. Most suppliers will request a membership for individual traders, such as **freelance** hairdressers, and will ask to see proof that they are operating as a business. This might be a letter head or a letter from their accountant. This prevents the discounts offered being given to the general public who might try to purchase professional products, by-passing the salon professionals.

Most suppliers offer hairdressing and beauty stock, ranging from small sundry items such as cotton wool and disposable capes, to full product ranges, and tools and equipment. Some larger wholesalers/suppliers also sell larger items such as salon fixtures and fittings. One of the biggest benefits to salons of using a supplier is that they deliver the goods order directly to the salon, which saves the salon time.

Wholesalers
Seller/trader of goods

Corporations
Companies

Franchises
Salons using a 'licensed name' or salons in part of a chain

Freelance
Working for yourself/self-employed

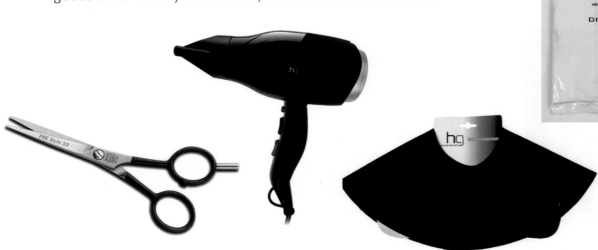

Salons can often access discounted education and training in the store, but the price or discount available and type of training might vary.

Freelance hairdressers often use their local wholesaler/supplier to access training and keep up to date with new services or product ranges available.

ACTIVITY

Research, using the Internet, three hairdressing suppliers in your area.

Find out the following information for each one:
- Do they have a store you can visit?
- Can you order online and/or via the telephone?
- Do you need to be a member?
- Do they offer training?
- Do they need proof that you have a salon or a freelance business?

From your research, decide which one would be more beneficial to a salon owner or a freelance hairdresser.

SALONS

When you first start out on your hairdressing career, you might decide you want to work in a quiet salon, a large busy salon or a salon that offers both hairdressing and beauty services. Whatever you decide, there are thousands to choose from!

Working in women's hairdressing, barbering, African-type hairdressing, or in a hair and beauty spa are options available to you. You can access further training to keep your hairdressing career alive and develop your skills and knowledge, enabling you to adapt your career pathway.

A salon's name

Salon names have often been areas for discussion and debate. Are 'fun' salon names really 'fun' or bad for business?

Fun names such as 'Jack the Clipper' or 'Curl Up and Dye' might bring a smile to your face, but is it a salon you would like to go to?

Creative names can be popular, such as 'His and Hairs', 'Grateful Heads' or 'All Tressed Up'.

Naming the salon with the owner's name has become more professional and business-like over the years, with names such as 'Toni and Guy', 'Nicky Clarke' or 'Trevor Sorbie'.

ACTIVITY

Using the Internet, search for salon names such as 'Shear Success', 'Shear Perfection' and 'A Cut Above'. How many of each salon name can you find? Search for fun and unusual names and list your favourite top five names.

PROFESSIONAL MEMBERSHIP ORGANISATIONS

There are several professional membership-based organisations for the hair and beauty industry, which are available to support salon owners, hairdressers, and beauty therapists and their clients. We even have a hairdressing charity to help us in our hour of need.

Professional membership organisation	Purpose of organisation	Membership benefits
The Fellowship for British Hairdressing **www.fellowshiphair.com** FELLOWSHIP FOR BRITISH HAIRDRESSING	The Fellowship for British Hairdressing was first set up in 1946. It aims to represent the top 10% of the country's stylists and salons. Its main features are to promote artistic and creative hairdressing by the way of shows, education and trendsetting.	Membership benefits can include: entry (sometimes free) to Fellowship events, opportunities to nominate for the Fellowship awards and the F.A.M.E. Team, attending education, skills and training events, as well as networking opportunities.
The National Hairdressers' Federation (NHF) **www.nhf.info** nhf national hairdressers' federation	The NHF was set up in 1942 by the **amalgamation** of The National Federations of Hairdressers Limited and The Northern Counties Hairdressers' Federation, and over the years other organisations joined too. The Federation represents hairdressing salons and beauty therapy businesses in Great Britain, and self-employed hairdressers and beauty therapists working in salons.	Membership benefits focus on the employment laws and **regulations**, offering salon owners and their staff support and advice on abiding with employment law. Membership is available to individuals, partners, directors and firms of the hairdressing or beauty trade.
The Hairdressing Council **www.haircouncil.org.uk**	The Hairdressing Council was set up in 1964 by an **Act** of Parliament. In the same way that doctors and nurses can become state registered, hairdressers can choose to do so too. The only difference is that it is completely voluntary to belong to the UK Register of qualified hairdressers. The Hairdressing Council also provides **consumer** information, recommending that they search for state registered hairdressers in their area, advice on choosing the right hairdressers and information on their consumer rights.	Registration benefits include: initials SRH after your name (State Registered Hairdresser) and official recognition under the law – The Hairdressers Registration Act, and includes a certificate that is underwritten by the law; an Act of Parliament. SRHs might also obtain cheaper insurance via the Hairdressing Council and have access to free hairdressing advice. Some SRHs are invited to a reception at the House of Commons. If you wish to work in Europe, America and other countries you might find you need to be state registered.

Professional membership organisation	Purpose of organisation	Membership benefits
The Freelance Hair and Beauty Federation **www.fhbf.org.uk**	The Freelance Hair and Beauty Federation represents hairdressers and beauty therapists working on a freelance and self-employed basis. To become a full member you must be qualified to at least Level 2 and have 2 years' experience, however a student membership is available.	Membership benefits include: a professional identity and ample opportunities to access training and continuous professional development (CPD). They have low cost insurance with a simplified skin testing policy, and benefits include AA membership cover for your car.
Hair and Beauty Benevolent **www.habb.org**	The Hair and Beauty Benevolent is the industry's official charity. It has been helping hair and beauty professionals (including their families) when they are facing hard times since 1853.	Anyone can support the charity by raising funds via charity events, attending their events or donating money.

Act
A law

Amalgamation
Combined

Consumer
User

Regulations
Rules

Legislation
Laws which are made or passed by parliament

INDUSTRY LEADING BODIES

Habia is the leading body for the hair and beauty industry. It stands for 'Hair and Beauty Industry Authority'. It is known as the 'standard setting body' and develops the 'national occupational standards' (NOS). Awarding bodies such as City & Guilds use these national occupational standards to develop hairdressing and beauty qualifications.

Habia offer support and advice to salons, providing them with guidance on employment law and health and safety **legislation**; to employees, offering advice on where to access suitable qualifications, trainers and centres delivering qualifications by supplying support manuals; and to learners, suggesting textbooks and providing advice on career pathways.

WHY DON'T YOU...
Refer to the Habia website **www.habia. org** for more information on the Hair and Beauty Industry Authority.

Awarding bodies
City & Guilds is the biggest name in the UK for vocational education. Every year they have over 2 million learners accessing over 500 qualifications in 28 different industries. They provide advice to learners, colleges, training centres and employers on qualifications; varying from short to long courses, which can be taken on a full- or part-time basis.

For this qualification alone (Level 2 Awards, Certificate or Diplomas in Hairdressing and Barbering – 3002) they offer 18 varieties to ensure your learning needs are met.

WHY DON'T YOU...
Refer to the City & Guilds website **www. cityandguilds.com** for more information on City & Guilds.

SmartScreen 201 activity assignment 1

MAIN SERVICES OFFERED

When referring to the hairdressing industry, we cover the following areas: hairdressing, barbering and African-type hairdressing. Each hairdressing area offers some general and traditional services and some that are more specific to their area.

HAIRDRESSING

Although most salons are now 'unisex' salons, many offer services that are not offered in barbers. Most people would expect a hairdressing salon to offer haircuts, blow drying and colouring; let's look at some of the other services that might be available:

Hairdressing
Including shampoo and conditioning and cutting/restyles

Vibro
Vibrating

Hair and scalp treatments	**Scalp massage and/or Indian head massage**	**Colour change**	**Colour correction services**	**Hair up or bridal/prom styles**	**Perming and straightening**	**Hair extensions**
Treating conditions of the scalp with tonics, oils and lotions	Massaging the head and scalp with hands or **vibro** machines	Chemically changing the natural or artificial colour of the hair	The stripping of colour or chemically changing hair colour	Setting and dressing hair into a style and/or adding accessories	Chemically changing the structure of the hair	Adding and securing additional hair to add length or volume

BARBERING

In the past, barbers would carry out surgery and dentistry in the salon. Although these services are no longer offered, some barbers still display the traditional red and white barbers' pole outside the salon.

Although we stated that most salons are now unisex, it cannot be said that most barbers are! The majority of services offered in barbers are aimed at the male clientele only. Let's look at what services barbers might offer:

Barbers
Including shampoo and conditioning, blow drying and cutting/restyles

Hair shaving
Removing hair length with the aid of clippers and/or a razor

Head shaving
Shaving the scalp with the aid of a razor

Face shaving/ hot towel shaves
Shaving facial hair with the aid of razors and steaming the skin with hot, wet towels

Face massage
Massaging the skin around the face with the hands, using creams or lotions to cleanse skin

Facial hair, hair shaping and trimming
Cutting facial hair, such as beards/moustaches into shape, with the aid of razors and clippers

Creating patterns
Creating patterns into cut hair with the aid of scissors, mini-clippers and/or T-liners

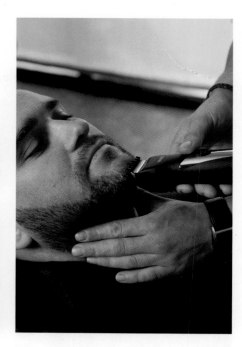

ACTIVITY

Research why the barbers' poles were red and white and why some of the more modern poles have introduced the colour blue too.

AFRICAN-TYPE HAIRDRESSING

African-type hairdressing is very different to **Caucasian** and European hairdressing and the services offered are very different too. Even the salons themselves vary immensely, often creating a community-type environment for customers, and some offering hairdressing services until late at night. Let's look at what services might be offered in African-type hairdressing salons:

Caucasian

Light-skinned people

 SmartScreen 201 handout 1

Hairdressing
Including shampoo and conditioning, blow drying, and cutting/restyles

Thermal styling	**Weaves, extensions and attaching added hair**	**Plaiting and twisting**	**Natural Afro**	**Perm hair**	**Chemically relaxing hair**	**Cutting in patterns**
Styling blow-dried hair with the aid of a heated tong	Extending the hair's length by weaving in pieces of additional hair	Plaiting and twisting the hair into strands, twists and corn rows	Shaping and enhancing the natural Afro style and working with the tight curls	Chemically changing the hair's structure to relax the curls	Chemically relaxing the hair to produce a straight effect to the hair	Cutting patterns into short shaved hair, using mini-clippers, a razor and/or T-liners

OCCUPATIONAL ROLES

When you first start out as a hairdresser, you need to learn the basics in all areas. Many services and skills are transferable across the industry, but you can become a specialist in your chosen field or the area you love the most when you are qualified.

Whether you choose to become a hairdresser, barber or work with African-type hair, you will need to learn how to:

- work hygienically and safely in the salon
- consult with clients
- shampoo and condition the hair and scalp
- create a positive impression of yourself within your organisation
- promote products and services to your clients.

As with all trades, you will need to start at the bottom; as a shampooist, assistant or trainee, and work your way up the career ladder.

WHY DON'T YOU...
Complete the activity in your logbook on page 6 – 'What kind of hairdresser are you?'

 SmartScreen 201 worksheet 1

11

The following diagram shows possible career paths you might wish to work towards and the various occupational roles available.

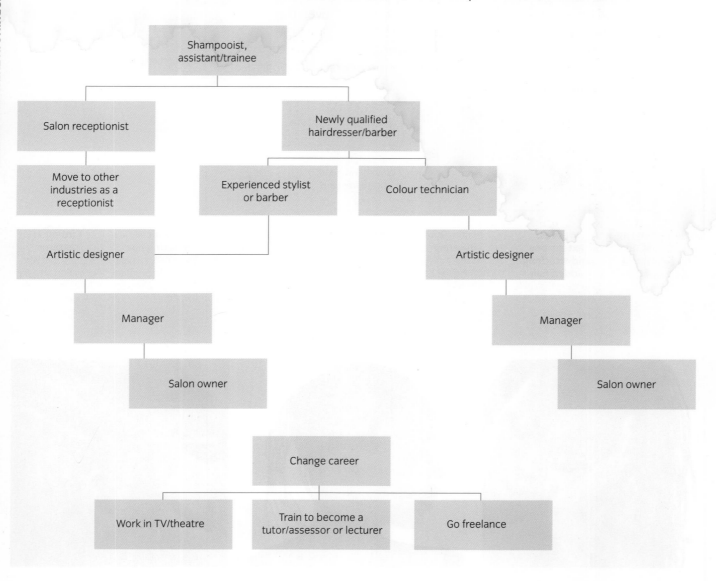

EMPLOYMENT CHARACTERISTICS

Within the hairdressing industry there is a huge range of employment variations, not only in your chosen field of work, but also how and when you work.

SATURDAYS AND LATE NIGHTS

It's probably fair to say that you should expect to work most Saturdays in the year and your salon is likely to restrict the amount of Saturdays you can book off as annual leave. It is just as likely that you will have to work at least one late night a week but, of course, as with every career there is variation depending on your salon requirements and where you work.

Some hairdressers and barbers working in the City of London get Saturdays off work. These salons are busiest Mondays to Fridays and after 5pm, so although the salon might close on Saturdays, they might have an early start or late night 4 days a week.

Most local salons will be at their busiest on Saturdays and expect staff to work every Saturday, offering a day off in the week, usually between Monday and Wednesday when the salon is quieter.

Some salons offer late-night appointments, maybe on Thursdays and/or Fridays. These salons might offer a rota system of week on, week off to cover late shifts, or expect staff to work until around 8pm at night, with a later start to the day of around midday.

FULL OR PART TIME

Working in the hairdressing industry offers you and the salon opportunities for flexible working patterns. It might be fair to say that when you first start out in hairdressing, you and the salon might share expectations of full-time work, but over the years your needs and the salon's might change. Perhaps after maternity leave it would suit an individual to work part time. Perhaps the salon is quieter Monday to Wednesday and both the salon and the employee decide that working Thursday to Saturday suits both parties. This might provide an opportunity for an individual to work on a freelance or part-time basis elsewhere.

WORKING AS EMPLOYED OR SELF-EMPLOYED IN A SALON

Rarely do salon stylists receive a flat rate as an employed stylist. This is often referred to as PAYE – Pay as You Earn. Most stylists receive some sort of bonus-type payment or a self-employed option. Most salons offer a 'commission type' payment system for stylists and this is the most common payment basis.

Commission

Basic and commission: stylists receive a flat basic wage to start with. When they have earned their wages, they receive commission as a percentage of all sales above their target.

Ratios: some salons offer the stylists a 50:50 ratio. This means that whatever the stylist earns, 50% goes to the salon owner and 50% to the stylist. The salon owner pays for the salon costs out of their 50%. This ratio can vary from 40:60 in the stylist's favour, to 60:40 in the salon owner's favour, but it all depends on what the salon owner is paying for. It is likely that the better the deal, the more the stylist has to pay for; this could range from paying towards their assistant's salary or paying towards the stock, etc.

Rent a chair

Some salons offer a 'rent-a-chair' option. This means the stylist literally rents the chair and floor space from the salon owner. They pay a flat fee for working there, but all the money that the stylist earns is kept by the stylist (subject to self-employed National Insurance and tax contributions).

CONTRACT WORK

On occasions there might be an opportunity for working under a short-term contract. Of course this option might not suit the stylist, but equally it might be a convenient opening. The short-term contract could be to cover the maternity leave of another stylist, long-term absence or sickness of an employee, **sabbatical** leave, or seasonal work over the Christmas period.

Sabbatical
Leave of absence

 SmartScreen 201 handout 2

CAREER PATTERNS

Although a long career within a salon is still a popular career path for lots of stylists, there are many career patterns and pathways available to you when you are a qualified stylist with some experience. A career in the hairdressing industry can be lifelong and rewarding; with fashion and trends changing on a regular basis, there are plenty of creative, flexible and development opportunities available.

The following table looks at potential career prospects and pathways available to you, and the skills required for the job.

Career prospects	Skills required for the job
Freelance hairdresser 	You will need to be a qualified hairdresser with at least 2 years' salon experience. The more experience you have as a salon stylist, the more confident and able you will be to solve any hairdressing problems that might arise. You will need additional skills for this role too, such as being qualified to drive and motivated to seek work and promote your own business. You will need an interest in maths and budgeting, to enable you to save and calculate your taxes due, purchase stock that is required for you to carry out the services you offer and tools and equipment needed to set up as a freelance hairdresser.
Owning your own salon 	Ideally you should be a salon manager or supervisor for a period of time before taking on this role. You will need patience and determination to make the salon work, after deciding on the salon you wish to buy and setting it up for business. You will be responsible for any staff you employ, and will need to follow employment law and have a reasonable understanding of tax and National Insurance contributions, although an accountant can help you with this area.
TV, film and theatre work 	Generally speaking you need a minimum of 5 years' experience for working in TV, film or theatre. If you have qualifications in hairdressing and beauty you will be more desirable for hire, but often you have to start as an assistant working for free. These jobs are normally on a freelance basis, so again you need to be able to promote yourself for work. Strong communication skills are needed, as you will have to network with the casting directors and work with some strong characters/demanding clients.
Fashion, media or photography 	With hairdressing qualifications and experience you might venture into working on hairstyles for photo shoots. This could also involve styling models' hair for catwalk shows, or even styling celebrities' hair for magazine work. You will need very good setting, dressing and hair-up skills for this kind of work.

Career prospects	Skills required for the job
Cruise-liners 	Working on a cruise-liner can be very exciting but hard work too. You need to be a good all-round hairdresser. Your skills need to include Level 3 hairdressing and creativity, and **dexterity** with long hair work. You must master the art of sales, as the commission targets can be hard to reach, or you might be on a commission-only basis. You will need patience, as the clientele can be demanding, and be willing to work long hours. You will also need to be independent, as you are often away from home for 6 months at a time. Visit **www.ukcruises.com** for more information.
Working abroad 	Other than your salon experience and being qualified, you will need to be independent to cope with life away from home. It would also be useful if you could speak additional languages.
Armed forces 	Other than your salon experience and being qualified, you will need to be independent to cope with life away from home. You would need to work flexible hours to suit your clientele and believe it or not, Level 3 hair-up skills might be required for styling the hair for any military formal occasions.
Salons in hotels, health clubs and/or spas 	This role will be quite similar to general salon work, but the focus of your skills will need to be in blow drying, setting and dressing and hair up.
Hospitals and clinics 	Working in hospitals and clinics can vary. You might travel around the hospital as a freelance hairdresser, styling the hair of patients who are sick, or working with patients after chemotherapy, advising them on how to deal with hair loss, discussing hair piece and wig options/fitting. If you are willing to attend university for up to 4 years and obtain a degree, you could have a career working in **trichology**.

Career prospects	Skills required for the job
Manufacturer technicians or demonstrators 	Along with your hairdressing qualifications you will need specific knowledge on the services and products sold by the manufacturer. A confident nature and projective voice will also be useful skills to have. You will need to be prepared to travel.
Training and assessing 	To become a trainer or assessor you will need to be qualified to Level 3 or have at least 5 years' experience in hairdressing as a qualified hairdresser. You will then need to train for your assessing and teaching qualifications. You can teach hairdressing in the salon, a college or training provider. There are also a limited number of hairdressing training posts in prisons, where inmates can work towards hairdressing qualifications. You will need tact, ability to show sympathy to the inmates and strength of character for this job role.

Dexterity
Skill with your fingers

Trichology
The science or study of hair

 SmartScreen 201 handout 3

EDUCATION AND TRAINING

As hairdressers we have to keep up with changes in the industry, such as new ideas in colour concepts, changing fashions and developments in technology and techniques. Although hairdressing is an expanding industry, we are fortunate that we can access plenty of education and training opportunities. This could be in the way of attending college for qualifications, attending 1-day seminars or visiting a trade show to identify what is new or coming up in the industry.

QUALIFICATIONS

Qualifications come in various levels and sizes and cross over several sectors. You might decide to apply for a course that offers hairdressing and beauty optional units to enable you to learn skills in new areas. These might include options like manicures and hand care, pedicures and foot care, facial treatments and make-up, to name a few.

The levels, ranging from Level 1 to Level 8, denote the level of difficultly. In hairdressing, Levels 1–3 are the most popular, but a Level 4 qualification is now available.

The size of these qualifications can vary too. An Award can be a short course, made up of one or a few units in hairdressing. You would most likely access this training at a college or training provider, who offers part-time short courses in the evenings so you can develop your skills while you are working.

A Certificate is a medium-size qualification and a Diploma is the largest qualification. These would be available at colleges and training providers offering full-time training courses or apprenticeships.

Level 1	Level 2	Level 3	Level 4
This basic qualification will prepare you to assist in a salon and work effectively as part of a team. To progress as a stylist you will need to achieve your Level 2 qualification.	This qualification is aimed at preparing you to become a stylist; this could be either 'salon-floor' ready or 'work-ready' depending on the type of Level 2 qualification gained. You will learn the basic hairdressing skills and techniques required to work in a salon and under supervision. To complete your Level 2 you can be 14–16 years old or an adult.	When you have gained your Level 2, and have been hairdressing for a while, the Level 3 qualification would enable you to become more experienced and competent in your hairdressing skills. You might wish to specialise in certain areas, such as advanced colour techniques, or learn more creative techniques for cutting/restyling or hair up and hair extensions.	When you are an experienced hairdresser or barber, you might wish to obtain a unit achievement in advanced hairdressing skills, such as colour correction. A Level 4 qualification could also prepare you for a supervisory or management role in the workplace.

ACTIVITY

Refer to the City & Guilds website **www.cityandguilds.com** to see the extensive range of courses they have available. Look at the different levels and sizes of the qualifications to give you an idea of what training you might wish to access next.

Trade shows

Attending a trade show such as Salon International, which is a yearly event held for hairdressers and similar industries, can help you stay abreast of the latest fashions and techniques available. These types of trade shows consist of free and pay-to-view hair shows which can motivate and inspire you, trade stands demonstrating the latest tools and equipment available, often allowing you to have practical hands-on experience, with opportunities to purchase tools of the trade at discounted prices.

HANDY HINTS

You can look in trade magazines such as *Hairdressers Journal* and search on the internet to find adverts for training and educational events:

www.hji.co.uk – Hairdressers Journal Interactive

www.fhbf.org.uk – Freelance Hair and Beauty Federation

www.habia.org – Habia

Workshops and seminars

Workshops and seminars can be accessed at colleges, training providers, manufacturers and also from your local wholesaler. You can often attend these cost-effective events for training on new products and techniques to improve your skills and knowledge. Manufacturers such as L'Oréal and Wella offer workshop days for techniques on cutting, colouring and perming, using and demonstrating their range of products. Other organisations such as the Freelance Hair and Beauty Federation also offer training and workshops with discounted prices for members.

TRANSFERRING TO OTHER SECTORS

Working within the hairdressing sector can open up opportunities to progress and transfer to other sectors and industries. It is becoming quite common for hairdressing salons to offer beauty treatments, such as manicures and Indian Head Massage, and you might decide you want to transfer across to the beauty industry or another sector.

When you have mastered the foundations in hairdressing, you can choose a variety of career pathways. You will have acquired skills that you can take with you from the world of hairdressing into the world of beauty therapy, working as a receptionist or working in spas and/or health clubs, etc. You will need to learn new skills and gain further qualifications, but most of your generic skills, such as consultation, awareness of the industry, communication and client care, and your health and safety knowledge will be transferrable across the sectors.

ACTIVITY

List all the skills that could be transferable from hairdressing to beauty therapy, health centres or spas, or work as a hotel receptionist.

WORKING PRACTICES IN THE HAIR INDUSTRY

During this part of the unit you will learn about:
- good working practices
- personal presentation
- opportunities to develop and promote your own professional image
- basic employment rights and responsibilities
- legislation affecting the industry.

GOOD WORKING PRACTICES

While working as a hairdresser it is very important that you follow good working practices in the salon. This will include salon **policies** as well as legal requirements such as health and safety legislation.

Salons need to ensure that staff are well-presented, working areas and surfaces are clean and tidy, and tools and equipment are well-maintained and sterilised.

Policies
Courses of action and recommended responses

Hair cuttings must be swept up from the floor

Staff must be well presented, wear personal protective equipment and have good personal hygiene

Work surfaces must be cleaned and sterilised with spray disinfectant

Salon and work areas

Gowns and towels must be washed after every client

Tools and equipment must be in good order and cleaned, sterilised, disinfected or sanitised

STAFF SAFETY

It is important that the salon staff are kept safe at all times. Salon employers must provide all employees coming into contact with harmful substances or chemicals with protective equipment. We call this personal protective equipment (PPE).

This includes:

- gloves to protect the hands when you are mixing and using chemicals/ colours, and for shampooing to prevent skin problems such as **dermatitis**
- eye protection to protect the eyes from chemicals and vapours
- aprons to protect clothes from damage
- masks to protect the lungs from chemical dust and vapours.

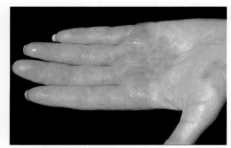

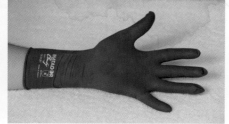

Dermatitis
Inflammation or allergy to the skin (hands)

Dermatitis

Salon employers must ensure that all staff are trained on how to use all of the equipment. The employer is responsible for ensuring the salon is safe for the staff to work in.

Employees must report to the salon owner any concerns that they have on health and safety, and work in a manner that does not put themselves or others at risk.

The employer must also ensure that staff are not at risk when they are using chemicals or harmful substances. They must follow a health and safety legislation called COSHH – Control of Substances Hazardous to Health.

Substances or chemicals that can cause harm to employees at work include:

- shampoos and conditioners
- colour and perming chemicals
- styling and finishing products
- washing powders and fabric softeners.

Employees must also make sure that they follow COSHH and use/handle these substances correctly to avoid harm to themselves and their clients.

We will cover more on health and safety in the next unit – 202 Follow health and safety practice in the salon.

CLIENT SAFETY

Not only is it important that staff are kept safe, the employer and the employee also have a responsibility to keep the client safe.

The employer is responsible for ensuring the building is safe, the staff are well-trained and that essential health and safety policies are put in place.

The employee is responsible for following the policies put in place, and looking after their own clients. Clients must be protected from salon products and their clothes covered with gowns and towels. Any tools or equipment that are to be used on the client must be clean and sterile/sanitised.

Sterilising tools and equipment

The three main methods of sterilising hairdressing tools and equipment are:

- Moist heat – a machine called an autoclave is used for this. It heats water to a temperature higher than boiling point and 'steam' cleans the tools.
- Chemical – one commonly used is 'Barbicide', a liquid that disinfects tools.
- Ultraviolet rays – an ultraviolet (UV) light cabinet is used to sanitise tools.

Any gowns and towels that need sterilising are machine-washed at high temperatures of 60–95°C.

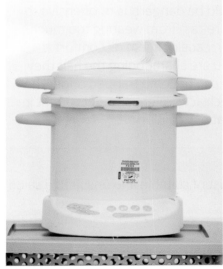
Autoclave

UV light cabinet

Barbicide

PERSONAL PRESENTATION

Hairdressing is all about image! Most clients have their hair done to improve their own image, so it is very important that the salon staff look well-presented. The image of the staff should reflect the image of the salon – one should complement the other.

You will have to follow the salon's policy on presentation. This might include wearing the salon's uniform or following its dress code, including wearing suitable footwear and ensuring that your hair is clean, well-styled and maintained.

Suitable salon wear	Reason for suitability
Closed-in shoes – no open toes	Closed-in shoes protect the toes from falling objects/injuries and stray hairs that can get into the skin and cause infections
Comfortable footwear	Hairdressing involves many hours on the feet, so it is essential that the feet are comfortable all day. Flat or low-heeled shoes are most suitable
Clothing of a suitable length	It is most important that the style of dress does not cause offence to clients. Shirts and tops should meet with the bottoms (skirt/trousers) and not be revealing Skirts must be of a suitable length
Tops with sleeves	When you are shampooing the hair, it is important that armpits are not on display, as this is unpleasant for the client. Tops should not be too loose, where sleeves could get caught in machinery, or so tight that they cause you to get hot and perspire

Although the hairdressing image is expressive and individual, some choices of clothing or accessories could be dangerous or offensive to others. Most salons request that staff refrain from wearing too much jewellery. This can catch in clients' hair, causing them discomfort. Additionally if rings are worn when you are shampooing the hair they can cause dermatitis, as the products can become trapped under the jewellery and cause allergies. Long necklaces might also get caught in machinery, putting the staff member at risk of injury.

ACTIVITY

Discuss with a colleague and make a list of suitable and unsuitable salon wear.

The following diagram shows areas of appearance that are important.

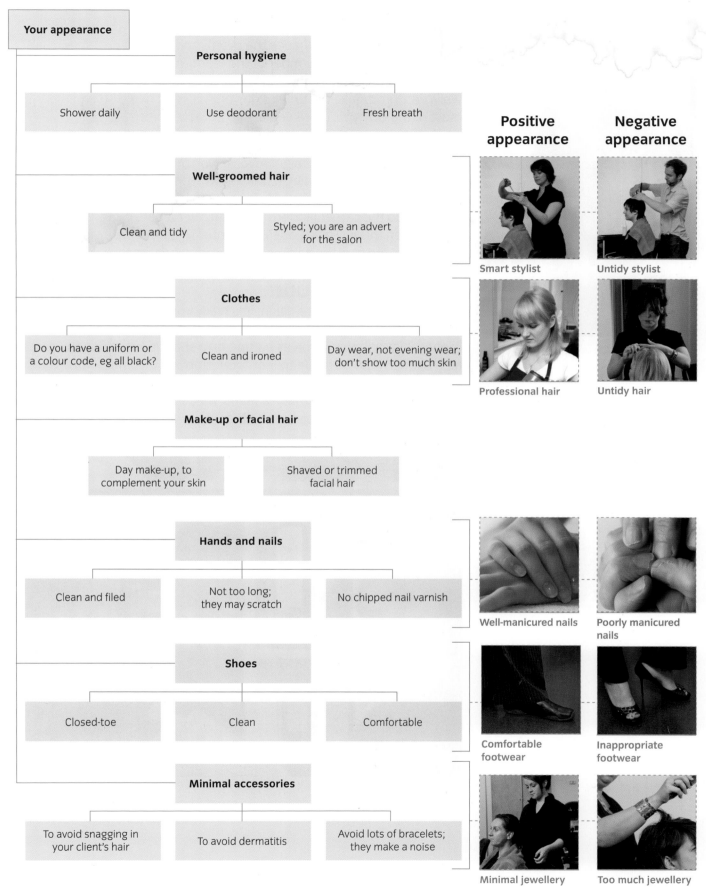

Your appearance

Personal hygiene
- Shower daily
- Use deodorant
- Fresh breath

Well-groomed hair
- Clean and tidy
- Styled; you are an advert for the salon

Clothes
- Do you have a uniform or a colour code, eg all black?
- Clean and ironed
- Day wear, not evening wear; don't show too much skin

Make-up or facial hair
- Day make-up, to complement your skin
- Shaved or trimmed facial hair

Hands and nails
- Clean and filed
- Not too long; they may scratch
- No chipped nail varnish

Shoes
- Closed-toe
- Clean
- Comfortable

Minimal accessories
- To avoid snagging in your client's hair
- To avoid dermatitis
- Avoid lots of bracelets; they make a noise

Positive appearance   **Negative appearance**

Smart stylist   Untidy stylist

Professional hair   Untidy hair

Well-manicured nails   Poorly manicured nails

Comfortable footwear   Inappropriate footwear

Minimal jewellery   Too much jewellery

DEVELOP AND PROMOTE YOUR OWN PROFESSIONAL IMAGE

Remember – first impressions always last! Promoting your own image in a positive manner will enhance the overall salon image and show that you are a professional member of the team. You should take every opportunity possible to develop yourself and always look smart and well-presented. Take the time to do your hair and make-up and make the most of the way you look – you are an advert for your salon.

When opportunities arise for you to develop yourself and your skills, you should embrace them. It might involve working a little later, putting in a few extra hours or attending a training workshop on your day off, but this is your career and every opportunity to learn more will help you to progress up the career ladder. If you can offer a better service to your clients, then this will give you the potential to earn more, improve your client base and give the salon a more professional image.

POSITIVE ATTITUDE

When you are working in a salon, it is really important to have a positive attitude. You should always smile and present a welcoming image to the clients. It is a job that involves putting on a show, no matter how you feel. Clients must be made to feel comfortable at all times – they want to visit a salon that has a harmonious working environment. All salon team members should be just that – a team! They should co-operate with one another, support and assist each other.

SmartScreen 201 worksheet 2

BASIC EMPLOYMENT RIGHTS AND RESPONSIBILITIES

When you start working in a salon or your place of work, you need to be aware of your rights. There are many legislation and laws to protect employees, but some of the basic ones include:

- being issued with a contract of employment
- being paid the correct wage
- working in a safe environment.

CONTRACT OF EMPLOYMENT

It is your legal right to have a contract of employment and you should receive it within 8 weeks of your starting date. You should read it and check it thoroughly before you sign it.

A contract of employment is a legally binding document between you and your employer, stating the terms and conditions which you have agreed to work to.

It is likely that your contract will include the following:

- your name and job title
- an outline of your roles and responsibilities
- who you report to
- start date with the salon
- your address and contact details
- days of work
- hours of work
- holiday allowance, including bank holidays
- sick pay agreement
- maternity/paternity agreement
- appraisal and review procedures
- period of probation and notice agreement
- salon procedures for disciplinary action, appeals and grievances
- pension scheme
- pay – the amount, how often, ie weekly, monthly and how you will be paid – cash, cheque or bank transfer.

It might also include any special arrangements agreed for you by the salon. This might be the amount of time allowed off for training and medical appointments, or agreements for other employment alongside your salon job.

Some employers might issue you with a company handbook which states your rights, how you should expect to be treated and how you should treat others.

MINIMUM WAGE

The National Minimum Wage (NMW) is a law ensuring that employees are not underpaid and receive a minimum amount per hour. It came into force on the 1st April 1999 and it is a legal right that covers all employees in the UK, depending on age and whether or not they are an apprentice.

 SmartScreen 201 worksheet 3

HANDY HINTS

For the most up-to-date rates on the NMW, refer to the Government website **www.direct.gov.uk**. Here, you can also obtain telephone numbers for Pay and Work Rights Helplines for confidential help if you are being underpaid.

ACTIVITY

Using the Internet, research the minimum wage for each of the five age categories listed.

HANDY HINTS

We will look at health and safety in a lot more depth in Unit 202 Follow Health and Safety Practices in the Salon.

The NMW rates are reviewed every year, usually around the 1st October, by the Low Pay Commission and they vary for each age group:

- 21 and over
- 18–20
- 16–17
- apprentices age 16–18, and in the first year of an apprenticeship
- apprentices age 19 and over, and in the first year of an apprenticeship.

SAFE WORKING ENVIRONMENT

To ensure that the workplace is safe for staff, clients and visitors, both the employer and the employees have responsibilities to adhere to.

Employers' responsibilities

Employers must follow all of the Health and Safety at Work Acts. The Health and Safety at Work Act (HASAWA) 1974 is the umbrella that all other 'Acts' sit under.

Overall the employer is responsible for ensuring the following:

- providing a safe working environment – the building and all of its fixtures and fittings must be in good working order
- ensuring that all electrical equipment is safe for use and fit for purpose
- putting in place procedures for assessing the risks that might be present in the salon
- putting in place policies for staff to follow to prevent risks and hazards
- training staff in the use of all equipment
- providing personal protective equipment (PPE)
- providing staff rest areas, clean drinking water and toilet facilities
- keeping the building and its contents secure
- ensuring that insurance policies are updated yearly.

Employees' responsibilities

All employees have a responsibility to follow the salon's policies and procedures and their responsibilities under the Health and Safety Act (HASAWA). This includes working in a safe manner so as not to put themselves or others at risk, by:

- wearing the provided PPE
- following the manufacturers' instructions on chemicals and other products
- using equipment for its intended purpose
- wearing suitable clothing and accessories
- protecting the clients' clothes and skin from chemicals and other products
- behaving sensibly at work, eg not running in the salon
- reporting problems to the employer, such as faulty electrical equipment
- dealing appropriately with problems that could cause a risk or hazard, such as mopping up a spillage.

LEGISLATION AFFECTING THE INDUSTRY

As an employee you have rights! These rights should protect you from harassment, bullying and any kind of discrimination in the workplace. You have the right to be treated fairly, whether you work full or part time, whether you are male or female, regardless of your religious beliefs, your nationality or ethnic origin.

DISCRIMINATION

Discrimination means treating someone differently from others. This does not mean that everyone has to be paid the same wage if you are doing different jobs, with different skills, but it does mean you should be paid the same if you are doing the same job. It does not mean that a part-time worker should have the same amount of holiday leave per year as a full-time worker, but it does mean they should have the same amount of holiday leave **pro-rata**.

Pro-rata
On a proportional basis

The Government has Equal Opportunity laws in place to ensure equality and diversity, and to protect all workers; to create a level playing field so that everyone is given the same opportunity in the workplace for wages, training, holiday, working conditions and promotion, etc.

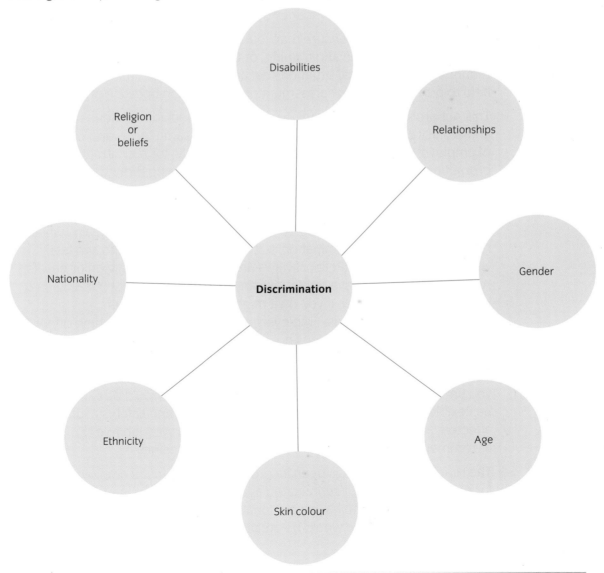

You cannot be discriminated against for any of these reasons

The following table lists the Acts and laws that protect you from discrimination and explains how.

Act or law	How it protects you
Disability Discrimination Act	This Act protects people with a disability from discrimination. Employers have to make reasonable adjustments to their premises to accommodate staff with a disability. Employers also have to make adjustments to application forms, interviews and working arrangements to make sure disabled people are not disadvantaged.
Sex Discrimination Act	Under the Equality Act 2010 it is unlawful for an employer to discriminate against you because of your gender. Men, women, married couples, gay and lesbian people must not be discriminated against because of their sexuality or sexual orientation. Everyone is entitled to receive the same terms and conditions of employment – salary and benefits, opportunities for recruitment, promotion and training – and must be treated equally during redundancy or dismissal situations.
Equal Pay Act	Men and women working for the same employer and doing the same job must receive the same terms and conditions of employment – salary and benefits, opportunities for recruitment, promotion and training – and be treated equally during redundancy or dismissal situations.
Age Discrimination Act	This Act is designed to ensure that you are not denied opportunities for recruitment, promotion and training, or treated differently during redundancy or dismissal situations because of your age. This law will also help to protect you from harassment or victimisation because of your age.
Race Relations Acts	This Act protects you from racial discrimination, including colour, nationality and ethnicity. Everyone is entitled to receive the same terms and conditions of employment – salary and benefits, opportunities for recruitment, promotion and training – and be treated equally during redundancy or dismissal situations regardless of their race, colour, nationality or ethnicity.
Religious or belief discrimination	It is against the law for you to be harassed or victimised because of your religion and/or beliefs. Although there is no specific list that explains what religious and belief discrimination is, it includes major religions and less widely practised ones. (Political views are not counted as religion or beliefs.) Although you do not have to disclose any information about your religion or beliefs to your employer, if you do it might help your employer accommodate your needs. Employers do not have to give you time off for prayers, etc or honour religious holidays, but they are expected to assist you where possible. If a room is available for you to pray in and it will not affect business while you are praying, the employer would be expected to allow you time out for prayers. Where possible, employers would be expected to be flexible with their dress codes, as long as health and safety is not affected, and make reasonable adjustments within your job role to accommodate your beliefs; without affecting the business.
Human Rights Act	The Human Rights Act has been incorporated into general employment law, for example, not to be discriminated against for your race, gender, age, etc. It is your human right to have a personal and family life. So discrimination against a gay employee would be breaking their right to a private life.

Act or law	How it protects you
Employment Rights Act	The Employment Rights Act includes all your employment rights, such as providing the right to statutory leave for maternity and paternity, and the right to a minimum wage, etc.
Employment Relations Act	The Employment Relations Act includes your rights to join a trade union, take time off work to look after dependants or take leave for family and domestic reasons, etc.
Bullying in the workplace	You cannot make a direct claim about bullying, but you can complain under the laws of discrimination or harassment. Bullying can be face-to-face, in writing, over the phone or via email. Examples are: • being constantly picked on • being humiliated in front of colleagues • regularly being treated unfairly, eg being overloaded with work so that you regularly fail to complete your work or meet deadlines • regularly being threatened with dismissal • being unfairly passed over for promotion or training opportunities • being verbally or physically abused. Your employer has a 'duty of care' towards you. You should talk to your employer if you think you are being bullied and your employer should take your concerns seriously.

ACTIVITY

Use the Internet to research direct, indirect and unintentional discrimination. Use the following websites to help you:

www.direct.gov.uk
www.acas.org.uk

 SmartScreen 201 worksheet 4

WORKING TIME REGULATIONS

The working time regulations set out the hours that can be worked in an average working week. These are set at 48 hours per week unless you, the employee, opt out and give written agreement to your employer to work more than 48 hours. You can change your mind and give your employer 7 days notice if you wish to opt back in. It is acceptable that some weeks you might work more than 48 hours, as long as it averages out at 48 hours per week over a period of 17 weeks.

If you have left school but are under 18 years old, you can only work 8 hours a day and a maximum of 40 hours per week. For young people there is no opt-out option, and these hours cannot be averaged out over a period of time.

Every employee is entitled to a break every 6 hours, 11 hours break between each day of work, 24 hours off in every 7 days and 48 hours off in every fortnight.

SmartScreen 201 worksheet 5

Holiday entitlement including bank holidays

All employees are entitled to paid holiday leave. Full-time staff are entitled to a minimum of 5.6 weeks per year, including the eight bank/public holidays.

- You are entitled to paid annual leave – a minimum of 5.6 weeks (28 days for someone working 5 days a week).
- Part-time workers are entitled to the same level of holiday pro-rata (so if you worked 2.5 days your holiday entitlement would be 14 days or 2.8 weeks).
- You start **accruing** holiday as soon as you start work.
- Your employer can tell you when you take your holiday.
- You get paid your normal rate for your holiday.
- If you leave a job, you get paid for any holiday you have not taken, but you might have to pay back money if you have taken more than you have accrued.
- Bank holidays can be included in your minimum entitlement.
- You accrue holiday throughout your ordinary maternity leave (and paternity and adoption leave).

Accruing
Building up

ACTIVITY

Work out your holiday entitlements:
- if you worked 1 day a week
- if you worked 3 days a week
- if you worked 4 days a week.

THE HEALTH AND SAFETY ACTS (HASAWA)

The Acts or laws that protect workers all come under the main Act: The Health and Safety at Work Act 1974. These include:

- The Workplace (Health, Safety and Welfare) Regulations
- The Provision and Use of Work Equipment Regulations
- The Manual Handling Operations Regulations 1992
- The Personal Protective Equipment (PPE) at Work Regulations
- The Control of Substances Hazardous to Health Regulations (COSHH)
- The Electricity at Work Regulations
- The Reporting of Injuries, Diseases and Dangerous Occurrences Regulations (RIDDOR)
- Health and Safety (Display Screen Equipment) Regulations

These Acts will be covered in depth in Unit 202 Follow health and safety practice in the salon.

SmartScreen 201 revision cards

SmartScreen 201 sample questions

Turn to page 485 for the answers.

1 Which **two** of the following are types of hairdressing organisations?
   a Manufacturers.
   b Sales representatives.
   c Cruise-liners.
   d Wholesalers.
   e Trichologists.

2 **Statement 1:**
   To become a freelance stylist, 2 years' experience in a salon, a good mind for business and a driving licence would be ideal.

   Statement 2:
   A stylist working in the fashion, film and media business would have to be trained to Level 4 as a minimum.

   Which **one** of the following is correct for the above statements?

	Statement 1	Statement 2
a	True	True
b	True	False
c	False	True
d	False	False

3 Which **one** of the following roles would a trichologist carry out?
   a Working on large groups of clients for photo shoots.
   b Dealing with clients having hair and scalp disorders.
   c Working on clients in the film industry.
   d Dealing with the armed forces.

4 Which **one** of the following is the **most important** reason why hairdressers update their training and qualifications?
   a To transfer to other sectors if needed.
   b To enable clients to see their certificates.
   c To keep up to date with changes in the industry.
   d To show the manager that they are willing and capable.

5 **Statement 1:**
   It is common for hair salons to offer beauty treatments. This might make it easy for hairdressers to transfer into the beauty industry.

   Statement 2:
   Transferable skills such as communication, client care and knowledge of health and safety make it easier to move from hairdressing to other sectors.

   Which **one** of the following is correct for the above statements?

	Statement 1	Statement 2
a	True	True
b	True	False
c	False	True
d	False	False

6 Which **one** of the following is the **best** example of good working practice for hairstylists?
   a Adhering to salon policy regarding health and safety.
   b Following clients' instructions regarding the use of chemicals.
   c Providing a range of drinks during the service.
   d Ensuring that all clients' belongings are locked away.

7 A contract of employment should be issued no more than:
   a 2 weeks after the start date.
   b 4 weeks after the start date.
   c 6 weeks after the start date.
   d 8 weeks after the start date.

8 Which **one** of the following websites is the **most reliable** source when researching the current national minimum wage?
   a www.wikipedia.org
   b www.businessblogs.com
   c www.hse.gov.uk
   d www.direct.gov.uk

CASE STUDY: HELLEN WARD

Having originally trained as a hairdresser upon leaving school at 16, I progressed up the ranks of the company from Salon Manager, then Regional Manager to General Manager of Harrods Hair & Beauty Salon before opening my own business with my husband Richard nearly 20 years ago. Now I run one of the largest independent hair and beauty salons and brands in the country, and I lecture at business seminars, educate salon owners, and write a monthly column for a beauty magazine. I have written 3 books for City & Guilds as part of the *Ultimate Salon Management* series: *Getting Established*, *Managing Finances* and *Team Performance* – which is part of the Level 4 Diploma in Salon Management and Advanced Techniques in the Hair & Beauty Sector.

Salon life is like no other – fun, varied, exciting and never, ever dull. Our industry is unique – where else could one person be able to create such a diverse career? My role encompasses accounting, management, brand development, marketing, PR, HR, journalism and now I'm an author, too! The talented therapists that I am lucky enough to work with never cease to amaze me with their skill sets – they have a unique ability to make people feel better about themselves through the treatments and services they conduct, which is immensely rewarding and hugely empowering. A career in our growing sector (we employ nearly 1% of the UK workforce) is a great choice, and with it's ever growing diversity, offers a multitude of opportunities to branch out and develop your hidden talents under one fabulous umbrella.

202
FOLLOW HEALTH AND SAFETY PRACTICE IN THE SALON

Health and safety may not be considered the most exciting part of hairdressing, but it is one of the most important. If you wish to enjoy your hairdressing career for many years ahead, pay careful attention to this unit because as with all jobs, there are risks! Health and safety in hairdressing is vital – the job involves strong chemicals and sharp tools, and working with these can put you at risk. The job also puts strains on your body through long hours standing and concentrated work with your hands.

There are two learning outcomes in this unit. The learner will be able to:

- maintain health, safety and security practices
- follow emergency procedures.

MAINTAIN HEALTH, SAFETY AND SECURITY PRACTICES

During this part of the unit you will learn:

- the differences between legislation, codes of practice and workplace policies
- health and safety legislation
- the differences between hazards and risks
- the purpose of personal protective equipment
- the importance of personal presentation, hygiene and conduct
- the importance of maintaining security of belongings
- the principles of hygiene and infection control
- the correct way to dispose of salon waste.

LEGISLATION, CODES OF PRACTICE AND WORKPLACE POLICIES

Like all things we do in life there are right and wrong ways of doing them in the workplace! So, to ensure we do them correctly we have to follow certain rules. These rules could be Parliamentary laws or your own salon's rules.

LEGISLATION

Legislation is the name given to laws or Acts made or passed by Parliament. If Parliament passes legislation and calls it 'The Health and Safety at Work Act', for example, we have to know which rules to follow. These rules are called **regulations**. There are many rules (regulations) to cover health and safety because it is a huge subject.

Regulations
The rules of the Act

Code of practice
The rulebook for your salon

Workplace policies
The individual rules in your salon

CODES OF PRACTICE

In your salon your employer makes the rules, which you should follow. This is called the 'salon **code of practice**'. It might include various rules for the workplace, such as:

- how you are expected to behave
- what you must wear/the salon's dress code
- expectations of the job role
- where you can eat or drink
- your **workplace policies**
- the salon's appeal and grievance procedure.

WORKPLACE POLICIES

Workplace policies are a collection of individual rules on several kinds of subjects. They might include various policies on:

- how and where to mix up colours
- how and where you should do the salon laundry
- how you should meet, greet and treat the clients
- how to behave in the salon
- how you must maintain the salon's hygiene
- how to dispose of the salon's waste.

ACTIVITY

If you work in a salon, list as many of your workplace policies as you can. If you do not work in a salon, list your college's workplace policies. Both should be very similar.

HEALTH AND SAFETY LEGISLATION

There are health and safety Acts that every employer and employee must follow, wherever you work; whether it is on a building site, in a retail shop or in a hairdressing salon. Let's look at the ones affecting the hairdressing industry.

HEALTH AND SAFETY AT WORK ACT 1974

The Health and Safety at Work Act (HASAWA) 1974 covers all health and safety legislation for everyone – employees, employers, self-employed people, and visitors including clients and representatives. This Act outlines everyone's responsibilities, including your own, and is about your health and safety in your place of work.

INDUSTRY TIP

It is important that salon staff follow workplace policies; they may be dismissed from work if someone's health is put at risk due to negligence.

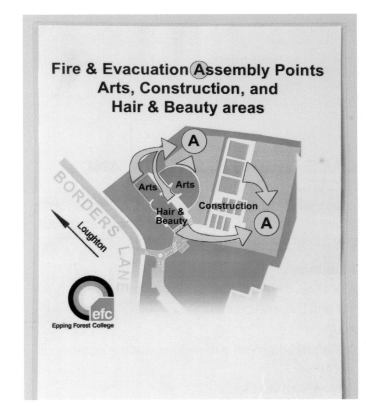

Employers' responsibilities

Your employer's responsibilities under the Health and Safety at Work Act 1974 are to staff, clients and visitors. The employer must:

- maintain the workplace and ensure it is safe to work in
- give staff appropriate training and supervision
- keep access and exit points clear and free from hazards at all times
- provide a suitable working environment and facilities that comply with the Act
- ensure that health and safety systems are reviewed and updated.

Employees' responsibilities

Your responsibilities under this Act are to yourself, your colleagues and your clients. You must:

- maintain the health and safety of yourself and others who might be affected by your actions
- co-operate and communicate with your employer about health and safety issues, so your employer can keep within the law.

YOU are the person responsible for reporting health and safety matters! If you see a health and safety problem you must deal with it or report it. Everyone is responsible for putting it right.

The main legislation that affect the hairdressing industry are listed in the following diagram.

SmartScreen 202 handout 1

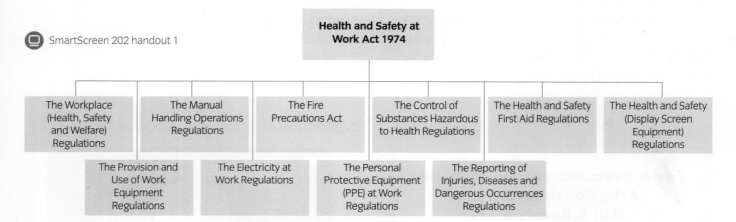

THE WORKPLACE (HEALTH, SAFETY AND WELFARE) REGULATIONS 1992

These regulations require everyone in the workplace to help maintain a safe and healthy working environment. You and your employer should follow environmentally friendly working practices.

Employers' responsibilities

Your employer's responsibilities under these regulations are to:

- maintain equipment and the workplace
- regulate temperatures
- ensure working conditions and room dimensions suit the number of staff employed
- ensure sufficient lighting and ventilation

- ensure all walkways are clear of hazards
- provide sanitary conveniences and washing facilities
- provide drinking water and facilities for staff to rest, eat meals and change clothing
- provide secure areas or lockers for employees' clothing and property.

Employees' responsibilities

Your responsibilities under these regulations are to:

- ensure all doors, fire exits and stairways are kept free of obstruction and hazards
- ensure you know the fire evacuation procedure
- keep the salon clean to prevent infection and **contamination**; this includes workstations, mirrors, floors, gowns, towels, equipment and tools
- keep the salon tidy to prevent accidents, such as tripping over trailing electrical wires. Spillages should be cleaned up immediately and hair cuttings swept up after the service to prevent slippery surfaces
- ensure all lights above the stairways and at fire exits are working
- report any problems that you are unable to deal with to your employer.

THE PROVISION AND USE OF WORK EQUIPMENT REGULATIONS (PUWER) 1998

All equipment (new and second hand) used in the salon must be used for its intended purpose only and kept in good working condition.

Employers' responsibilities

Your employer's responsibilities under these regulations are to:

- provide you with training to use the equipment
- ensure that equipment is properly constructed and fit for use.

Employees' responsibilities

Your responsibilities under these regulations are to:

- ensure you are competent when you are using equipment in the salon
- use equipment only for its intended purpose.

Contamination

The presence of something unwanted that might be harmful

WHY DON'T YOU...
Help the environment and switch off lights when they are not in use. Saving power helps to save money and energy, and cuts greenhouse gas emissions!

THE MANUAL HANDLING OPERATIONS REGULATIONS 1992

You are sometimes required to move equipment and stock around the salon; this is called manual handling. There are correct ways to lift so you do not injure yourself.

According to the **HSE** more than a third of all injuries resulting in over 3 days' absence from work are caused by manual handling. Recent surveys have shown that over 12.3 million working days are lost each year due to work-related **musculoskeletal disorders** that have been caused or made worse by poor manual handling.

HSE
The health and safety executive

Musculoskeletal disorders
Muscle and bone disorders

Employers' responsibilities

Your employer's responsibility under these regulations is to:

- carry out risk assessments on all employees for manual lifting.

Employees' responsibilities

Your responsibility under these regulations is to:

- always ask yourself 'Can I lift this?' If the answer is no, then don't! Ask for help. If you are able to lift it, remember to bend your knees and keep your back straight. Lift the weight with your knees not your back and keep the item you are lifting close to your body.

The HSE guide to manual handling

 SmartScreen 202 handout 2

STEP 1 – Bend your knees.

STEP 2 – Keep your back straight.

STEP 3 – Lift the weight with your legs.

STEP 4 – Check the area in front is clear and hazard free.

THE ELECTRICITY AT WORK REGULATIONS 1989

Use electrical appliances with caution. Electrical equipment must be handled correctly, checked and tested. Plug sockets must be safe, and faulty electrical equipment must be labelled, removed and reported to the relevant person. After use, equipment must be correctly stored away.

Employers' responsibilities

Your employer's responsibilities under these regulations are to:

- ensure that a qualified electrician completes a portable appliance test (PAT) on electrical items and sockets in the salon each year
- keep a record of these tests.

Employees' responsibilities

Your responsibilities under these regulations are to:

- not use electrical appliances until you have been trained
- use appliances correctly and switch them off after use
- check each item is in working order before using it – check wires, switches and plugs
- report, label and remove any faulty items from use.

A faulty hairdryer without a vent cover

Checking equipment – body, wires and plugs

Incorrect use of hairdryer

THE FIRE PRECAUTIONS ACT 1971

This Act ensures that all premises have a basic standard of fire prevention and control.

Employers' responsibilities

Your employer's responsibilities under this Act are to:

- ensure all fire exits are unlocked and accessible
- train staff in fire evacuation procedures
- supply suitable fire-fighting equipment and ensure that it is maintained.

Employees' responsibilities

Your responsibilities under this Act are to:

- know where the fire extinguishers and blankets are located
- know which extinguishers should be used on different types of fire
- know your evacuation procedure and identify your meeting point.

THE PERSONAL PROTECTIVE EQUIPMENT (PPE) AT WORK REGULATIONS 1992

Personal protective equipment (PPE) is for the worker, not the client. PPE comes in the form of gloves, aprons, masks and eye protection for hairdressing employees. It is important that you wear the appropriate PPE to protect yourself from harm when you are working with chemicals.

Employers' responsibilities

Your employer's responsibilities under these regulations are to:

- supply free of charge any PPE required for you to carry out your job
- maintain supplies of PPE
- train staff in knowing when to use PPE
- carry out risk assessments and recommendations of when to use PPE.

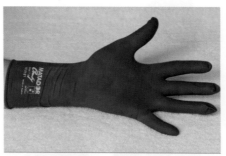

Gloves – protect your hands

Apron – protects your clothes

Mask – protects your lungs

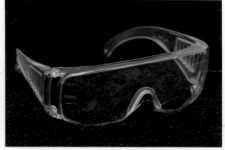

Glasses/eye protection – protect your eyes

Employees' responsibilities

Your responsibilities under these regulations are to:

- wear PPE when you are mixing, handling and using chemicals or other potentially hazardous substances
- report any shortages of or damages to PPE to the relevant person.

THE CONTROL OF SUBSTANCES HAZARDOUS TO HEALTH REGULATIONS (COSHH) 2002

Chemicals and hazardous substances can enter the body through ingestion, absorption and inhalation, so they present a high risk to salon staff. According to the HSE website, every year thousands of workers fall ill as a result of hazardous substances, contracting lung diseases such as asthma or cancer, or skin diseases such as dermatitis. These diseases cost many millions of pounds each year; for the industry to replace trained workers, for society in disability allowances and for individuals who might lose their jobs.

Hazardous substances must be:

- **s**tored correctly, ideally on a low shelf and in a cool, dark, dry, secure, fire-proof cabinet
- **h**andled correctly, ensuring you wear PPE when mixing chemicals
- **u**sed correctly according to the manufacturers' instructions, ensuring you and your client are protected from chemicals
- **d**isposed of correctly, in an environmentally friendly and safe manner.

We refer to this as **SHUD** – store, handle, use and dispose.

When following SHUD, you must abide by the manufacturers' instructions (MFIs), the **local by-laws** and your salon policy. The MFIs will instruct you on how to store, handle, use and dispose of the chemicals or substances. The local by-laws will tell you how to dispose of the chemicals or substances in an environmentally friendly manner, and how to follow the local authority's guidelines on waste and refuse. Your salon policy will explain where to store and mix the chemicals and where to dispose of them in the workplace.

Local by-law
A local council rule

Employers' responsibilities

Your employer's responsibilities under these regulations are to:

- ensure COSHH information sheets are available for substances and chemicals in the workplace
- supply PPE free of charge
- ensure waste disposal is suitable for the environment and follow the local by-laws.

Employees' responsibilities

Your responsibilities under these regulations are to:

- follow SHUD
- read MFIs, follow local by-laws and your salon policy
- know where to find the COSHH information sheets.

ACTIVITY

COSHH substances include all powders, liquids, creams and lotions in your salon – everything from washing powder to peroxide. Take a look around your salon, laundry room, staff areas and washrooms and identify all substances that need to be controlled under COSHH. Make a list.

THE REPORTING OF INJURIES, DISEASES AND DANGEROUS OCCURRENCES REGULATIONS (RIDDOR) 1995

The Reporting of Injuries, Diseases and Dangerous Occurrences Regulations 1995 includes reporting the following to the HSE:

- injuries, eg falls, sustained by you, your colleagues, clients or visitors in the workplace that cause you to take 3 or more days off work; major injuries such as amputation, dislocation, fractures (not fingers or toes) loss of sight and any other eye injuries
- more than 24 hours in hospital
- accidents and injuries sustained from violence in the workplace
- death in the workplace
- diseases such as occupational dermatitis or work-related asthma
- dangerous occurrences, eg a gas leak, even if this occurred outside working hours and no one was injured.

All of the situations listed above need to be reported immediately to the HSE by telephone, and then in writing within 10 days of the incident.

Employers' responsibilities

Your employer's responsibility under these regulations is to:

- report any of the above occurrences.

SmartScreen 202 worksheet 2

Employees' responsibilities

Your responsibilities under these regulations are to:

- report any work-related disorders to the person responsible for health and safety
- prevent any work-related disorder by wearing PPE such as gloves, etc
- report any accidents or injuries that you sustain
- prevent any accidents or injuries by maintaining a safe and tidy working environment.

THE HEALTH AND SAFETY FIRST AID REGULATIONS 1981

These regulations apply to all workplaces in Great Britain, including those with less than five employees and self-employed staff. Their aim is to protect everyone in the workplace by ensuring risk assessments are carried out to prevent accidents and injuries at work.

Employers' responsibilities

Your employer's responsibilities under these regulations are to:

- take immediate action if employees are injured or taken ill at work
- consider providing a first-aider
- nominating an appointed person to be responsible for the first-aid arrangements
- provide a well-stocked first-aid container.

According to the HSE website **www.hse.gov.uk/firstaid/legislation** there is no mandatory list of items to be included in a first-aid container. They recommend (as a guide only):

- a leaflet giving general guidance on first aid (for example, HSE's leaflet *Basic advice on first aid at work*)
- around 20 individually wrapped sterile plasters (assorted sizes), appropriate to the type of work (hypoallergenic plasters can be provided, if necessary)
- two sterile eye pads
- four individually wrapped triangular bandages, preferably sterile
- six safety pins
- two large sterile individually wrapped un-medicated wound dressings
- six medium-sized individually wrapped un-medicated wound dressings
- a pair of disposable gloves.

The appointed person should check the contents of the first-aid container frequently and ensure it is restocked soon after use. They should ensure the safe disposal of items when they reach their expiry date.

SmartScreen 202 handout 3

Employees' responsibilities

Your responsibilities under these regulations are to:

- avoid taking any unnecessary risks that might put you or others in danger
- report any first-aid supply shortages to your appointed person.

THE HEALTH AND SAFETY (DISPLAY SCREEN EQUIPMENT) REGULATIONS 1992

The Health and Safety (Display Screen Equipment) Regulations aim to protect the health of people who work with Display Screen Equipment (DSE). Computer workstations or visual display units (VDU) can be associated with neck, shoulder, back or arm pain, fatigue and eyestrain.

Periodic
A set period of time

That does not mean that DSE work is risky – it isn't, providing the user follows good practice like setting up their workstation well and taking **periodic** breaks from work.

Employers' responsibilities

Your employer's responsibilities under these regulations are to:

- risk assess new workstations or changes to current workstations
- reassess if staff suffer from any discomfort
- train employees in the risks of working with DSE
- plan scheduling of work, regular breaks, changes of activity
- pay for employees to have eyesight tests if required.

SmartScreen 202 worksheet 1

Employees' responsibilities

Your responsibilities under these regulations are to:

- work with a good posture
- take regular breaks and adjust your seating position regularly
- organise your desk space effectively
- keep your 'mouse' arm straight and rest it lightly on the 'mouse'
- keep your keyboard close to your body and do not over-stretch
- adjust the screen or lighting position where possible, to suit.

HAZARDS AND RISKS

Almost anything can be a hazard in the salon. It is your responsibility, along with your employer, to prevent these hazards from risking the safety of yourself and others. Maintaining a clean and tidy salon helps to reduce hazards.

A hazard is something with the potential to cause harm. A risk is the likelihood of the hazard's potential being realised. Trailing wires and hair cuttings on the floor are both hazards. If the trailing wire is neat and tidy against the wall it poses a lesser risk than if it is trailing across a workstation where someone might trip over it. Hair cuttings on the floor pose a

HANDY HINTS

When you are working in the salon, always use safe methods of working and follow health and safety rules and regulations.

potential risk if not swept up as soon as the client leaves the workstation, but there is a lesser risk to the client while s/he is sitting in the chair.

Hazards that are commonly found in the workplace according to the HSE website **www.hse.gov.uk/firstaid/legislation** are shown in the table below.

INDUSTRY TIP

It is your duty to maintain the health and safety of yourself and others who may be affected by your actions.

Hazard	Causes of accidents	Examples of injury requiring first aid
Chemicals	Exposure during handling; spillages; splashing	Burns, eye injuries
Electricity	Poorly maintained electrical equipment	Electric shock, burns
Machinery	Loose hair or clothing becoming tangled in machinery	Lacerations, eye injuries
Manual handling	Repetitive and/or heavy lifting, bending and twisting; exerting too much force; handling bulky or unstable loads; handling in uncomfortable working positions	Fractures, lacerations, sprains and strains
Slip and trip hazards	Uneven floors; trailing cables; obstructions; slippery surfaces due to spillages; worn carpets and mats	Fractures, lacerations, sprains and strains
Work at height	Overreaching or overbalancing when using ladders; not using suitable ladders to work at height	Head injury, loss of consciousness, spinal injury, fractures, sprains and strains

HAZARDS THAT MIGHT OCCUR IN THE SALON

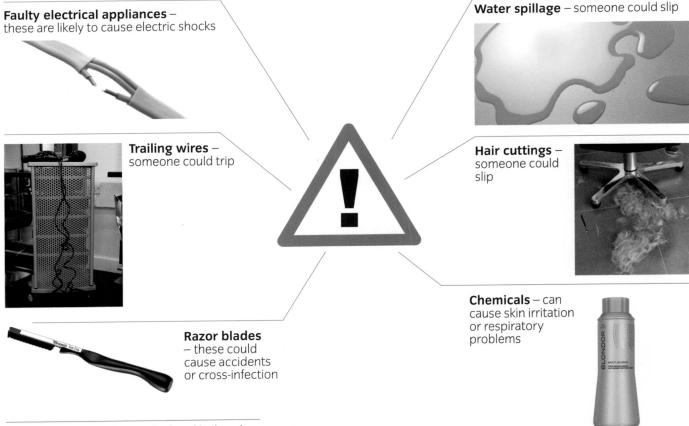

Faulty electrical appliances – these are likely to cause electric shocks

Water spillage – someone could slip

Trailing wires – someone could trip

Hair cuttings – someone could slip

Razor blades – these could cause accidents or cross-infection

Chemicals – can cause skin irritation or respiratory problems

Examples of hazards that may be found in the salon

45

HAZARDS THAT MIGHT NEED TO BE REFERRED

ACTIVITY

Copy and complete the table below, identifying potential hazards in the salon that you can deal with and those that must be referred. How would you control each listed potential hazard to reduce risks?

Potential hazards in the salon	My responsibilities within my job role and workplace policies	How I would control and reduce potential risks, to safeguard myself, colleagues and clients	Who I would report health and safety matters to when they are outside my limits of authority
EXAMPLE: Faulty electrical equipment	Label, report and remove item from salon	Visually check all electrical items prior to use	Salon manager
Trailing wires			
Spillages			
Hair cuttings on the floor			
Chemicals			
Sharps – scissors or razor blades			
Obstructions to access and **egress**			
Loose floor tiles			

Egress
Way out

HANDY HINTS

Always remain alert to hazards and risks to minimise potential accidents to yourself and others.

 SmartScreen 202 worksheet 5

PERSONAL PROTECTIVE EQUIPMENT (PPE)

Personal protective equipment for the employee should be supplied by the employer.

PPE for the stylist and the assistant are:

- gloves to protect your hands from chemicals and staining
- an apron to protect your clothes from chemical damage.

If you suffer from asthma or allergies:

- wear a particle mask when you are mixing chemicals, particularly when you are using bleach powders, to prevent inhalation
- wear eye protection when you are handling chemicals, to prevent chemicals from entering the eyes.

PROTECTING YOUR HANDS

It is important to protect your hands to avoid occupational dermatitis. Dermatitis can occur when your skin comes into contact with substances that can cause irritation and allergies. Each person's skin will react differently to substances, and dermatitis can occur at any time during your career. Hairdressers are more likely to contract occupational dermatitis than any other profession.

Dermatitis is not **contagious**, but it can spread over your own skin. Although most commonly found on the hands, it can appear on the face, lips, arms and cause irritation to the eyes. The good news is that it can be avoided.

Follow these five simple steps to healthy hands:

1 Wear non-latex disposable gloves for shampooing, conditioning, removing colours and neutralising, etc.
2 Dry your hands thoroughly after they have been in water.
3 Moisturise your hands regularly.
4 Use new gloves for every client.
5 Check your hands regularly for signs of contact dermatitis.

Dermatitis can be recognised by:

- dry hands
- itchy hands
- redness of the hands
- cracking of the skin
- bleeding and swelling
- blistering.

PERSONAL PRESENTATION, HYGIENE AND CONDUCT

Your personal presentation, hygiene and conduct must protect the health and safety of yourself and others. It must also meet with legal requirements and follow your workplace policy.

PERSONAL PRESENTATION

Your personal image reflects on your salon's professional image. Always ensure you are healthy and free of infections. Seek guidance from your manager before going to work if you have a potentially infectious condition, eg a cold, flu, eye infection or stomach bug.

HYGIENE

Start your day after a good night's rest, ensuring you brush your teeth, shower or wash before work, and use a deodorant. Wear clean, ironed clothes that are well-presented. If you are a smoker, enjoy coffee or spicy foods, always ensure you have mints or similar handy to freshen your breath. Your hair should always represent the industry you are in and look clean and tidy. Ladies might choose to wear a little make-up to help them look well-groomed, and nails must be clean and not chipped if painted. For men, facial hair should be neatly trimmed.

Dress in layers that can be taken off so you do not get too hot. Becoming too hot can lead to body odour and cause offence or discomfort to others. This is especially important as hairstyling involves working very close to your clients and often leaning over them. Some salons require you to wear a uniform or a certain colour code, such as black. Always ensure you prepare your work clothes in advance.

Contagious
When a disease is passed on by contact with an individual or object.

INDUSTRY TIP
Dermatitis can prevent you from having a career in hairdressing and can be painful and uncomfortable. You must look after your hands and always follow the five steps to healthy hands.

HANDY HINTS
Refer to Personal Protective Equipment at Work Regulations 1992.

Remember – wear PPE and always follow MFIs when using and mixing chemicals to prevent the risk of harm or injury to yourself and others.

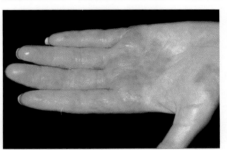
Dermatitis

HANDY HINTS
Always cover any cuts or open wounds to prevent **cross-contamination** and further harm.

Cross-contaminate
Pass unwanted and harmful things to others

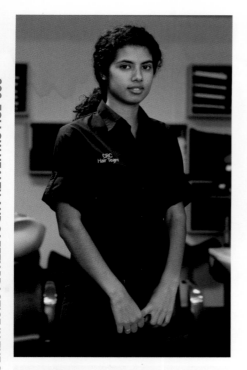

HANDY HINTS

Remember – poor standards of health and hygiene can cause offence to your clients, spread germs and allow cross-contamination.

WHY DON'T YOU...

Identify infectious conditions that may keep you away from work.

Equality

Treating people the same, regardless of differences

Diversity

Mixture or range

 SmartScreen 202 handout 4 and worksheet 4

Staff should ensure that their own personal hygiene is maintained. The following diagram shows you how:

CONDUCT

Your conduct should reflect the standard expected of you in the salon and reduce the risk of harm to yourself and others. You are representing your salon and the image you present has an impact on the whole business. Always act professionally, speak politely to visitors and clients, and promote **equality** and **diversity** for all.

SECURITY OF BELONGINGS

Your salon should ensure the protection of your clients' and staff's personal belongings, salon equipment and the reception area – the till point and products on display. Client and salon records must also be protected by following the rules of the Data Protection Act (DPA).

MAINTAINING THE SALON'S SECURITY

Each salon will have a different policy for maintaining security of the premises and stock, and the safety of staff and clients. Some salons might have a shutter that covers the salon doors and windows when it is closed for the day; others might have a 'buzz' entry or video entry system, which allows entry to authorised clients and salon visitors only. Most salons will have a front door that allows access and entry to all; this is often best kept closed, for your personal safety and those around you.

To prevent breaches in security you must follow your salon's policy.

This could include:

- storing minimal cash in the till
- keeping the till drawer locked at all times and the key removed when the receptionist leaves the reception area
- rarely leaving the reception area unattended

THE CITY & GUILDS TEXTBOOK

- tidying away the salon equipment and not leaving expensive items, such as hair straighteners, out on display
- keeping staff personal belongings in a locker or secured in the 'staff only' areas
- ensuring clients keep their personal belongings with them at all times
- displaying retail stands either behind the reception desk, away from the entrance door or in a lockable glass display cabinet.

> **INDUSTRY TIP**
>
> By law, every workplace must have public liability insurance and display the current insurance policy certificate. If you do not look after your clients' belongings and they are damaged or stolen, they may need to make a claim on the salon's insurance.

PROTECTING INFORMATION

Clients will give you their personal information, such as their address, phone number and credit card details. They give you this information because they trust you and the salon to use it correctly, but there are laws to protect personal data. Clients' information must be protected and you must always follow the Data Protection Act.

The Data Protection Act 1998

The Information Commissioner's Office is the UK's independent authority, set up to uphold information rights in the public's interest.

It sets the rules for the Data Protection Act (DPA), which protects people's rights to confidentiality and privacy. When completing client record cards and taking contact details at reception, you must ensure you follow this legal requirement.

You must adhere to the following:

- All client information, including handwritten and computer records, must be kept in a secure place.
- The information you have must be accurate and up to date and must not be disclosed to anyone else.
- Clients have the right to request access to all written and stored information about them at any time.
- Your salon must be registered with the Data Protection Registry to hold client (and staff) personal information.
- Any out-of-date information and records that are no longer required must be shredded or disposed of in a secure way. You must not store client information for longer than is necessary.
- You have responsibilities under this Act to ensure you maintain client confidentiality and do not **divulge** any information about them to unauthorised persons.
- You must use your clients' information only for the purpose for which it was supplied.

Failing to protect client confidentiality could result in loss of clients, a bad salon reputation or a client suing the salon. You might even lose your job. Your clients could contact the Information Commissioner's Office if they feel their information is not being protected under the DPA guidelines.

HYGIENE AND INFECTION CONTROL

It is essential that the staff's and salon's cleanliness is maintained throughout the day. This will ensure that a professional image is projected to your clients and you maintain infection control. The following diagram shows you how:

HANDY HINTS

The DPA protects you and all data/information stored about you. This includes doctor/dentist records, bank records, and employment and college records. You have a right to access this information if and when you wish to, and you should expect it to be kept confidential.

Divulge

Make known to others

INDUSTRY TIP

Never give clients your personal information, such as address and phone number, as this may put you at risk. A contract of employment may also state this, preventing staff from encouraging clients to have their hair done privately in their homes.

 SmartScreen 202 worksheet 9

INFECTION CONTROL TECHNIQUES

Tools and equipment must be sterilised in an appropriate manner. Salon sterilisers consist of chemicals – disinfectants, moist heat – sterilisers and ultraviolet (UV) light – sanitisers.

The most commonly used salon steriliser is Barbicide – a liquid disinfectant, but some salons might use sprays and wipes or even a bleach solution. Items that are suitable for a liquid disinfectant are cleaned and then placed in the solution for about 20 minutes; they are then rinsed and are ready for re-use.

Using heat to sterilise is the most effective method of sterilising equipment. In hairdressing the appliance is called an autoclave. It heats water to create steam, which cleans and sterilises the equipment. This method usually takes about 20 minutes. (Due to the amount of moisture these sterilisers release to the immediate environment, they are not commonly used in salons.)

HANDY HINTS

Sterilising varies between salons, some will **sterilise** or **disinfect** and others just **sanitise**.

Sterilise

To destroy all micro-organisms

Disinfect

To destroy all harmful and most other micro-organisms

Sanitise

To make hygienic and clean by destroying most micro-organisms

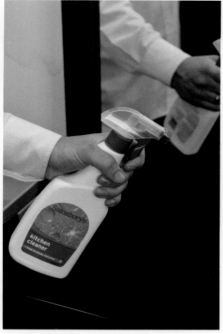

Chemical sprays

Barbicide

Chemical wipes

WHY DON'T YOU...
Ask your line manager about your salon's procedures for cleaning hairbrushes and combs in between clients.

HANDY HINTS
To remove hair and dirt deposits from between the teeth of a comb, use a small brush (eg toothbrush) with hot soapy water.

SmartScreen 202 worksheets 6 and 7

Sanitising using UV lights take longer, as the equipment needs to be placed in the cabinet for about 20–30 minutes and then turned over for a further 20–30 minutes. This method is only effective if used with cleaned equipment and if the equipment is turned properly.

Always wash brushes and combs with warm soapy water before sterilising them. A hair-covered brush will not be effectively sanitised after the UV light process, and will look unprofessional and unclean. Also remove excess hair from scissors, clippers and razors prior to sterilising.

UV light cabinet

Autoclave

WHY DON'T YOU...
Ask your line manager what the salon's procedures are for cleaning scissors in between clients.

HANDY HINTS
Clean equipment and tools with detergent and water, sterilise in an autoclave, disinfect with a chemical liquid and sanitise in UV light.

Types of sterilisers and their uses

Type of tools and equipment	Liquid disinfectant (chemical)	Autoclave (heat)	UV light (ultraviolet)
Towels and gowns	Yes – in a washing machine at temperatures between 60 and 95°C	No	No
Combs, clips, plastic brushes and clipper attachments	Yes – Barbicide, sprays and wipes	Yes – although not all plastic equipment can withstand the heat of the autoclave	Yes
Wooden-handled brushes	No	No	Yes
Scissors and razors	Yes	Yes, this method is the most suitable	Yes
Clippers	Wipes and sprays only	No	Yes
Work surfaces, trolleys, wash basins, salon floor and styling chairs	Yes – sprays and wipes	No	No

DISPOSAL OF SALON WASTE

Quantities of waste will accumulate in the salon over the course of a working day. This must be disposed of in a safe and environmentally friendly manner. Always follow the local by-laws as well as the MFIs for disposal. Salons and businesses will have set days for refuse collection, and most rent large waste bins for commercial waste, preventing a build-up of refuse sacks in the workplace.

Dispose of salon waste in the following manner:

- Any waste from staff lunches must be placed in the staffroom waste bin, which should have a lid to avoid smells.
- Hair cuttings and colour meshes or foils must be disposed of in the dedicated salon waste bin with a lid.
- Packaging from products, such as plastics, cardboard and paper, should ideally be recycled. Recycling signs are generally colour-coded to help identify where and how you can recycle an item.
- Small quantities of unused chemicals can be rinsed down the sink with plenty of cold water to dilute the product. Always follow your MFIs and COSHH datasheets to ensure you do not harm the environment or cause a hazard.
- Razor blades and other sharps must be carefully disposed of in a sharps bin and either collected by the council or taken to a chemist that has a drop-off service.
- Contaminated waste, such as used plasters, must be carefully disposed of in a contaminated waste bin with a lid, to avoid the spread of bacteria.

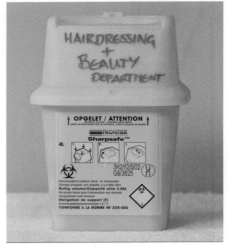

Dispose of sharps in a sharps box

Recycle where possible – look for this logo

 SmartScreen 202 worksheet 8

FOLLOW EMERGENCY PROCEDURES

During this part of the unit you will learn:

- the correct use of fire-fighting equipment
- the importance of reporting and recording accidents.

FIRE-FIGHTING EQUIPMENT

The most widely used extinguishers in salons contain water or carbon dioxide (CO_2). Currently all extinguishers are red and can be identified by their coloured label. The types of extinguisher found in the hairdressing industry are listed in the table below, which explains where they should be located, how they should be used, how they work and the dangers of using them incorrectly.

Type of extinguisher	Identified by?	Used for?	Location	How to use	How it works	Dangers
Water extinguisher	Red label and a thin hose	Class A fires involving wood, paper, hair and textiles	Salon; staff areas; corridors	Point the jet at the base of the flames and move it across the burning area until the flames are out.	Water is very efficient at cooling the fuels' surfaces; the pressure enables the spray to cover a wide surface area, removing the fire by extinguishing the flames and cooling the heat source.	Do not use on electrical fires, as electrical shock may occur and the fire may spread. Do not use on chip-pan fires, as water is heavier than oil and sinks to the bottom. It produces a blast of steam, causing the fire to spread.
Foam extinguisher	Cream label and a thin hose	Class B fires involving flammable liquids (except cooking oils)	Salon; staff areas; corridors	Aim the jet around the side edge of the fire – do not aim the jet directly into the liquid. Allow the foam to build up across the liquid.	As the extinguisher is mainly water based, with a foaming agent, the foam floats on top of the burning fluid and breaks the contact between the flames and the fuel's surface.	Do not use on electrical fires, as electrical shock may occur and the fire may spread. Do not use on chip-pan fires as the oils get extremely hot and may explode.

Type of extinguisher	Identified by?	Used for?	Location	How to use	How it works	Dangers
CO₂ extinguisher	Black label and wide nozzle	Class C fires involving electrical fires and flammable gases	Salon; office area	Direct the nozzle at the base of the fire and move the nozzle over the flames.	CO_2 does not burn and it replaces the oxygen in the air. Fire needs oxygen to burn; CO_2 suffocates the fire by removing the oxygen.	Not good at cooling fires. The extinguisher horn gets very cold and can cause 'freeze' burns and blisters, so it must not be touched when in use.
Dry powder extinguisher	Blue label and a thin hose	Class C fires involving electrical fires and flammable liquids	Salon	Aim the jet at the base of the flames and sweep it over the flames.	Dry powder helps to reduce the chemical reactions needed for the fire to continue.	Not good at penetrating into appliances, so electrical fires may re-ignite. Not very good at cooling a fire down.
Fire blanket and wet chemical extinguisher*	Blanket	Class F fires involving cooking fats. Also to be used to wrap around people if their clothes are on fire.	Staff kitchen area	Wrap the person on fire in the fire blanket or cover the item on fire.	Suffocating the flames by removal of oxygen while the person is wrapped or item is covered.	Needs to be left to cool, to prevent re-ignition when the person is unwrapped or item uncovered and exposed to oxygen.

*Wet chemical extinguishers can also be used for fires involving cooking fats, but these are not required in the hairdressing environment.

The table below shows what each class of fire involves, and which extinguisher to use in each case.

SmartScreen 202 worksheet 3

Class of fire	Involving:	Type of extinguisher
A	Wood, paper, hair, textiles	Water, foam, dry powder, wet chemical
B	Flammable liquids	Foam, dry powder, CO_2
C	Flammable gases	Dry powder, CO_2
D	Flammable metals	Specially formulated dry powder
E	Electrical fires	CO_2, dry powder
F	Cooking oils	Wet chemical, fire blanket

ACTIVITY

Draw a simple plan of your salon and add the location of and type of fire extinguishers available.

REPORTING AND RECORDING ACCIDENTS

The reporting and recording of accidents, injuries and emergency occurrences in your salon are very important. Your employer must always be informed if someone has been injured, had an accident or something has happened in the salon which could lead to accidents or injuries. Not only must you report the occurrences to your employer, under the health and safety of RIDDOR, it is a legal requirement for your employer to report to the Health and Safety Executive (HSE) too.

PROCEDURES FOR REPORTING AND RECORDING ACCIDENTS

It is a legal requirement for all staff to know where the first-aid box and the accident book are stored. Your employer should explain where these are, who is responsible for maintaining the contents and how to complete the accident book.

If an accident occurs in the salon, always ensure that firstly you treat the person; secondly, as quickly as possible inform your employer or line manager and ensure the accident is written up in the accident book immediately.

The salon's accident book must be kept in a safe place and every member of staff must know where this is. Any accidents, even a cut to a stylist's finger, must be reported in the accident book.

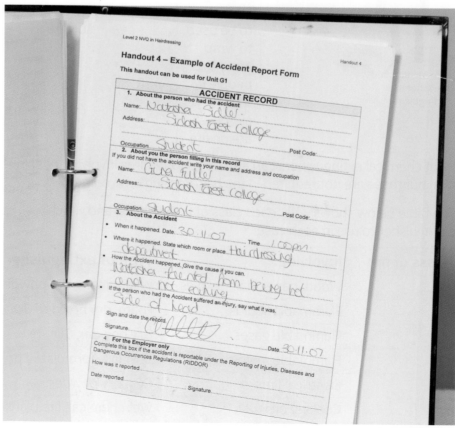

THE CITY & GUILDS TEXTBOOK

You need to record the following information:

- the date and time of the incident
- the name and address of the person involved
- the name and address of any witnesses
- clear descriptive details, eg 'a cut to a stylist's third finger on her left hand, resulting in a small bleed'
- treatment given or whether none was required.

The recording of accidents must be completed in case of any legal consequences arising from the injury. Since personal details are recorded, these pages must be removed from the accident book and kept confidentially in order to follow the Data Protection Act. Forward the accident book page to the person responsible for health and safety.

ACTIVITY

Use your salon diagram from the previous activity. Add the location of the first-aid box and accident book.

DEALING WITH EMERGENCIES

If you discover a fire you should raise the alarm in a calm and safe manner, notify staff and evacuate clients to the assembly point. Dial 999, ask the operator for the fire service, clearly give the salon address and describe the current situation.

You should only fight a fire if you have been trained to do so, or if the fire is blocking your exit route.

ACTIVITY

Add the fire exits and assembly meeting point to your salon diagram.

SmartScreen 202 revision cards

Turn to page 485 for the answers.

1 Which **one** of the following is the name given to laws or Acts?
   a Regulations.
   b Legislation.
   c Codes of practice.
   d Workplace policies.

2 Which **one** of the following does **not** come under the Health and Safety at Work Act 1974?
   a COSHH.
   b RIDDOR.
   c The Fire Precautions Act.
   d The Sale and Supply of Goods Act.

3 Which **one** of the following is a hazard found in a hairdressing salon that will need to be referred to a senior?
   a Slippery surface.
   b Chemical spillage.
   c Heavy obstruction.
   d Trailing wires.

4 Which **one** of the following is an item of personal protective equipment and should be provided by the employer under the Personal Protective Equipment Regulations?
   a Gowns.
   b Sterile towels.
   c Gloves.
   d Waterproof capes.

5 An autoclave is not commonly used in salons because:
   a It creates a lot of moisture.
   b It does not sterilise effectively.
   c It sanitises work areas but not towels.
   d It is a large machine and takes up salon space.

6 Small amounts of unused hairdressing chemicals should be disposed of by:
   a Wrapping in newspaper and placing in a covered bin.
   b Placing in a yellow bin.
   c Rinsing into the outside drain.
   d Rinsing down the sink with plenty of cold water.

7 **Statement 1:**
   The most common type of fire-fighting equipment seen in salons contains carbon dioxide (CO_2); this is ideal for use on electrical fires.

   Statement 2:
   The dangers of using a CO_2 fire extinguisher is that it can cause 'freeze burns' and blisters.

   Which **one** of the following is correct for the above statements?

	Statement 1	Statement 2
a	True	True
b	True	False
c	False	True
d	False	False

8 The correct procedure on discovery of a fire is to:
   a Dial 999 and calmly evacuate the salon.
   b Take the clients that you think are in danger to the assembly point.
   c Dial 999 and start to use fire equipment.
   d Take time to ensure everyone has their personal belongings before evacuating.

CLIENT CONSULTATION FOR HAIR SERVICES

What makes a good hairdresser? Many clients would say effective communication skills, followed closely by creativity and styling skills. A popular stylist listens to what the client really wants, discusses how achievable the result is and shows a genuine interest in the client and their needs. Making a client feel good about themselves and a valued customer is as important as making the client look good. Your communication skills are vitally important if you want to become a 'great' stylist. In this unit you will learn how to improve your communication skills and the complete consultation process.

There are two learning outcomes in this unit. The learner will be able to:

- consult and advise clients
- know the characteristics of the hair.

CONSULT AND ADVISE CLIENTS

During this part of the unit you will learn:

- how to communicate effectively
- how to carry out hair tests for different services
- how to identify contra-indications that limit or prevent services
- how to identify factors that limit or affect services
- the importance of client records cards
- the importance of maintaining client confidentiality
- the importance of following legislation when selling and promoting retail products.

COMMUNICATING EFFECTIVELY

 SmartScreen 203 handout 1

An effective consultation must take place before every hairdressing service. This includes services such as shampooing and conditioning treatments, cutting, styling, colouring and perming. The giving and receiving of accurate information is a very important part of communicating with your client and colleagues, as this aids the understanding process. It also enables all staff members involved with the service requirements to know their roles and responsibilities.

COMMUNICATION TECHNIQUES

You will need to adapt your style of communicating and consultation to suit the different needs of your clients. Clients' personalities vary immensely and although it is fair to say that most people enjoy visiting the salon, a few compare it to visiting the dentist!

It is important that your communication puts your client at ease, so they can enjoy their salon visit.

VERBAL COMMUNICATION

Jargon
Specialised language concerned with a particular subject

Always speak to your client in a friendly manner, avoiding **jargon** and too many technical terms. Ask plenty of questions to identify accurately what they would like the outcome to be and to clarify both your own and your client's understanding. You should observe your client's body language to ensure they look comfortable with what has been discussed and is in agreement.

Questioning your client

Your questioning techniques should include open and closed questions. Open questions demand more than one-word answers and therefore help you to get information and details from your client to enable you to understand what they want. These questions usually start with 'what', 'why', 'when' or 'how'.

Some useful open questions are:

- What service would you like today?
- Why would you like this particular service/technique?
- What result would you like your colour service to achieve?
- When did you last visit the salon?

- How do you manage your hair at home and what do you do to your hair on a daily basis?
- What products do you use on your hair at home?
- When did you last have a perm/colour?

Closed questions are questions that can be answered with either 'yes' or 'no'.

The following are examples of closed questions:

- Are you having a colour service today?
- Are you happy with your hair condition at the moment?
- Would you like to have your hair restyled today?
- Do you want to book in for a restyle on your next appointment?

Towards the end of the consultation, closed questions can be very useful, as these help to confirm that you and your client are thinking along the same lines.

ACTIVITY

List five open and five closed questions that you could ask a client about their hair.

WHY DON'T YOU...
Practise using some open and closed questions with your colleagues to help gain more information or clarify a point.

INDUSTRY TIP
Listen to the stylists in a salon carrying out consultations with their clients to gain an understanding of how to carry out effective consultations.

INDUSTRY TIP
Stylists should always clarify their client's understanding of the consultation process and what has been agreed, and encourage the client to ask questions about areas they do not understand.

INDUSTRY TIP
Always consult with your client face-to-face and avoid talking to them through the mirror. However, during the service, in order to keep to time, your conversation is likely to take place through the mirror.

Language and tone of voice

You can judge how you think your client is feeling by listening to the manner in which they speak to you, their tone of voice and the vocabulary used. Always confirm that your client understands and agrees with the service requirements. Equally, you must adjust your language style and tone of voice to suit the needs of your client.

The table shows how you might adapt your style of conversation and behaviour with each type of client.

Children	Young adults	Middle aged	Older clients
You should keep your tone light and friendly; most young children do not like having their hair done. Try to make the experience fun and behave in a non-formal manner. Avoid technical terms and grown-up words. Talk to the child to put them at ease. Explain what you are doing, every step of the way.	A more informal approach could work well with young adults, to relax them, and the friendly atmosphere you create will encourage them to return. Use a younger style of language and a light, friendly tone of voice, but ensure you always remain professional. Explain what you are doing and why, and offer ideas on how to style their look in various ways to maximise their style.	Middle-aged clients expect good customer service and are more likely to remain loyal to the salon. They might be confident in expressing their wishes and articulating what they want. Ensure you listen carefully and advise alternative options if their requests are not the most suitable. Ensure you use professional language, but avoid hairdressing jargon and keep your tone light and friendly.	Older people are used to good, old-fashioned values and customer service. Always remain respectful and a little more formal. If an older client has mobility or hearing problems, be sensitive and helpful at all times. Older clients are happiest returning to a regular stylist and building a solid relationship. Some personal chit-chat about their families often goes down well.

NON-VERBAL COMMUNICATION

When you communicate, you do so verbally and non-verbally. Listening is a form of non-verbal communication, as is body language. Non-verbal communication can be negative as well as positive. It can give away secrets about whether you are telling the truth, listening to your client and interested in what your client is saying.

Listening to your client and actually 'hearing' what they are saying is a skill you need to master. Not every client will use the correct terms, or express themselves clearly, so it is down to you to work out what they actually want!

Our eyes can give away how we really feel. Always maintain eye contact with your client. Look for tell-tale signs that they are comfortable with what is being discussed and what you are doing, and always ensure that your smile reaches your eyes and not just your mouth.

Body language

The chart below shows examples of positive and negative body language.

Positive body language		Negative body language	
Smiling – indicates you are happy and approachable		**Mouth is smiling but eyes are not** – indicates that the smile is not genuine	
Eye contact – indicates you are listening		**Poor posture/slouching** – looks unprofessional, indicates tiredness and makes you look uninterested	
Good open body posture – indicates you are alert and ready for work		**Crossed arms/closed in body posture** – indicates defensive behaviour and a closed mind	
Open palms – indicates openness and honesty		**Talking with your hand in front of your mouth** – indicates to your client that you are not being honest or truthful	
Keeping a little distance from your client – shows respect of personal space		**Scratching behind the ear or rubbing the back of the neck** – indicates that the listener is uncertain	

USE OF VISUAL AIDS

If your client is requesting a new style, cut or colour, you should use visual aids to help you both get a clearer picture of the desired look.

Styling magazines help your client describe what the finished result should look like. With the image in mind you can discuss with your client how feasible the outcome will be. Remember, as the expert, it is up to you to suggest alternative ideas if the style chosen will not suit your client's face shape, hair type or texture, or even their lifestyle. Always be prepared to suggest other positive options.

The use of colour charts is very important when you are discussing a colouring service with your client. Most manufacturers have colour charts with removable samples that you can drape through your client's hair and against their skin to check that the colours suit their skin tone and their existing hair colour.

SmartScreen 203 worksheets 1 and 2

If your client is a regular client, always refer back to the record card and talk about the previous services that he/she has had before. This helps to get a good starting point, as you can identify whether your client would like a similar service or a complete change.

CARRYING OUT HAIR TESTS FOR DIFFERENT SERVICES

Before every service you need to carry out a variety of tests on the hair. Even if you are shampooing and conditioning the hair, you need to know if the hair is porous and whether the hair has good elasticity or if it is weak. This information helps you to decide whether the hair needs an extra-moisturising shampoo or a deep-penetrating conditioner; it even indicates how careful you should be when untangling the hair. So, if we need to know this for shampooing and conditioning, we must need to know a lot more before we add heated appliances and chemicals to the hair!

You must carry out tests before and during all services. These tests must be completed following the manufacturers' instructions, salon policies and legal requirements to ensure that you follow health and safety guidelines.

- The manufacturers' instructions (MFIs) – these will vary, particularly for colouring and perm tests. If you do not follow the MFIs and your client suffers an allergic reaction or the hair condition deteriorates, not only can your client take legal action, so can the manufacturer.
- Your salon's policy – each salon will have their own policy on where and when tests are carried out, but they must be in line with the MFIs and any legal requirements. If you do not follow your salon policy and something goes wrong, not only could the client take legal action, you might lose your job too.
- Any legal requirements – along with the MFIs and your salon policy, you must ensure you follow the legal requirements too. These will include the health and safety Acts, such as COSHH and the Data Protection Act (DPA), so ensure you wear your PPE when using chemicals and follow the DPA when recording the outcomes of these tests on the client record card. (We will cover more on the DPA later in this unit.) If you do not follow legal requirements and a service goes wrong, you and your employer could find yourselves into serious trouble with the Health and Safety Executive (HSE).

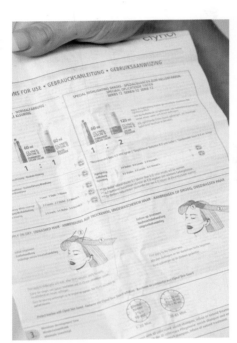

The following table shows you all the common tests you need to do on the hair before styling, cutting, colouring and perming. The outcomes of these tests will help you to decide the best tools to use, the best products to use and whether you can add chemicals to the hair for colouring and perming.

Tests	When to carry out the tests	How to carry out the tests	Why carry out the tests?	Expected results of the tests	Consequences of not carrying out the tests
Porosity test	Before any service on dry hair	Take a few hairs and slide your fingers up the hair shaft in the direction of point to root.	To test the cuticle layer to identify if the cuticles are smooth or rough	Hair cuticles should feel smooth if the hair is non-porous, and rough or raised if the hair is porous.	Damage to clients' hair might occur or the desired outcome might not be achieved. There is a risk that the client will take legal action.
Elasticity test	Before any service on wet hair	Take one or two hairs and mist them slightly with water, then stretch the hair a couple of times between your finger and thumb.	To test the strength of the cortex	Wet hair should stretch about 30% more than its original length and then return when released.	Damage to clients' hair might occur or the desired outcome might not be achieved. There is a risk that the client will take legal action.
Incompatibility test	Before chemical services, if you suspect **metallic salts** are present in the hair	Take a small cutting of your client's hair and place it in a solution of 20 cc liquid 6% peroxide and 1 cc of perm solution (or a solution of 20:1 liquid peroxide and ammonium hydroxide). Leave for up to 30 minutes.	To test the hair to identify if any metallic salts are present which would react with professional chemical products	If metallic salts are present the hair might change colour, the solution might bubble and fizz and/or give off heat.	Damage and/or disintegration to clients' hair and/or skin could occur. There is a risk that the client will take legal action.

Metallic salts

These can be found in products which contain lead compounds or a variety of other metals depending on the shade of colour required

Tests	When to carry out the tests	How to carry out the tests	Why carry out the tests?	Expected results of the tests	Consequences of not carrying out the tests
Skin test	24–48 hours before a colour	Always follow MFIs as these might vary. As a guide you must clean an area in the inner elbow or behind the ear. Then apply your client's chosen colour to the area and leave it exposed to dry.	To test for an allergic reaction or sensitivity to the product/para-dyes	A positive reaction is red skin and/or sore areas that might weep and itch. A negative reaction is no change to the skin area.	Allergic reaction, anaphylactic shock, contact dermatitis or damage to clients' skin could occur. There is a risk that the client will take legal action.
Colour test	Before a colour or lightening service	Apply the chosen colour to a section of the hair (either a test cutting or on the head).	To see if the desired result is achievable	The desired result should be achieved, or further development might be required.	Damage and/or disintegration to clients' hair could occur. The desired outcome might not be achieved. There is a risk that the client will take legal action.
Strand test	During the colouring or lightening service	Wipe off the colour or lightener from a few strands of hair.	To see if the colour result has been achieved, or if the lightener development is sufficient	If permanent colour is developed, then the desired result should be achieved. If the bleach is regularly checked, the level of lift should be achieved without damage to the hair. Further development might be required if the colour result has not been achieved.	Damage and/or disintegration to clients' hair could occur if over-developed. The desired outcome might not be achieved if under-developed. There is a risk that the client will take legal action.

Tests	When to carry out the tests	How to carry out the tests	Why carry out the tests?	Expected results of the tests	Consequences of not carrying out the tests
Perm skin test	Prior to a perm service	Always follow MFIs as these might vary. As a guide you must clean an area in the inner elbow or behind the ear. Then apply the chosen perm product to the area and leave it exposed to dry for 24 hours.	To test for an allergic reaction or sensitivity to the product	A positive reaction is red skin and/or sore areas that might weep and itch. A negative reaction is no change to the skin area.	Allergic reaction, contact dermatitis or damage to clients' skin could occur. There is a risk that the client will take legal action.
Pre-perm test curl	Before the service	Weave the hair and wind a roller section on the head. Protect the rest of the hair and complete the full perm process on one or two rods. Or take a cutting of hair and complete the perm process on the hair cutting.	To identify if the rod size and perm lotion choice is suitable to achieve the desired result	The curl should be suitable and as expected. If too tight, you need a larger rod; if too loose you need a smaller rod; if too dry or frizzy a weaker lotion is required or a pre-perm conditioner should be used.	Result might be too loose, too tight or the hair condition might be too dry or damaged. There is a risk that the client will take legal action.
Development test curl	During the development process of a perm	Unwind a perm roller partially and push the hair back towards the root area. Do this in three to four areas around the head.	To check if the perm development time has been sufficient	A positive result shows an adequate 'S' bend in a similar size to the roller. A negative result will be either a weak 'S' bend, meaning the development time is insufficient or an over-tight 'S' bend meaning the hair is over-developed.	Damage and/or disintegration of clients' hair or skin could occur if over-developed. The desired outcome might not be achieved if under-developed. There is a risk that the client will take legal action.

SmartScreen 203 worksheet 7

IDENTIFYING CONTRA-INDICATIONS THAT LIMIT OR PREVENT SERVICES

There are many contra-indications and factors that hairstylists need to consider when they are carrying out hairdressing services.

Some contra-indications prevent the service from being carried out; by this we mean the service cannot take place, for example, allergic reactions to perm lotion or permanent colours might prevent a perm or colour service from taking place.

Some contra-indications and factors limit the service; by this we mean restrict what can be carried out, for example, hair in poor condition might be able to sustain having a semi-permanent colour but would not withstand having any permanent colourants put on the hair.

Other factors can affect the service or the end result, for example, if your client's hair was too fine and sparse the end result of a new style might not be the desired result.

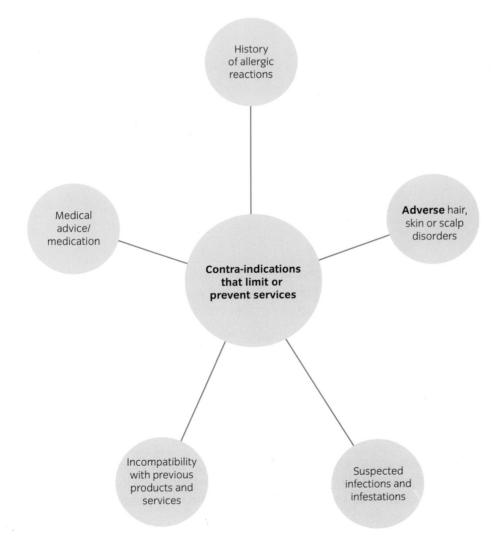

Adverse
Unfavourable, poor or difficult, not suitable

Contra-indications	Limitation on/prevention of the service
Allergic reactions	Allergic reactions could prevent a chemical service from taking place but an alternative, milder product might be acceptable to your client and the colour/perm aims adapted. Clients can be allergic to tint, perm lotions and even the adhesive used to bond hair wefts. Some allergic reactions might result in irritations or contact dermatitis, but acute allergic reactions can result in anaphylactic shock or even death. You will put your client at risk of harm if you do not carry out the relevant allergy tests. If your client has a history of allergic reactions you might need to suggest alternatives to chemical treatment.
Adverse hair, skin and scalp conditions	Adverse hair conditions are where hair is physically or chemically damaged; further services could make the condition of the hair deteriorate or cause breakage. Physical damage can be caused by back-combing the hair, overuse of electrical heat appliances or excessive brushing. Chemical damage can be from colouring, bleaching and perming the hair, but also from chemicals like chlorine if your client is a regular swimmer. Adverse skin and scalp conditions vary, but most can affect which services you can offer your client. A client with psoriasis can have a cut and blow dry but you might decide that colouring treatments are best avoided. Other adverse conditions of the skin and scalp could be: ■ warts ■ cuts and abrasions ■ cysts. Any open, weeping or infected conditions will prevent the service from taking place.
Suspected **infections** and **infestations**	Contagious infections, infestations or disorders of the scalp will prevent services being carried out, as they could cause **cross-contamination**.
Incompatibility of previous products or services	There might be factors that affect potential services due to previous treatments or products. For example, tint will not lift tint, so if a client wants a full-head tint but already has tint on their hair, the desired look might not be achieved. Although it is rare, some products will react with other products on the hair and could cause the hair to break and disintegrate. Metallic salts that are found in a few hair-colouring products available in high street shops will react with the chemicals in professional brands. Some clients' hair might not be suitable for further chemical treatments, for example if the hair is in poor condition as a result of previous services or products.
Medical advice/ medication	Some medical disorders and associated medications might affect the service that you can offer. Always ask your client if they are taking any medication and whether they have been advised by their GP that it might affect the hair. Check for signs of weakened hair if your client is taking any medication.

Infectious

Infectious means contagious, so these conditions can be passed from one person to another. Salon services, therefore, must not be carried out on clients with infectious conditions

Infestations

Parasites living on the body in large numbers. These are also contagious and salon services should not be carried out on clients with infestations

Cross-contamination

Spreading from one person to another

ADVERSE HAIR CONDITIONS

The following chart shows some defects that cause adverse hair conditions:

Adverse hair conditions – non-infectious conditions				
Adverse hair or defect	**Description**	**Cause**	**Symptoms**	**Possible treatment**
Fragilitas crinium	Split ends	Physical damage or chemical treatments	Dry, split ends, damage to cuticle and cortex at the end of the hair shaft	Regular use of surface conditioners and deep-penetrating conditioners improve the condition. Cutting the hair removes the split end.
Trichorrhexis nodosa	Swollen, hardened areas of the hair shaft	Physical damage or chemical treatments	The hardened swelling can break off and cause the hair to split	Regular use of surface conditioners and deep-penetrating conditioners improve the condition. Cutting the hair might help to remove the damaged area.
Monilethrix	Beaded hair shaft	A rare hair defect that is hereditary and caused by an uneven production of the hair's **keratin**	Very weak hair that might break off near the root. The hair feels bumpy where the 'beads' are formed	Treat with caution and care. Conditioners and treatments might help. Refer to a GP.

Keratin

Protein found in the cuticle cells of the hair

SmartScreen 203 worksheet 10

ADVERSE SKIN AND SCALP CONDITIONS

The following chart shows some non-infectious adverse skin and scalp conditions:

Adverse skin and scalp conditions – non-infectious conditions

Condition	Description	Cause	Treatment	Infectious?
Eczema 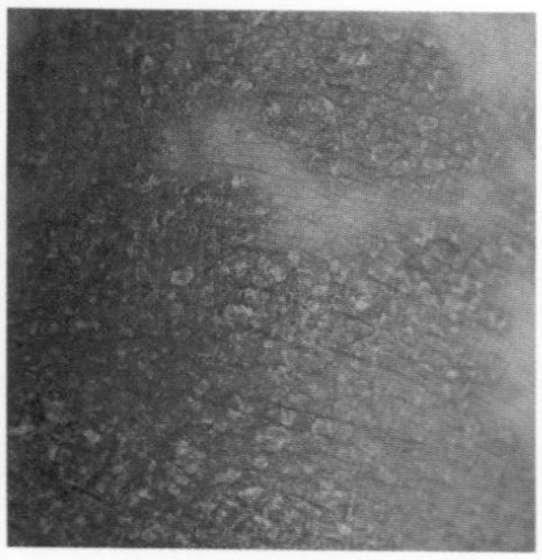	Red inflamed itchy skin, sometimes split and weeping	Can be caused by physical irritation or allergic reaction. Internal factors can also cause eczema.	Refer to GP or **dermatologist**. Salon services can be carried out but avoid chemicals on any skin that is broken.	No
Psoriasis 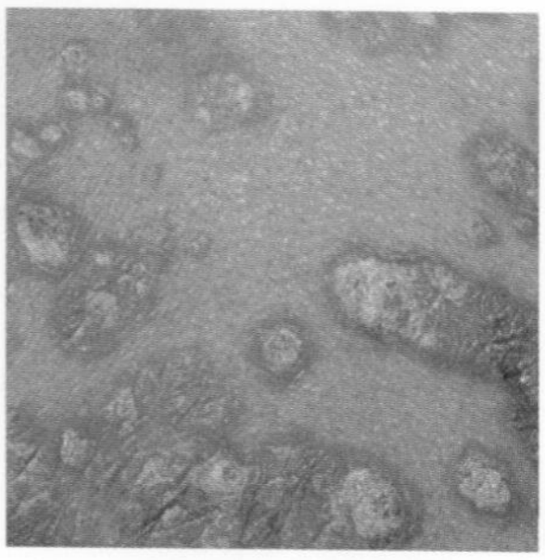	Silvery yellow scales and thickening of the skin	Unknown	Refer to GP or dermatologist. Salon services can be carried out but avoid chemicals on any broken skin.	No
Alopecia – male pattern baldness, alopecia areata, alopecia totalis 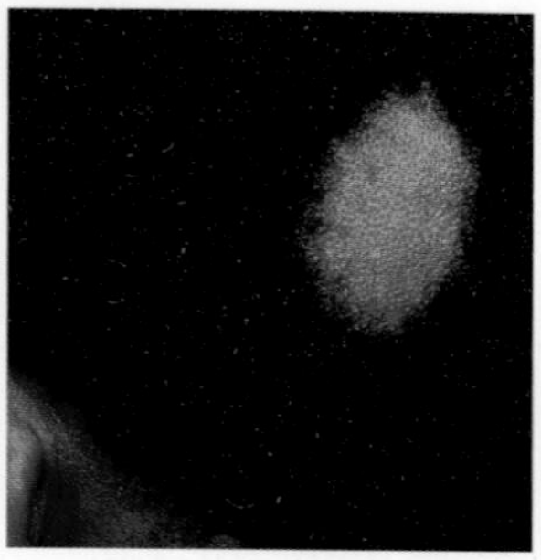	Baldness in areas of the scalp (alopecia areata) or the whole head (alopecia totalis)	Can be caused from stress or shock. It can also be hereditary, eg male pattern baldness. Trauma to the follicles caused by excessive tension can also cause hair loss.	Avoid chemicals in weaker areas but otherwise continue with services. Advise visit to a **trichologist**.	No
Seborrhoea 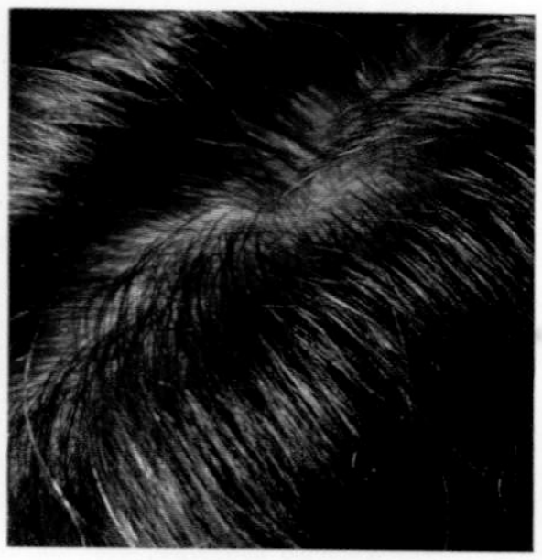	Excessively oily hair and scalp	Over active sebaceous glands. Can also be caused by irritants – physical or chemical.	Scalp treatments will improve the condition. Normal salon services can be offered. Refer to a trichologist in extreme cases.	No

Adverse skin and scalp conditions – non-infectious conditions

Condition	Description	Cause	Treatment	Infectious?
Acne	Raised spots on the face, inflamed and sore	Increased sebum and blocked pores	Refer to GP or dermatologist. Salon services can be carried out but avoid chemicals on any broken skin and take care with the comb when cutting around the hairline.	No

Dermatologist

A specialist who diagnoses and treats skin disorders

Trichologist

A person who is qualified to diagnose and treat hair and scalp diseases and disorders

 SmartScreen 203 handout 5 and worksheet 11

SUSPECTED INFECTIONS AND INFESTATIONS

Condition	Description	Cause	Treatment	Infectious?
Bacterial infections				
Impetigo	Yellow crusty spots on the skin	A bacterial infection, sometimes caused as a secondary condition to head lice as a result of scratching	No salon services can be offered. Refer to GP.	Yes
Folliculitis	Inflammation of the hair follicles	A bacterial infection, which can be caused by harsh physical or chemical actions	No salon services can be offered. Refer to GP.	Yes

Condition	Description	Cause	Treatment	Infectious?
Furunculosis 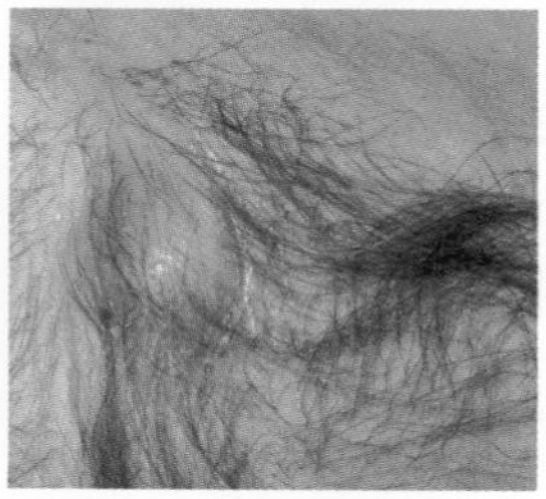	Boils or abscesses	A bacterial infection of the hair follicle	No salon services can be offered. Refer to GP.	Yes

Viral infections

Condition	Description	Cause	Treatment	Infectious?
Herpes simplex 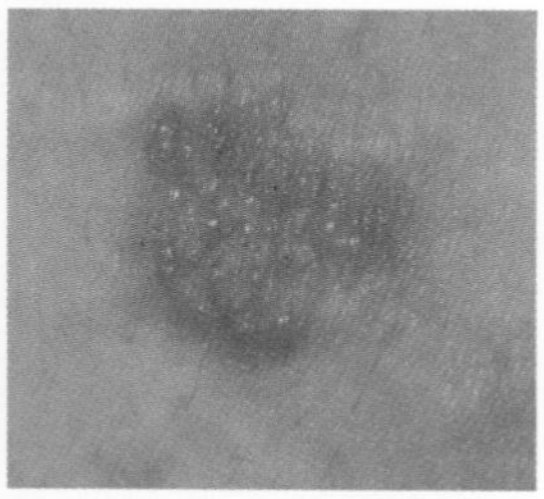	Cold sore	Exposure to heat or cold, cross-contamination or reaction to food or drugs	As this infection is on the face, treatment on the hair can be carried out with care. Refer to GP.	Yes
Influenza 	Common cold and infection of the body	Viral infection attacking the cells in the body	Refer to GP or pharmacy. Avoid treating infectious clients.	Yes
Warts 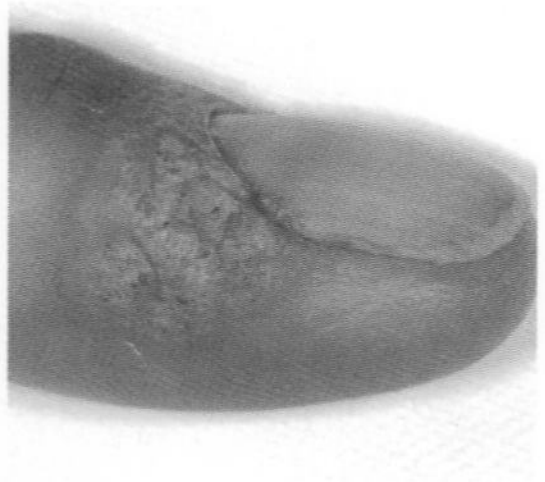	Warts or verrucas look like hard raised lumps on the skin	Viral infection in the lower epidermis, causing the cells to multiply and harden	If there are warts on the head avoid the area. Do not proceed with the service if the warts are open, sore or weeping.	Yes

Fungal infections

Condition	Description	Cause	Treatment	Infectious?
Tinea capitis 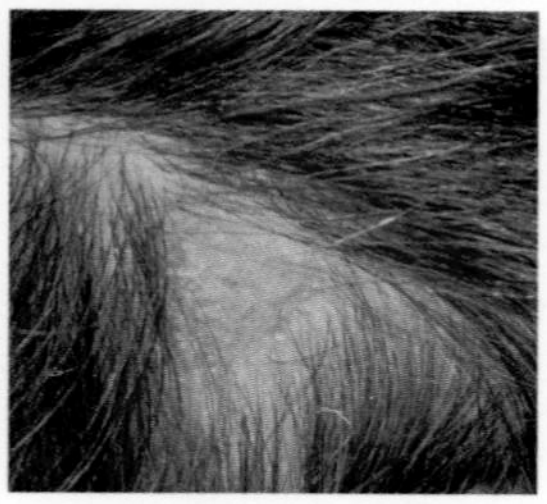	Ringworm – red ring surrounding a grey patch of skin	Fungal infection	No salon services can be offered. Refer to GP.	Yes

Condition	Description	Cause	Treatment	Infectious?
Pityriasis capitis	Dandruff Dry or oily scaling scalp, yellow in appearance and can smell	Over-production of skin cells or a fungal infection. Can also be stress-related or caused by irritants – physical or chemical	No salon services can be offered **if** caused by fungal infection. Refer to GP/ pharmacy.	Yes, if fungal infection

Infestations

Condition	Description	Cause	Treatment	Infectious?
Scabies	A very itchy rash in the folds of the skin, normally the midriff or inside of arms and thighs	Infestation of an itch mite, burrowing into the skin and laying its eggs	No salon services can be offered. Refer to GP.	Yes
Pediculosis capitis	Head lice and nits (eggs)	Infestation and cross-contamination. The head louse feeds off the blood in the scalp and lays its eggs on the hair shaft close to the warmth of the scalp	No salon services can be offered. Refer to GP/ pharmacy.	Yes

HANDY HINTS

Always record any contra-indications identified on the client record card for the following reasons:

- to prove what action you have taken
- for future reference
- in case of any legal action.

WHY DON'T YOU...

Research other infectious and non-infectious conditions, such as sycosis, tinea pedis and herpes zoster.

HANDY HINTS

If you are unsure of your diagnosis, ask for a second opinion from a senior stylist. Refer your client to the chemist or to their GP for further guidance.

Do not name any diagnosis when discussing the service with your client – just in case your diagnosis is incorrect.

IDENTIFYING FACTORS THAT LIMIT OR AFFECT SERVICES

The diagram below shows factors that might affect the service and must be considered.

The points shown in the diagram might only have minor effects in some cases. The following table shows the effects the factors might have on the service.

Factors	Effect on the service
Hair growth patterns 	Hair growth patterns may affect the choice of certain hairstyles; fringes may need to be avoided if a client has a cowlick or the hairline may need to be left longer to hide or work with a nape whorl.
Hair length 	The client's hair length may be too short and prevent a hairstyle looking as the client imagined. It will affect the size of rods or rollers that can be used when perming and setting the hair, and also for colouring techniques.

Factors	Effect on the service
Hair texture and density 	The client's hair texture and density may be too thick and coarse, or too fine and sparse to achieve the desired effect.
Client requirements 	Client requirements must always be taken into consideration but cannot always be met, due to the factors above and/or results of hair tests.
Head and face shapes 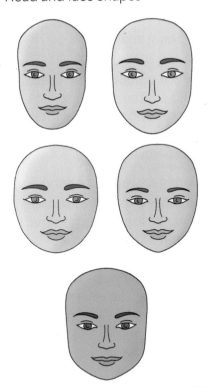	The head shape should be considered for the overall shape of the style. The ideal head shape looks a little like a question mark from a side view. The head should be rounded from the crown to the **occipital** bone and then dip in slightly towards the nape. Face shapes are taken into consideration when cutting and styling to ensure the style enhances the client's face shape. A person's head and face shape can affect the choice of style. For round face shapes, avoid styles that add more roundness, such as too much width or height; try to suggest styles that come onto the face. For oblong face shapes, avoid styles that come onto the face; encourage width, avoid height and suggest a fringe to shorten the illusion of a long face shape. For heart face shapes, avoid width at the temple area and add width near the jaw-line area; try to avoid the finished length being at the jaw-line. For square face shapes, suggest styles that soften the jaw-line. Always aim to achieve a style that makes the face look oval shaped.

Occipital
The bone between the crown and the nape area

Factors	Effect on the service
Lifestyle 	Your client's lifestyle must be considered for most services, to determine whether your client will be able to maintain their hair between visits. It would be wrong to recommend a vibrant fashion colour service to a client whose workplace would not allow it. Equally, if your client has a shy personality, a vibrant fashion look that draws attention to them would not be suitable. A mother with a hectic lifestyle might not have the luxury of the time needed for a high-maintenance hairstyle; a quick-style look is what is really required.

 SmartScreen 203 worksheet 9

ACTIVITY

In pairs, discuss which services could create restrictions to future services and might not be compatible with the client's requirements.

CLIENT RECORD CARDS

Ideally every client who visits the salon should have a client record card. Some salons create record cards for clients who have chemical services and treatments only. Whatever your salon policy is, you must follow it!

A client record card should include the following information:

- name and contact details of the client
- services carried out – including when, which products were used, how long they were on the hair for, who carried out the service/stylist's name, whether the client was happy with the end result and total charge for the service
- any contra-indications or medical advice/instructions.

Record cards can be referred to before, during and after the service:

- Before a service – have a look at the outcomes of previous services and chat to your client to identify if they would like the same service again or any variations. Check to ensure that all the details are accurate and up to date.
- During the service – update the record card with today's service and ensure you record any contra-indications. Make sure you record any client responses to questions asked about their hair, skin and scalp.
- After the service – record the outcome of the service and whether the client was satisfied with the end result. Add any additional relevant information, such as aftercare purchases made at the reception.

Consult client record cards to ensure:

- previous services are considered
- responses to client consultations are recorded
- contra-indications are recorded clearly
- all service and product details have been entered
- their personal details are accurate and up to date.

 SmartScreen 203 handout 4

MAINTAINING CLIENT CONFIDENTIALITY

Your salon will have a policy on where and how you store your clients' details and personal data. Breaking the salon rules of confidentiality can result in damage to your professional image, loss of clients and possible legal action. Your salon's competitors might also find out about company information that could be **detrimental** to the business and salon trade.

Some record cards are kept on the salon's computer and others are handwritten. For handwritten record cards, ensure you write clearly and accurately. Whether the records are stored on the computer or in a record card box, you must ensure that the client data is stored confidentially and that you follow the Data Protection Act.

THE DATA PROTECTION ACT (DPA)

The DPA states that any personal information stored must be kept confidential. Always ensure that you follow these rules:

- Only authorised staff can have access to the records.
- They must be kept in a secure location.
- They must be accurate, relevant and up to date.
- They must be disposed of (shredded or deleted) when they are no longer required.
- They must be used for professional purposes only.
- Clients must be granted access to their own record card.
- If records are stored on a computer, the salon must be registered with the Data Protection Registry, who will ensure the computer is secure.

FOLLOWING LEGISLATION WHEN SELLING AND PROMOTING RETAIL PRODUCTS

When promoting services and retail products, you should do so in a manner that promotes goodwill and is in your clients' interest, not based around your commission or salon targets.

You must follow the legal requirements of these Acts which protect the buyer:

- Sale and Supply of Goods Act
- Supply of Goods and Services Act
- Trade Descriptions Act
- Consumer Safety Act
- Prices Act.

These laws are clearly stated on the following website: **www.direct. gov.uk/en/Governmentcitizensandrights/Consumerrights**.

THE SALE AND SUPPLY OF GOODS ACT 1994

When you go shopping, anything you buy is covered by an Act called the Sale of Goods Act 1979, which forms part of this Act. This means that when you buy a product it should be:

- as described
- fit for purpose
- of satisfactory quality.

Detrimental
Unfavourable

SmartScreen 203 handout 6

SmartScreen 203 handout 8

As described means that the item you buy should be the same as any description of it. A description could be what the seller has said to you about the item or something written in a brochure.

Fit for purpose – what you buy should be able to do the job that it was made for. Goods should also be fit for any specific purpose that you agreed with the seller at the time of sale. For example, if you are looking to buy a shampoo and ask the seller how many washes it will give you, then the advice you are given has to be correct.

Of satisfactory quality – goods that are of satisfactory quality are free from minor defects (problems), of a good appearance and finish, strong and safe to use.

THE SUPPLY OF GOODS AND SERVICES ACT 1982

The Supply of Goods and Services Act 1982 is an Act that requires traders to provide services to a proper standard of workmanship. Furthermore, if a definite completion date or a price has not been fixed then the work must be completed within a reasonable time and for a reasonable charge.

In addition, any material used or goods supplied in providing the service, must be of satisfactory quality. The law treats failure to meet these obligations as breach of contract and consumers would be entitled to seek compensation, if necessary through the civil courts.

THE TRADE DESCRIPTIONS ACT 1972

The Trade Descriptions Act 1972 prevents sellers from misleading their customers as to what they are spending their money on.

You should be aware that the Trade Descriptions Act 1972 makes it an offence for a trader to quote false or misleading statements, or to knowingly make such statements about goods and services. Generally speaking, this means you have rights as a consumer – when you make a purchase the item should do what it says it does.

THE CONSUMER SAFETY ACT 1978

This is a requirement to reduce the possible risks to consumers from any product that might be potentially dangerous.

THE PRICES ACT 1974

The price of products has to be displayed in order that a false impression is not given to the client.

SmartScreen 203 handout 7 and worksheet 12

THE CHARACTERISTICS OF HAIR

During this part of the unit you will learn:

- the basic structure of the skin
- the basic structure of the hair
- the characteristics of hair
- about general factors that contribute to healthy hair.

THE BASIC STRUCTURE OF THE SKIN

It is vital that you analyse your client's hair, skin and scalp during the consultation and throughout the service to identify factors that may affect the service or the products available for use. Before you can begin to understand how and why you analyse the hair, skin and scalp, you must first understand their structure and functions.

The hair on our head helps to protect our scalp and keeps us warm. The skin and scalp have three main layers, each with a role to play.

THE EPIDERMIS LAYER

The outer layer of the skin is called the **epidermis**. There are a few nerve endings but no blood supply to this layer. The epidermis is made up of five main layers, which protect us from bacteria and temperature changes and are regularly replaced. House dust is partly made up of the epidermis that our bodies have shed. Our whole body is covered with the epidermis, which varies in thickness; it is thickest on the soles of our feet and is thinnest on our eyelids.

The epidermis is made up of five layers: stratum corneum, stratum lucidum, stratum granulosum, stratum spinosum and stratum germinativum.

The top three layers contain dead cells, one layer contains old cells and the bottom layer is constantly producing new cell growth.

THE DERMIS LAYER

The **dermis** attaches the epidermis to the **subcutaneous layer** and passes nutrients between the two layers. It is this layer that provides strength and elasticity to the skin. The nerve endings, hair follicles, **arrector pili muscles**, **suderoforous glands** and **sebaceous glands** stretch from here to the epidermis.

THE SUBCUTANEOUS LAYER

The subcutaneous layer is fatty tissue that is attached to the dermis layer. Its functions are to keep us warm and supply nutrients via the blood supply. This layer is much thicker on the body than on the head.

HANDY HINTS

The main activities of the skin take place within the dermis and subcutaneous layers.

Epidermis
Outermost layer of the skin

HANDY HINTS

The function of the epidermis is to protect the dermis.

Dermis
Middle layer of the skin

Subcutaneous layer
Layer of fatty tissue

Arrector pili muscle
Muscle attached to the hair follicle at one end and dermal tissue on the other

Suderoforous glands
Glands in the skin that secrete sweat

Sebaceous glands
Glands in the skin attached to the hair follicle that secrete oil

Along the hair follicles are **sebaceous glands**. These produce oil called sebum which naturally protects and conditions the hair. An average hair follicle contains up to three sebaceous glands. Overactive sebaceous glands – or more than three – can cause excessively oily hair.

Above the hair bulb is the **hair follicle**, where the hair grows from. The follicle stretches from the hair bulb through to the epidermis. The hair seen outside the follicle and above the epidermis is known as the hair shaft; the remainder, below the skin's surface, is the hair root.

The **arrector pili** muscle is attached to the hair follicle and the epidermis. When we are cold or scared this muscle contracts and causes the hairs to lift. As we only have very fine downy hair on the body this action does not do much to keep us warm, but in mammals with hair or fur all over their bodies, it traps a warm layer of air between the hairs and protects them from the cold.

Suderoforous glands (sweat glands) travel from just above the subcutaneous layer through the dermis and up to the epidermis. They contain water which is released as perspiration through sweat pores to cool us down when we are hot.

Hair shaft

Sweat pore

Nerves travel through the **subcutaneous layer**, into the dermis and attach to the lower layers of the epidermis. When we shed skin it does not hurt, but cutting or bruising ourselves does because we have triggered the nerve endings. Nerves also attach to the hair follicle, causing discomfort if the hair is pulled.

Epidermis

Dermis

Subcutaneous layer

The **matrix**, which is wrapped around the dermal papilla, forms the new hair bulb by producing cells called melanocytes. These are made from keratin and are the fastest growing cells in the body.

The **dermal papilla** nourishes the hair follicles and supplies food and oxygen to the hair and skin from blood cells via capillaries, arteries and veins.

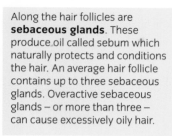 SmartScreen 203 worksheet 4

Vellus hair

Fine, downy hair that appears all over our bodies, except for the palms of the hands and soles of the feet

Terminal hair

The hair on our heads, underarms and genital areas of the body

THE BASIC STRUCTURE OF THE HAIR

Hair covers the entire body except for the palms of our hands and soles of our feet. Body hair is called **vellus hair**; the hair on the head is referred to as **terminal hair**.

THE HAIR SHAFT

The hair shaft is made up of three main layers, two of which you must be familiar with: the cuticle and cortex layers. These two layers play a huge part in all areas of hairdressing and can affect the outcomes of services and products available for use. The third layer is the medulla.

The cuticle layer

The outer layer of the hair is called the **cuticle** and is made up of many layers of transparent, overlapping scales which protect the hair. The cuticle scales lift when chemicals are added to the hair to allow penetration of the chemical into the layer underneath. Heat can also open the cuticle layer. Ideally the cuticle scales should be closed and lie smoothly from root to tip. Shiny, healthy hair that reflects light does so because the cuticle scales are closed and smooth, and therefore non-porous. Dull, **lacklustre**-looking hair appears flat and absorbs the light because the cuticle scales are damaged or open, and the hair is therefore **porous**.

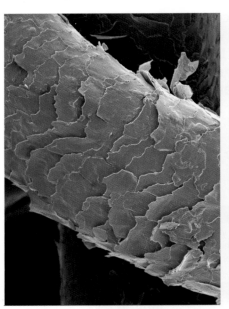

Damaged cuticle absorbing light

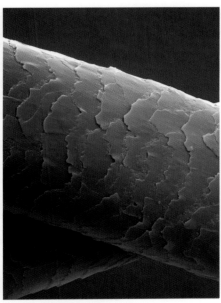

Smooth cuticle reflecting light

Cuticle
Outer layer of the hair

Lacklustre
Drab

Porous
Absorbs liquid

> **HANDY HINTS**
>
> Cuticle scales are often described as looking like 'fish scales' or 'overlapping roof tiles'; they overlap from root to point.

> **HANDY HINTS**
>
> Different hair types have varying layers of cuticle: **Caucasian** hair types have four to seven layers, African hair types have seven to eleven and Asian hair types have up to eleven layers.

Caucasian
Light-skinned

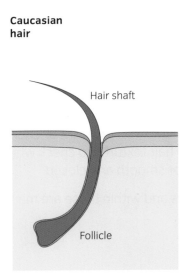

Caucasian hair

Hair shaft

Follicle

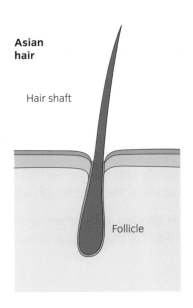

Asian hair

Hair shaft

Follicle

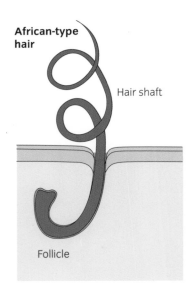

African-type hair

Hair shaft

Follicle

Cortex
Middle layer of the hair

Medulla
Central layer of the hair

The structure of the hair

SmartScreen 203 handout 3 and worksheet 3

The cortex layer

The **cortex** is the middle section and most exciting layer of the hair. Your natural hair colour is determined by the cortex: it is here that artificial colouring takes place. It is this layer that holds the bonds which hold the components of your hair in place and determine whether your hair is naturally curly, wavy or straight. When hair is temporarily or permanently changed from curly to straight or straight to curly, this takes place here in the cortex. The cortex is the main body of the hair, giving the hair its strength and elasticity.

The medulla layer

The **medulla** is the least interesting layer of the hair and does not play any real part in hairdressing. It is the central layer of the hair but it is not always present. Little is known about what the medulla is for, or its significance. In a single strand of hair the medulla may fade in and out, be present the whole way through or not be there at all. In thicker hair it appears to be present more often than not.

ACTIVITY

Draw and label the three layers of the hair and describe two or three facts about each layer.

HANDY HINTS

To help you remember the three layers of the hair you can think of a pencil. The cuticle is like the varnish/paint on the outside of a lead pencil and this area sometimes gets a little flaky. The cortex is like the main body of the pencil, which gives it its strength, and the medulla is like the lead.

THE CHARACTERISTICS OF HAIR

Hair is described as fine, medium or coarse. Fine hair has a small circumference and fewer layers of cuticle scales. Medium hair is greater in circumference than fine hair with an average amount of layers. Coarse hair has a large circumference and the most layers of cuticle scales. Fine hair will absorb chemicals much faster than coarse hair because there are fewer cuticle scales. Coarse hair can often be resistant to chemicals. A porosity test can be carried out on all hair textures to check whether the cuticle scales are rough and open, or smooth and closed.

Hair is divided into three main hair types and within these are many variations of thickness and texture.

HAIR TYPES

Caucasian or European hair is generally referred to as wavy; this is because of the way the hair grows out of the hair follicle. The hair shaft is oval with around four to seven layers of cuticle scales.

Asian hair is very straight and grows directly up from the hair follicle. It is round shaped and has about eleven layers of cuticle scales.

African-type hair is very curly and grows out of the follicle at an acute angle. The hair shaft is kidney shaped with around seven to eleven layers of cuticle scales.

 SmartScreen 203 worksheet 5

Caucasian hair

Asian hair

African-type hair

THE HAIR GROWTH CYCLE

The hair grows in three stages or cycles. Our hair grows on average 1.25 cm per month (½ inch). We have thousands of hairs on our heads, all at different stages of the hair growth cycle; we each lose on average 100 hairs per day.

Anagen
During this part of the growth cycle up to 80% of the hair follicles are active and the hair is growing. The blood and oxygen from the capillaries form the hair follicle in the dermal papilla and can grow for up to 7 years or stop growing after as little as 1½ years. Clients trying to grow their hair might find it stops when it reaches a certain length; this could be due to the limited hair growth in their anagen cycle.

Catagen
During this part of the cycle the hair growth slows down for an average period of 2 weeks. The follicle starts to shrink and detaches from the dermal papilla.

Telogen
During this phase the hair is resting; it can last for 10–12 weeks.

New anagen
Towards the end of the resting cycle, new activity and cell division take place in the dermal papilla and the anagen cycle begins again. The new

hair growth pushes the old hair further up the hair follicle, which is often then completely removed from the follicle when the hair is brushed or combed.

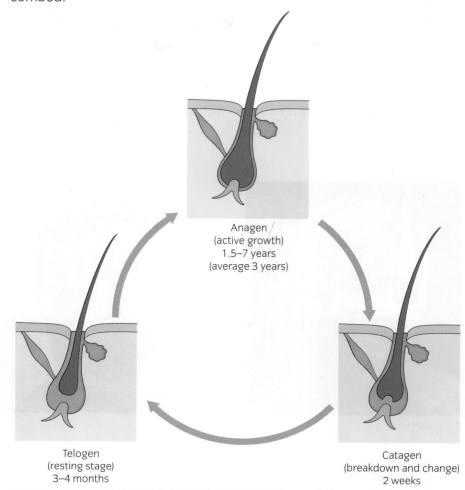

Anagen
(active growth)
1.5–7 years
(average 3 years)

Telogen
(resting stage)
3–4 months

Catagen
(breakdown and change)
2 weeks

Hair growth cycle

 SmartScreen 203 handout 3 and worksheet 6

FACTORS THAT CONTRIBUTE TO HEALTHY HAIR

Our physical health and diet contribute to our hair's condition. Eating healthily and maintaining a balanced diet help to feed the hair and skin with the nutrients they require. Exercise helps to improve blood flow and move oxygen around the body, improving the condition of the hair and promoting new hair growth. However, too much wind or sun can have a negative effect on the hair's condition, so it might be necessary to advise your client to wear a hat and use conditioning treatments and sun protections. Medication and illness can affect the hair, as can pregnancy and hormonal changes. Excessive use of heated appliances and chemical work on the hair will also cause physical damage to the hair. You must always discuss these issues sensitively with your client to get a thorough understanding of their situation, and to be able to offer the most suitable services.

 SmartScreen 203 worksheet 8

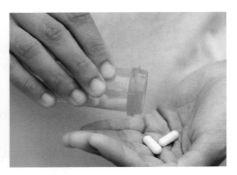

HANDY HINTS

Avoiding excessive heat and chemicals, using good conditioning products and maintaining a balanced diet with exercise all help to contribute to healthy hair.

SmartScreen 203 revision cards and sample questions

Turn to page 485 for the answers.

1 A good consultation before the service is essential:

   a To support understanding between the stylist and client.

   b To ensure that the client is happy.

   c To enable the client to manage their own hair.

   d To diagnose any medical conditions affecting the service.

2 **Statement 1:**
During consultation it is advisable to avoid technical jargon.

Statement 2:
Open questions are a good method of gaining information and closed questions will help to confirm service requirements.

Which **one** of the following is correct for the above statements?

	Statement 1	Statement 2
a	True	True
b	True	False
c	False	True
d	False	False

3 Which **one** of the following identifies the tests that must be carried out before every colour treatment?

   a Skin, porosity, elasticity and strand.

   b Skin, porosity and incompatibility.

   c Test cutting, strand and skin.

   d Elasticity, porosity and skin.

4 Which **one** of the following is not a contra-indication to hairdressing services?

   a History of allergies.

   b Suspected infections.

   c Cuts to the scalp.

   d Excessively oily scalp.

5 **Statement 1:**
Pediculosis capitis can be treated in the salon with a mildly medicated shampoo to stop itchiness and flaking.

Statement 2:
Herpes simplex is an infectious condition of the skin, but hairdressing services may be carried out with care.

Which **one** of the following is correct for the above statements?

	Statement 1	Statement 2
a	True	True
b	True	False
c	False	True
d	False	False

6 Which **one** of the following identifies the factors that may affect styling?

   a Face shape, lifestyle and incompatibility of chemicals.

   b Lifestyle, client requirements and length of hair.

   c Allergies to para-dyes and density of hair.

   d Hair growth patterns and strength of peroxide.

7 Which **one** of the following is the correct name for scalp hair?

   a Terminal.

   b Vellus.

   c Lanugo.

   d Cortex.

8 **Statement 1:**
Anagen is known as the growth phase and can last for up to 7 years.

Statement 2:
Limitations to the length of the hair may be attributed to a shortened anagen phase.

Which **one** of the following is correct for the above statements?

	Statement 1	Statement 2
a	True	True
b	True	False
c	False	True
d	False	False

CASE STUDY: PHILIP KINGSLEY

People suffer great anxiety when their hair is not looking or behaving in the way they wish. Being unhappy with your hair makes you feel miserable; a 'happy hair day' lifts your spirits. Consultations are very important for trichologist Philip Kingsley, who aims for a highly professional and sympathetic approach at all times, with the highest standards in advice and treatment.

At the Philip Kingsley Clinic, consultations include a thorough examination of the scalp and hair, taking a detailed history. Patients are seen in a private room with the trichologist, where they can feel at ease and confident enough to discuss diet, lifestyle, health history and concerns. This is followed by a relevant hair treatment. Philip Kingsley Clinics adopt a holistic approach to all problems, investigating general health, family history, nutrition, lifestyle, medication and other relevant factors.

Most scalp and hair complaints can be treated in the clinic or with clinical prescription products at home, for those who cannot attend regularly.

A clinical treatment can include the application of scalp and hair creams, steam, scalp massage, infra-red, radiant heat or ultraviolet light therapy. All treatments are individually prescribed, depending upon what is required. It may be that only the cosmetic appearance needs to be improved.

Complaints, such as hair loss and scalp problems, are thoroughly investigated – often there is a combination of problems to address. Blood tests are frequently required; in some cases the trichologist may liaise with the patients' doctor or other specialist.

204
SHAMPOO AND CONDITION THE HAIR AND SCALP

The shampoo and conditioning process is often a favourite with clients, and it can be the first impression that a client has of the service about to be offered in the salon, so you need to make a positive impression. Massaging techniques can be relaxing for the client, but you need to remember that you are treating the hair and scalp too. The range of shampoos and conditioners available to enhance the condition and look of the hair is vast and you need to know which products to use to produce the most effective results.

There are two learning outcomes in this unit. The learner will be able to:

- prepare to shampoo and condition the hair and scalp
- shampoo and condition the hair and scalp.

PREPARE TO SHAMPOO AND CONDITION THE HAIR AND SCALP

During this part of the unit you will learn:

- safety considerations for shampooing and conditioning the hair and scalp
- communication and behaviour requirements
- consultation techniques that should be used
- the range of shampoos and conditioning products
- the range of shampooing and conditioning equipment
- about hair and scalp conditions.

SAFETY CONSIDERATIONS

You must always follow the salon's policy with regard to how you prepare the salon for the day ahead. Preparing for the service will involve preparing yourself, the salon – reception, workstations and shampoo areas – and when your client arrives you will need to prepare them too.

PREPARING YOURSELF

Arrive at work in good time and ensure you are well-presented and ready! Your personal preparation and presentation should include:

- a fresh face – from a good night's sleep
- personal hygiene
- clean, fresh hair
- clean, ironed clothes/uniform
- minimal day make-up (if required)
- well-groomed facial hair (if applicable)
- clean, manicured nails/unchipped nail polish (if relevant)
- clean, comfortable suitable footwear
- minimal jewellery (rings and bracelets, etc).

SmartScreen 204 handout 4

PREPARING THE SALON

Upon your arrival you should ensure that the salon is ready for the first clients to arrive. The reception area will be the clients' first impression, so ensure that it is clean and tidy. Then check and prepare the salon areas; they need to be cleaned and sanitised in readiness for your clients' arrival.

You must work effectively and manage your time successfully. Ensure the shampoo area is well-prepared, clean and tidy, with a supply of fresh towels and gowns. If you are using a trolley and applying a **treatment** at the workstation, you must ensure you have the trolley to your favoured side of working to suit whether you are left- or right-handed.

Treatment

A process to apply a product or similar – in this instance we mean a penetrating conditioner that improves the cortex condition. It could also be a scalp treatment that remedies a scalp disorder

Make sure that there is sufficient stock of shampoos and conditioners and that conditioning treatments are available. If you notice you are running low on resources, such as towels and gowns, you must inform the relevant person, or reload the washing machine/dryer to ensure a plentiful supply. If stock, such as shampoos, needs re-ordering, inform the relevant person or note it on the stock list.

PREPARING YOUR CLIENT

You must always protect your client during a shampoo or conditioning treatment with a fresh, clean gown and towel, using a shoulder cape for clients with longer hair to prevent moisture from damp hair soaking through to their clothes. The shoulder cape will also protect your client from accidently getting wet if you have not taken adequate care during the shampoo process.

INDUSTRY TIP

Some salons place the gown on the client with the opening at the front and others with it at the back; most put the towel on over the gown but some place the towel on under the gown. You should always follow your salon's policy for this.

 SmartScreen 204 handout 1

HYGIENIC WORKING PRACTICES

You must always ensure you are fit and ready for work, maintaining your personal health and hygiene at all times. Do not attend work if you have a contagious condition, such as influenza, or an eye infection. Ensure you cover any open wounds and refer any potential cross-infection, hazards or risks to your manager.

A common workplace disease is contact dermatitis and sadly this disease can play havoc with hairdressers, especially when you are shampooing and conditioning the hair. This can leave you unfit for work and in the worst case scenario, you might need to leave the industry. Dermatitis can be recognised by inflamed skin that might be red and sore, and the skin can weep and crack.

To avoid contracting dermatitis, you must:

- rinse and dry your hands thoroughly after every shampoo and conditioning treatment
- wear non-latex gloves whenever possible for shampooing and conditioning
- use a moisturising hand cream/barrier cream after the service.

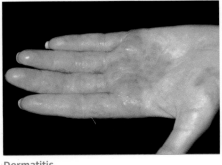

Dermatitis

 SmartScreen 204 handout 3 and worksheet 1

KEEP YOUR WORK AREA CLEAN AND TIDY

Working safely, cleanly and tidily minimises the risk of harm and injury to yourself and others and prevents cross-contamination. It projects a professional image to clients and visitors. Ensure the shampoo area is clean, free of waste and ready for your clients' service. Clean basin areas and work surfaces with detergent and water, disinfect the basin and your equipment using either suitable chemical liquids or a UV light, and sterilise tools in an autoclave.

If you have encountered an infection or infestation, remove all infected waste immediately and dispose of it in the dedicated salon bin with a lid. Boil wash the towels and gowns, and sterilise tools for about an hour. Always follow your salon's policies and procedures for dealing with infections and infestations. If you encounter an unrecognised scalp disorder, you must refer this to a senior staff member to prevent possible cross-contamination and infestation.

> **HANDY HINTS**
> Poor standards of health and hygiene can cause offence to others, cross-contamination and present a poor salon image.

> **HANDY HINTS**
> Cover any open wounds to prevent cross-contamination.

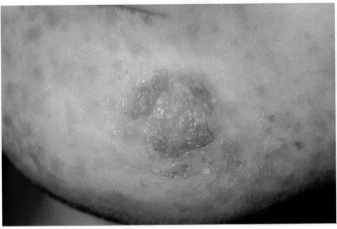

Avoid spreading infections and infestations

HEALTH AND SAFETY LEGISLATION

Always follow the Health and Safety at Work Act and when you use electrical equipment near water or on wet hair, be aware of the potential hazards and follow the Electricity at Work Regulations. Always ensure your equipment is in good working order and fit for use, to prevent harm. Use it correctly, following the manufacturers' instructions (MFIs).

When using substances such as shampoo and conditioning products, you must always follow COSHH, and as you can contract contact dermatitis. You should wear your PPE, ie non-latex gloves, to protect your hands. It is also good practice to wear an apron to protect your clothes from any conditioner splashes when you are combing the products through.

You must dispose of any empty containers following your salon policy and local by-laws, ensuring you do not harm the environment. Always rinse any empty bottles and dispose of them in the salon waste bin with a lid; ideally recycling where possible.

POSITIONING OF YOU AND YOUR CLIENT

During the shampoo process you will need to lean over, and if shampooing from a side basin you will also need to twist your body slightly. Make sure your balance is evenly distributed; stand with your feet slightly apart and avoid stretching and twisting where possible to prevent back problems and **fatigue**. You can sometimes be standing over the basin for as long as 15 minutes, eg when shampooing long hair or applying conditioning treatments, and this is a long time to spend leaning over. You need to stand correctly to avoid risk of injury.

Always ensure your client is comfortable, especially when leaning backwards in the basin. Always support their neck when they lean backwards, adjust the basin position to suit, and ensure they sit with their back supported and legs uncrossed.

WHY DON'T YOU...
Refer back to Unit 202 and list your responsibilities under the Electricity at Work Regulations.

SmartScreen 204 handout 2

Fatigue
Tiredness

Twisting and leaning at the basin can cause back problems. Standing correctly at the basin reduces the risk of fatigue

COMMUNICATION AND BEHAVIOUR

Whenever you are working in the salon, you are on show and presenting your salon's image, so you must behave professionally at all times. You should avoid cross-chatting over clients to other staff members and always ensure your conversations include clients and promote respect, equality and diversity for all.

You must always be polite and friendly to clients and work colleagues, speak clearly and use positive body language. When you are communicating, make sure you listen to what is being said and respond appropriately. Any clients that raise concerns or seem unsure about what you are saying need to be reassured in a confident, professional manner, using jargon-free but suitable terminology to suit your client's needs.

Remember to be safe at all times – follow your salon policies and the manufacturers' instructions and record on a client card any relevant information about today's service, as you or another stylist might need to refer back to it.

CONSULTATION TECHNIQUES

The consultation for any service is very important; you must relax your client and try to obtain as many facts about their hair as possible. When consulting with your clients, you will need to question them about their requirements. Along with verbal communication techniques, you will use non-verbal communication, such as body language, and demonstrate good listening skills.

OPEN AND CLOSED QUESTIONS

As we mentioned in the last unit (203 – Consultation) open questions are those which begin with 'why', 'when', 'how' and 'what' and generally give you a more in-depth answer. Closed questions are generally answered with 'yes' or 'no' responses.

When discussing your client's requirements, you should use the open questions to gather as much information as you need, and the closed questions to confirm their requirements. For example:

As you can see from the conversation on the previous page between the stylist and Aimée, the stylist was able to find out that not only does Aimée have an oily scalp, but she is damaging her own hair too, with overuse of straightening irons. She was able to recommend more suitable products from this discussion. The stylist could also ask Aimée whether she uses any heat protectors on her hair, and suggest further products if required.

As the consultation draws to a conclusion, you should use closed questions to confirm that you have obtained accurate information and to obtain clarity where required. For example:

From the second part of the stylist's and Aimée's consultation, the stylist was able to confirm that Aimée agreed and was happy with the recommendations made.

ACTIVITY

Try some open and closed questions with a colleague to get you into practice.

USE OF VISUAL AIDS

Using visual aids during a consultation can help to give you and your client a clearer understanding of what is being suggested and discussed. Visual aids can be anything that is literally visual, including colour charts for colour consultations, magazines for suggested styles and even products, so your clients can feel, smell and see the suggested products. For you as a stylist, looking at a client's previous record card can act as a visual aid too.

During the shampoo and conditioning consultation, show your client the products that you are recommending or are going to use on their hair.

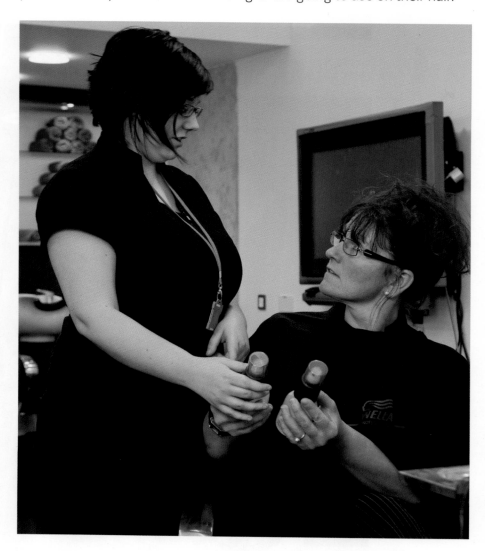

BODY LANGUAGE

During the verbal part of your conversation, you need to **articulate** what you want to say. You should use non-technical words which are jargon free. Along with your verbal communication, your client will be watching your body language too, so you need to ensure that it is friendly, approachable and giving off honest and open vibes.

Maintaining eye contact with your client will help put them at ease; smiling will make you look approachable; open palms will make you appear honest and open to ideas.

Articulate
Speak clearly

You should avoid invading your client's personal space, as this will show a lack of respect. Do not speak behind your hands as you will appear dishonest, and a poor posture could make you look idle or lazy. As well as being mindful of your own body language, you must look at your client's, as the same rules apply. If your client is rubbing their neck or scratching behind the back of their ears, it could mean they are not convinced by what you are saying. If their arms are crossed, they could be getting a bit defensive and you might need to adapt what you are saying or how you are saying it!

Listening skills

A stylist's listening skills are one of the skills most valued by clients. Sadly, many clients leave salons because they simply feel that the stylist did not listen to their requirements. As you listen to your client, repeat what is being said and agreed. You will find your client gains confidence in you and what is being suggested. Repeating suggestions, instructions and what has been said by your client gives them confirmation that you really have heard what they want, are actually listening to them and responding appropriately to their needs. Positive body language helps to confirm that you have listened, eg smiling, nodding and encouraging facial expressions.

SmartScreen 204 handout 8

WHY DON'T YOU...
Refer back to Unit 202 and:
- explain why dermatitis is reportable under RIDDOR
- list your responsibilities under COSHH
- explain what RIDDOR, COSHH and SHUD stand for.

SHAMPOO AND CONDITIONING PRODUCTS

When using shampoos and conditioning products, you must do so safely and economically. Always ensure you follow COSHH regulations. Using too much product is wasteful and the salon will lose profit; excessive use of products can overload the hair, affecting further services. Always read the MFIs to ensure you use the correct amount and achieve the best results.

THE RANGE OF PRODUCTS

Shampooing cleanses the hair and scalp, and prepares the hair for the next service. Conditioner provides shine by smoothing the cuticle scales, which improves the handling of the hair and makes combing and brushing easier.

Shampoos and conditioners are available for every hair type and scalp condition. Using the incorrect shampoo or conditioner could cause the hair and scalp to dry out, or using products that are too moisturising on an oily scalp could make the condition worse. You must always read and follow the MFIs on the products.

The following table shows the likely ingredients in shampoos and conditioners for different hair and scalp conditions.

Scalp condition	Likely ingredients used for shampoos and conditioners
Normal	Rosemary, soya, aloe vera and jojoba oils are often key ingredients in all shampoos and conditioners.
Dry	Coconut oil, jojoba oil, honey and almond or brazil nut oil are some of the main ingredients found in shampoos and conditioners to help treat dry hair and scalps. These products are naturally moisturising and nourish the hair.
Dandruff-affected	Tea tree oil, medicated products, zinc pyrithione and selenium sulphide are the main ingredients in shampoos and conditioners that treat dandruff. Ginger, eucalyptus, lavender and sage might help to soothe the scalp.
Oily	Lemon, camomile, egg and citrus fruits are the main ingredients in shampoos and conditioners for oily conditions. They help to break down the oils and slow down the production of sebum from the sebaceous glands.

The following table will help you to identify which shampoos and conditioners you should use for each hair and scalp condition:

Hair and scalp condition	Which products should I use?
Normal 	For normal hair/scalp condition, you can use a normal shampoo and surface conditioner.
Dry scalp 	Use a moisturising shampoo and a dry scalp treatment. You may need a light surface conditioner on the mid-lengths and ends of the hair too.
Dandruff-affected (pityriasis capitis) 	If it is dry or stress-related dandruff, caused by an over-production of skin cells, then a medicated shampoo can be used. Use a conditioner to suit the hair condition and a leave-in scalp treatment to aid dandruff control.
Oily (seborrhoea) 	If the hair is in need of a good cleanse, use a shampoo for oily hair and a surface conditioner on the mid-lengths and ends only. If the client has seborrhoea, use a shampoo for oily hair, a surface treatment on the mid-lengths and ends and a leave-in scalp treatment to aid seborrhoea control.
Product build-up 	A thorough shampoo process with a clarifying shampoo will be required. A light surface conditioner is recommended after your shampoo.

Hair and scalp condition	Which products should I use?
Heat damaged 	You will need to use a moisturising shampoo and surface conditioner. A penetrating conditioning treatment may also be required.
Chemically damaged 	You will need to use a moisturising shampoo for coloured or chemically treated hair and a penetrating conditioning treatment to strengthen the cortex and smooth the cuticle scales.
Environmentally damaged 	You will need to use a moisturising shampoo and surface conditioner. A penetrating conditioning treatment may also be required.

SmartScreen 204 handout 10 and worksheets 5 and 6

Surface, penetrating and treatment conditioners

HANDY HINTS

Porous hair will absorb the moisture from the shampooing process and take longer to blow dry. It may also catch in brushes and combs so extra care must be taken.

ACTIVITY

List the range of shampoos, conditioners and treatments available in your salon for dry, normal, oily and dandruff-affected hair and scalps. Make a list of the main ingredients for each.

CORRECT USE OF PRODUCTS

You must always refer to the MFIs for the correct use of products; how much to use and whether heat is required. If the incorrect shampoo or conditioner is used, the product could coat the cuticle and cause a barrier to the following service. When shampooing the hair prior to a perm, you should use a pre-perm shampoo. This is pH neutral and lifts the cuticle scales, ready for the perm solution to enter the cortex. Never condition the hair and smooth the cuticle scales before a perm, as this will cause a barrier to the perm solution.

Always use the correct shampoo and conditioning product for the hair and scalp condition.

- Fine hair – excessive conditioner or deeply moisturising products can cause fine hair to become limp and lank.
- Oily scalp – using a moisturising shampoo could cause the hair to become oily quickly, and the sebaceous glands might produce more sebum.
- Dry hair and scalp – using a shampoo for oily scalps might cause the hair to feel dryer with rough cuticle scales. The product is designed to break down the natural oils needed for the hair, which might cause irritation to dry scalps.

SHAMPOO AND CONDITIONING EQUIPMENT

The following diagram shows the equipment you might use throughout the shampoo and conditioning service:

SmartScreen 204 worksheet 7

HANDY HINTS

A salon assistant could complete the shampooing and conditioning service to help you keep to time.

HANDY HINTS

A brush should not be used on wet hair because it can cause the hair to over-stretch and break.

Before shampooing, you could use a soft bristle brush through the dry hair to remove tangles and loosen products such as hairspray.

After you have conditioned the hair, untangle with a wide-tooth comb.

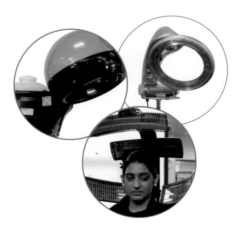

After shampooing, you can detangle the hair with a wide-tooth comb before applying a surface conditioner.

If you are using a penetrating conditioning treatment you can use a bowl and brush, climazone, rollerball, steamer or hood dryer.

While the surface conditioner is on the hair, comb through again with a wide-tooth comb.

HAIR AND SCALP CONDITIONS

As the stylist it is your responsibility to identify which products should be used to suit your client's requirements, the following service and their hair and scalp condition.

The table below shows common hair and scalp conditions that you must be able to recognise and treat.

Scalp condition	Likely cause
Normal	Healthy diet, exercise and/or using correct products.
Dry scalp	There are many causes of dry scalps, such as a natural moisture imbalance, changes in seasons and heat, and product and chemical reactions. Diet, health issues and underactive sebaceous glands can also cause dry scalps. Dry scalps look whiter than normal and have white flakes close to the scalp.
Dandruff-affected (pityriasis capitis)	Can be caused by fungi, stress or chemical irritants.

Scalp condition	Likely cause
Oily (seborrhoea) 	It can be oily because it is due for a shampoo, has been insufficiently cleansed, the client has been sweating (eg from exercise) or if the client has overactive sebaceous glands, which produce an over-production of sebum. Diet can also cause the scalp to become oily.

Hair condition	Likely cause
Product build-up 	This can be caused by the overuse of some products. Applying too much or using an incorrect product can cause a build-up on the hair. An incorrect shampoo may also prevent the products from being effectively removed from the hair. Oil-based products, such as wax, do not mix with water and need a good detergent to break them down. Excessive hairspray, sprayed too closely to the hair, can often leave a coating on the hair that can be difficult to remove. Product build-up can cause a barrier to the following service.
Heat damaged 	The continued daily use of excessive heat from hairdryers, straightening irons or curling tongs can damage the cuticle scales and remove moisture from the cortex layer. This is due to the heat from the appliances, incorrect usage and/or failure to use heat protector products when styling the hair. This causes the hair to become porous, with the cuticle scales open/rough, and decreases elasticity in the cortex.
Chemically damaged 	Too many harsh chemical treatments, such as colour and bleaching, may leave the hair dry and porous and the cuticle scales open and rough. The cortex may be weak and the elasticity poor. This can affect further services and may cause the hair to tangle easily.

Hair condition	Likely cause
Environmentally damaged 	The sun and wind can affect the hair's condition, causing colours to fade and the cuticle scales to open, resulting in porous hair. Chlorine and seawater can also affect the hair.

WHY DON'T YOU...
Refer back to Unit 203 to remind yourself about other hair and scalp conditions, and their likely causes.

HANDY HINTS
Repeating the shampoo process is recommended for oily/dirty hair.

HANDY HINTS
Repeating the shampoo process is recommended on hair with product build-up.

WHY DON'T YOU...
Identify the hair and scalp condition of three of your colleagues.

HANDY HINTS
For long hair, your hands must be removed from the head regularly to prevent tangles, and you should return to the effleurage technique in between to untangle and soothe the scalp.

 SmartScreen 204 worksheet 4

SHAMPOO AND CONDITION THE HAIR AND SCALP

During this part of the unit you will learn:

- massage techniques
- step-by-step guides
- the direction in which the cuticle lies and its importance
- the effects that pH values have on the hair's structure
- the way in which shampoo and water act together to cleanse the hair
- the effects that water temperature has on the hair's structure
- aftercare advice that should be given to clients.

MASSAGE TECHNIQUES AND BENEFITS

Effleurage is a gentle stroking movement, using the palms of your hands to apply the products to the hair. It is particularly good for long hair to prevent tangles. When applying the shampoo product, use rotary massage movements to cleanse the hair.

Rotary massage involves quick, small circular movements used to loosen the dirt from the scalp and hair. Your hands are positioned in a claw-like manner and you use your finger pads to work around the head in a methodical way to cleanse the whole head. For clients with long hair, remove your hands from the head regularly and comb through with your fingers, as continued rotary movements could cause tangles. The quick circular rotary massage benefits your client by stimulating the blood supply and relaxing your client.

Friction massage is fast and firm, it involves plucking movements used to massage around the head after the rotary massage. You spread out your hands and use your finger pads only. This method must not be used on oily scalps or long hair. For clients with a dry scalp you could use friction; as this method stimulates the sebaceous glands and the fast, plucking movements stimulate blood flow.

To condition the hair apply the product with effleurage massage techniques in exactly the same way and then use petrissage massage.

Petrissage massage is circular and very slow and relaxing. You work your way gradually around the head slowly massaging each area. Your fingers are spread apart and you use your finger pads. The slow, circular massage movements stimulates the scalp and the sebaceous glands. This can be very relaxing for your client, but must be avoided on oily scalps.

STEP-BY-STEP GUIDES TO SHAMPOOING

In this part of the unit we look at how to shampoo the hair and scalp using the correct massage techniques.

Follow the step-by-step guide below when you are shampooing the hair.

STEP 1 – Ensure your products are at hand.

STEP 2 – Gown your client and brush their hair to remove tangles.

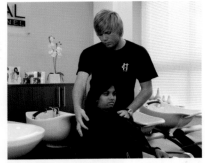

STEP 3 – Position your client comfortably at the basin.

STEP 4 – Test the water temperature cautiously on your wrist.

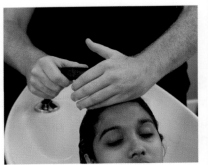

STEP 5 – Protect your client's face from spray as you apply the water.

STEP 6 – Apply a small but suitable amount of shampoo.

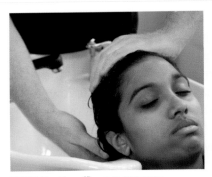

STEP 7 – Use effleurage massage movements to apply the shampoo.

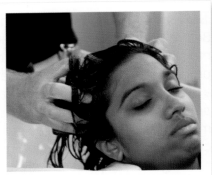

STEP 8 – Use rotary massage movements to cleanse the hair.

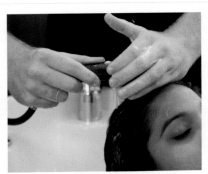

STEP 9 – Rinse the shampoo thoroughly from the hair after the massage.

HANDY HINTS

Always check that the hair is not caught between the basin and your client's neck as you position your client.

 SmartScreen 204 handout 5

When rinsing, use your free hand to move the hair, allowing the water flow to remove the product and lather from the hair. Ensure the water flow follows the direction of the cuticle scales to help smooth them. Push the hair back so that water does not drip on your client's face. Ensure that the water flow is directed away from your client's face. For your client's comfort, make sure you use your finger pads and not your finger nails on the scalp. Ensure you rinse the hair thoroughly to remove the product from the hair. If the product remains in the hair it can affect the next service and might cause irritation and discomfort.

If the hair has evident product build-up or is dirty/oily, repeat the shampoo process again – steps 6–9. If this completes your service requirements and you are not applying conditioner to the hair, follow the next steps, 10–12.

STEP 10 – Squeeze the excess moisture from the hair and blot dry with a towel.

STEP 11 – Comb through the hair with a wide-tooth comb from root to point.

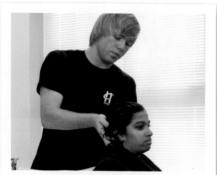

STEP 12 – Support the client's neck as they rise from the basin.

HANDY HINTS

Save water – always turn off the taps in between rinses and when massaging the hair.

HANDY HINTS

Do not rub the hair as this will cause friction on the cuticle scales and tangle the hair. Ensure the hair is free from excess moisture so that when the client sits up they will not get wet and uncomfortable. Ask the client to sit up, and support their head and back as they rise.

HANDY HINTS

Brush dry hair before shampooing to untangle, but use a wide-tooth comb when the hair is wet. Always comb or brush the hair in the direction of the cuticle, starting at the points and working progressively towards the roots.

STEP-BY-STEP GUIDES TO CONDITIONING

In this part of the unit we look at how to condition the hair and scalp using the correct massage techniques, depending on the product needed.

Surface conditioners add moisture to the surface of the hair and smooth the cuticle scales. Penetrating treatments enter the hair shaft and can help to repair the hair's structure and strengthen the cortex. Scalp treatments treat scalp conditions, such as oily/dry scalps and dandruff.

SURFACE CONDITIONER

Before applying surface conditioner, ensure the hair is free from excess moisture by using a towel to blot dry the hair, as the water will dilute the product. Apply the product to the palms of your hands (about the size of a 50 pence piece) and use effleurage massage techniques followed by petrissage to apply the conditioner to the hair. To carry out petrissage massage movements, spread out your fingers and use slow, deep, circular, kneading movements. This slow massage movement is very relaxing if carried out correctly and stimulates blood flow and the sebaceous glands. After petrissage massage, return to effleurage for a few seconds before continuing. Using a wide-tooth comb, comb the product through the hair starting from the points and follow the direction of the cuticle scales, working in sections progressively towards the roots. Ensure all tangles are removed without causing any discomfort to your client.

Follow the step-by-step guide below when you are conditioning the hair.

Having completed steps 1–9 in the shampooing procedure, you can now apply a surface conditioner; you do **not** need to complete steps 10–12 before you carry out steps 13–15.

HANDY HINTS

Hair stretches when wet, so always use a wide-tooth comb so you do not damage and snag the hair as you brush.

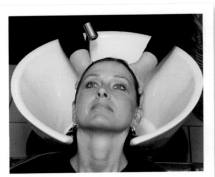

STEP 13 – Apply the conditioner and use effleurage massage to coat all of the hair.

STEP 14 – Use petrissage massage to stimulate the scalp.

STEP 15 – Comb the hair using a wide-tooth comb, starting at the points of the hair, and rinse thoroughly.

Follow steps 10–12 to prepare the hair for the next part of the service.

PENETRATING CONDITIONERS

Use a penetrating conditioner instead of a surface conditioner if the hair is dry or damaged. Care must be taken when you are using petrissage massage movements on long hair to avoid tangling the hair and causing discomfort to your client. Do not use petrissage massage movements on oily scalps as it will activate the sebaceous glands and make the hair more oily.

For long hair and oily scalps only use effleurage massage movements. For oily scalps use a conditioner on the mid-lengths and ends only.

Complete steps 1–12 for shampooing and removing the moisture, then carry out steps 13a–15a if applying a penetrating conditioner.

HANDY HINTS

Ensure the water flow follows the direction of the cuticle scales to help smooth them. If you notice there is still conditioning product in the hair, rinse the hair again, otherwise it may create a barrier on the hair, making it lank and limp.

HANDY HINTS

Before applying penetrating conditioner, ensure the hair is free from excess moisture, as the water will dilute the product.

HANDY HINTS

Using the incorrect shampoo/conditioner can create a barrier by coating cuticle scales and preventing penetration of chemical services. They can also cause irritation to the scalp, or the hair to become lank.

STEP 13A – Divide the hair into four sections (hot-cross bun – ear to ear and front to back).

STEP 14A – Apply the product using a bowl and brush. Keep hair clipped out of the way.

STEP 15A – After the massage, apply heat from an accelerator to aid penetration into the cuticles/cortex layers, then rinse thoroughly.

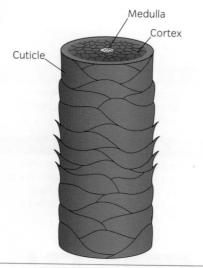

The structure of the hair

SmartScreen 204 worksheet 2

You can apply a penetrating treatment to the hair with a tint brush, and then comb the product through with a wide-tooth comb. Clip up long hair to prevent moisture from the hair soaking through the towel to your client's clothes.

Section the hair from the centre to each side. Each section should be approximately 2 cm in depth apart. The treatment can also be applied to mid-lengths and ends only, if this is more suitable for the scalp. If you are applying the product to the scalp, and when you have coated the product through the entire surface of the hair, use petrissage massage movements to stimulate blood flow to the scalp. Always follow your MFIs to ensure you choose the correct product to achieve the best result, and that you use an adequate amount.

If heat is recommended – to allow the treatment to open the cuticle scales and penetrate into the cortex – use the appliance safely. Steamers are the preferred method of applying heat with penetrating treatments as they add moisture and are kinder to the hair. Always accurately monitor the time, following the MFIs.

SCALP TREATMENTS

Most scalp treatments come in the form of tonics, oils or lotions, and are applied directly to the scalp. If the product is very watery, apply it at the basin and ensure your client keeps their head back. If it is sprinkled onto the hair, then it can be applied at the workstation. These products are not shampooed out of the hair and can be applied after a surface or penetrating conditioner. Other types of scalp treatments can be applied in the same way as a surface conditioner.

DIRECTION OF THE CUTICLE

The cuticle scales overlap each other and lie flat from root to point along the hair shaft when closed. When untangling the hair after the shampoo and conditioning service, you should always use a wide-tooth comb. Start at the ends of the hair (points) and work progressively towards the root area. This ensures that you work with the direction of the cuticle scales. After chemical processes you must always use a pH-balancing conditioner to smooth and close the cuticle scales, and lock in the moisture to prevent the hair from drying out and becoming brittle.

HAIR TESTS

Safe methods of working when you complete shampoo and conditioning treatments include carrying out the relevant hair tests prior to the service. You must carry out a porosity test to identify whether the cuticle scales are open or closed and if the hair is porous or non-porous. If the cuticle scales are open, the hair is porous and will need more conditioner and maybe even a treatment. You must also test the strength of the cortex with an elasticity test, and weak hair will need treating.

HOW pH VALUES AFFECT THE HAIR'S STRUCTURE

Our hair and skin are acidic and have a natural **pH** of 4.5–5.5. Therefore the day-to-day shampoos and conditioners we use must be pH balanced to our hair and skin, ie also pH 4.5–5.5. This ensures that the hair and skin's natural moisture is maintained, and the cuticle scales are closed. The pH scale has a range of pH 0–14. Acidic products (pH 0–6.9) close the cuticle. Alkaline products (pH 7.1–14) open/lift the cuticle scales.

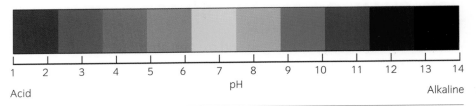

Acid

pH

Alkaline

The pH scale showing acid through to alkaline

Acid products, pH 0–6.9

- pH 0–1 strong acids, which would destroy the hair
- pH 1.5–4 mild acids, which would shrink and harden the hair
- pH 4.5–5.5 weak acids, found in shampoos and conditioners that are balanced to the hair and skin's natural pH.

pH neutral, pH 7

- water
- soapless shampoos – shampoos used to cleanse and clarify the hair before a perm are pH 7, which lifts the cuticle scales slightly to aid the perming process.

Alkaline products, pH 7.1–14

- pH 7.1–7.9 weak alkali, slightly lifts the cuticle scales
- pH 8–10 mild alkali, swells the hair, opens cuticle scales, allows penetration into the cortex
- pH 10–14 strong alkali, causes **depilatory** action.

The diagram below shows the effects of acid and alkali products on the hair shaft.

HANDY HINTS

To help you remember which products lift or close the cuticle scales:

Acid closes the cuticle scales.

The '**C**' in a**c**id helps you to remember that it **c**loses the cuticle scales.

Alkaline lifts the cuticle scales.

The '**L**' in a**l**kaline helps you to remember that it **l**ifts the cuticle scales.

Depilatory
Hair removal

SmartScreen 204 worksheet 3

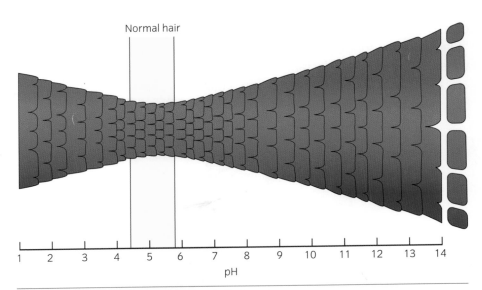

Normal hair

pH

How the hair shaft is affected by acid and alkali products

You would most commonly use alkaline products when you need to lift the cuticle scales so that chemicals can penetrate into the cortex.

- Alkali perm solutions are pH 7.5–9.5.
- Permanent colouring products are pH 8–9.5.

HOW SHAMPOO AND WATER ACT TOGETHER TO CLEANSE THE HAIR

Water is made from both hydrogen and oxygen atoms (H_2O). There is a strong attraction between the water molecules which causes them to be pulled inwards at the surface of the water, creating a skin-like layer. This is commonly known as **surface tension** and can be seen by the way water forms droplets and the way they pool together.

Surface tension
The skin-like surface layer of a liquid

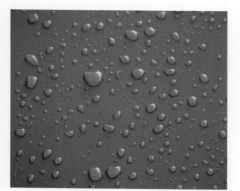
Surface tension forms water droplets

ACTIVITY

Completely fill a glass with clean, fresh tap water until it is overflowing. You should be able to see that the water's surface is dome shaped, and the level is higher than the glass! This is due to the surface tension of the water.

Gently lay a small metal paperclip on the surface of the water. It should float on the surface, again because of the surface tension. Keep this glass of water, as we will return to this activity again soon.

Oil and water do not mix! We know this from washing greasy roasting dishes in the kitchen, where we have to use plenty of washing-up detergent. This is because oil is less dense than water and therefore the oil floats on the top. Shampoos work in the same way as washing-up detergents.

SHAMPOO

Shampoos are made from cleansing agents called surfactants (the name surfactant is derived from **surf**ace, **act**ive and **agent**) – it is an **agent** that **act**ively reduces the **surf**ace tension.

Surfactants contain molecules that are attracted to water at one end and oil at the other. A surfactant molecule has a hydrophilic (water-loving) 'head' and a lipophilic (oil-loving) 'tail' (we refer to this as hydrophobic – a water-hating tail). A surfactant molecule dissolves in both oil and water and joins them together, enabling the breakdown of oils within water.

Water and oil do not mix

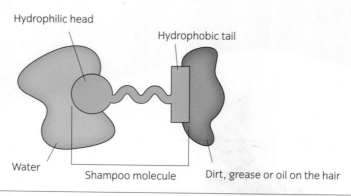

Hydrophilic head

Hydrophobic tail

Water

Shampoo molecule

Dirt, grease or oil on the hair

Hydrophilic head attached to the water and hydrophobic tail attached to the grease and dirt

SmartScreen 204 worksheet 8

When applying a shampoo and water mix to the hair, you create lather. The hydrophilic head of the surfactant is drawn to the water, while the hydrophobic tail is drawn to the oil and grease on the hair and scalp. The oil and grease contain dirt and skin particles. The lathering action of the 'head' and 'tail' of the surfactant creates a push and pull effect on the oil and grease, lifting it from the hair shaft. The more oil and grease there is to bond with the surfactant molecules, the less the shampoo will lather. This is why a second shampoo always lathers more richly, because the majority of the oil and grease has already been removed by the initial shampoo. When you use fresh water to rinse away the shampoo's lather, which now contains the oil and grease from the hair, it leaves a clean, oil-free hair shaft.

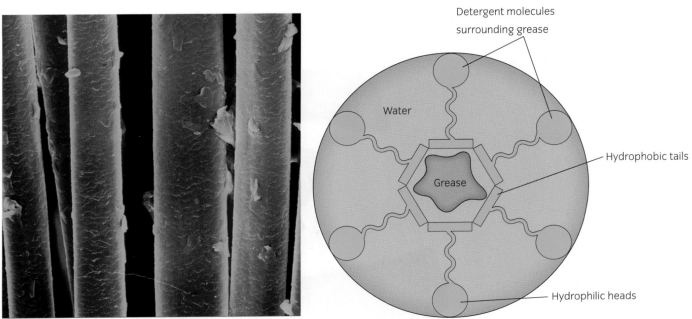

Grease and dirt on the hair

HANDY HINTS

Until a lather can be formed by the shampoo's application, it would indicate that oil still remains within the hair, and therefore further applications are required.

ACTIVITY

Coat a small metal paperclip lightly in detergent and add it to your glass of water with the floating paperclip. What happened when you added the second paper clip that was coated in detergent?

ACTIVITY

- Almost fill a glass with fresh tap water and add a couple of tablespoons of oil (cooking oils work best as you can see the colour difference). What happens?
- Now add a small squirt of detergent. Watch through the side of the glass and look at the oil pattern on the top. What happens?
- Give it a stir, wait a while, and see what happens next.
- Now try it in a different order. Fill a glass with water, add detergent and then add the oil. What happens?

HANDY HINTS

To help you remember which end of the surfactant molecule is water loving, think of ducks! Ducks go underwater head first (hydrophilic – water-loving head), leaving their tails poking out of the water (hydrophobic – water-hating tail).

HOW WATER TEMPERATURE AFFECTS THE HAIR'S STRUCTURE

Temperature affects the cuticle scales in a similar way to the effects of acid and alkaline products. Heat aids the opening of the cuticle scales and is often used to reduce the processing time of chemical services. Heat is used to open the cuticle scales during a penetrating treatment so that the product can enter the cortex to strengthen the hair and aid repair. Excessive heat, either from an **accelerator** used during a treatment, or from very hot water, can damage your client's hair and scalp. Avoid hot water when you are shampooing oily scalps as the heat can activate the sebaceous glands and produce more sebum. It is essential that you consider the temperature of the water to ensure your client's comfort. While very hot water might scald, cold water is unpleasant and will cause discomfort. After shampooing and conditioning, a cooler rinse might benefit your client to close the cuticle scales.

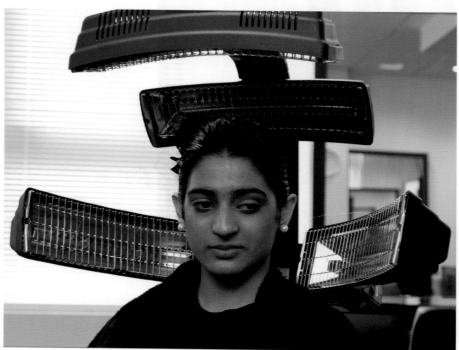

Climazone – an accelerator

Accelerator

Appliance used to apply heat to the hair and speed up a service, eg steamers, rollerballs and climazones

INDUSTRY TIP

You must always carefully check the water temperature on your hands or wrists before you apply it through the hair and take care when combing through the hair if the cuticles have been opened, as you may cause damage.

SmartScreen 204 handout 6

AFTERCARE ADVICE

The products you use in the salon to shampoo and condition the hair and scalp should be explained, demonstrated and recommended to your client for use at home. When advising your clients about retail products, you must give clear and accurate information about why you are recommending these products, and their benefits. Openly and constructively discuss the condition of your client's hair and scalp, and how these retail products will help to improve or maintain the condition.

When you are giving aftercare advice, use positive body language that promotes an open and trusting relationship. Use eye contact and check your client's body language to identify any areas of uncertainty. Use open and closed questions to really understand your client's needs for home hair-care.

You will need to know your salon's brands of products that are available to be able to give the most effective aftercare advice to your client. Give them advice for maintaining the condition of their hair and scalp between salon visits, and include how the products should be used and how often. Suggest the benefits of other salon services, such as conditioning treatments, regular haircuts, alternative colouring services, if their current colouring service is making their hair feel dry or damaged.

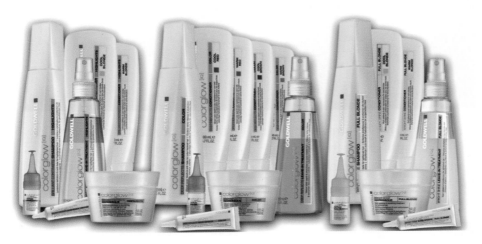

Always consider your client's lifestyle – does your client have time for further salon treatments, or would they be best suited to maintain the condition of their hair at home? Would your client prefer the convenience of surface conditioners, rather than having to find 20 minutes to develop a penetrating conditioner?

If your client's hair had product build-up, you should suggest alternative products that will still suit their particular hairstyle, but will work more effectively with the hair and scalp. If your client wants to keep working with their current styling product, offer advice on how your client could improve the removal process; perhaps suggest that your client uses neat shampoo on the hair if they have used wax products. The neat shampoo will attach to the oil-based product prior to the introduction of water and enable a more thorough removal.

Clients with damaged hair should be given advice on how to comb and brush their hair to avoid further damage, and how to use tools correctly. This could include advice on how to use straightening irons with a heat-protective lotion, how to style their hair with certain brushes to smooth the cuticle scales and even using a nozzle on a hairdryer to control the direction of the heat and airflow.

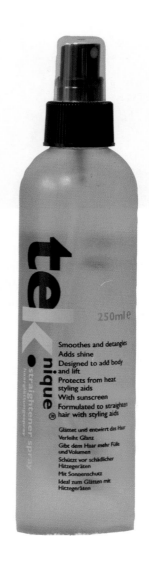

For clients who are off on holiday, offer advice on hair protection from the sun and wind, and perhaps suggest they wear a hat.

Caroline has long, fine, coloured hair and is going on holiday next week in the sun. What advice would you give her?

Claire has oily, medium-length hair, which is a little dry at the ends from previous colour treatments. What advice would you give her?

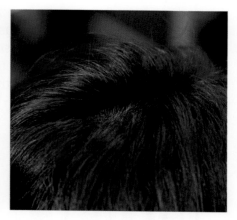

Gita has a dry scalp, medium-length red-tinted Asian hair and swims regularly. What advice would you give her?

Anita has dandruff caused by an allergic reaction. She has long, abundant hair that is very dry on the mid-lengths and ends. What services would you recommend and what advice would you give her?

Suzie enjoys going for a spin on her motorbike, but her long hair suffers in the wind. What advice would you give her?

Paul has oily-looking hair, and uses a lot of wax products to support his hairstyle. What styling products would you recommend and how would you suggest he shampoos his hair?

 SmartScreen 204 handout 7

 SmartScreen 204 revision cards and sample questions

Turn to page 485 for the answers.

1 Replenishing stocks of shampoo and conditioner will ensure that the salon:
  a Runs smoothly and efficiently.
  b Maintains a healthy profit.
  c Projects a professional image.
  d Is clean and ready for the day.

2 Which **one** of the following is the **best** course of action to take if the stylist has an infectious condition?
  a Advise the client to consult their doctor.
  b Report to the manager and do not attend work.
  c Treat the condition in the salon.
  d Immediately inform your GP.

3 Which **one** of the following minimises the risk of dermatitis?
  a Wearing non-latex gloves during shampooing.
  b Wearing an apron when completing wet work.
  c Applying cream at the start and end of every day.
  d Applying lotion to the scalp before the service.

4 A likely ingredient in a shampoo for dry hair is:
  a Jojoba.
  b Lemon.
  c Selenium.
  d Tea tree.

5 Which **one** of the following identifies the reason for using a pre-perm shampoo?
  a To ensure that the hair is prepared and the cuticle is closed.
  b To cleanse the hair and maintain strength in the cortex.
  c To ensure the hair is moisturised beforehand.
  d To cleanse the hair and minimise barriers.

6 **Statement 1:**
It is best to use a wide-toothed comb on wet hair to minimise damage by over-stretching.

Statement 2:
Hair should be brushed thoroughly before shampooing to loosen dirt and prepare the hair.

Which **one** of the following is correct for the above statements?

	Statement 1	Statement 2
a	True	True
b	True	False
c	False	True
d	False	False

7 A typical sequence of massage when shampooing is:
  a Rotary, friction, effleurage.
  b Effleurage, rotary, friction.
  c Friction, pettrisage, effleurage.
  d Pettrisage, effleurage, friction.

8 Which **one** of the following identifies the reason for using a penetrating conditioner?
  a To open the cuticle.
  b To close the cuticle.
  c To strengthen dry and damaged hair.
  d To add moisture to dehydrated hair.

CASE STUDY: RAE PALMER

Leading hairdresser Rae Palmer was named Southern Hairdresser of the Year in the British Hairdressing Awards 2008–09. She opened her own salon in 1997, which has been regional finalist at the L'Oréal Colour Trophy eight times, with a regional win in the Young Colourist category. She also raises money for charities by organising glamorous parties and modelling competitions. Here are her six essential shampooing and conditioning tips for you!

1 Always deep cleanse the hair once a week or before a treatment to remove any product or chlorine build-up. Deep cleansing the cuticles of the hair will allow any conditioning treatments to work more intensively, but also stop the hair from looking dull and lifeless.

2 Hair needs protein and moisture for good health, so when you are shampooing and conditioning the hair, use products with these essential ingredients.

3 Always brush the hair before shampooing to remove old hair and knots; it will make it easier for you to shampoo and condition the hair.

4 Always try to comb through any conditioner, as this seals the cuticles of the hair, creating shine and manageability.

5 Treatments penetrate into the cortex of the hair and replace lost proteins and moisture; conditioners coat and protect the cuticles. The two products are different; our hair and scalp need a conditioner every time the hair is washed, and a treatment every five washes.

6 Always blot the hair dry – never rub. Rubbing the hair together will damage the cuticles, leaving the hair looking dry.

205
PROMOTE PRODUCTS AND SERVICES TO CLIENTS IN THE SALON

In today's world it is an employer's market and with so many salons available for clients to choose from, they will opt for a salon which offers the best value for money, the top services and the finest customer care. So you must have the skills that salons and clients desire! Salons' ranges of services and retail products are increasing, so effectively promoting your salon's services and products enhances salon business. It is vital that you maintain your knowledge of the latest services, new product ranges and how these benefit your clients and the salon; of course you will benefit from this knowledge too.

There is one learning outcome in this unit. The learner will be able to:

- promote products and services to the client.

PROMOTE PRODUCTS AND SERVICES TO THE CLIENT

During this unit you will learn:

- the benefits to the salon of promoting products and services to clients
- varied terms used to describe the features and benefits of products and services
- consultation and communication techniques used
- the importance of effective personal presentation
- the importance of good product and service knowledge
- stages of the sale process
- legislation affecting the selling of products and services
- methods of payment that can be used.

SALON BENEFITS OF PROMOTING PRODUCTS AND SERVICES

You will need to ensure that you are knowledgeable on the entire range of services and retail products available in your salon, in order to promote them effectively to your clients. Although you personally might not be able to offer every service that the salon promotes, they need to be offered and made available to all clients. It will be your responsibility to know which staff members carry out these services and when they are available. Armed with this information, you will be able to offer the best service and make future recommendations to your clients.

The **benefits** of promoting products and services, to you and the salon, are shown in the following diagram.

Benefit
Advantage

The salon business can grow and maintain stability

Encourages clients to try new services or products

Increases in retail sales means an increase in salon profit and turnover

Improves the professional image of the salon

Benefits of promoting products and services, to you and the salon

Maintains the client's interest in your salon services and clients are more likely to return

Enhances the salon's reputation and new clients may visit the salon, increasing its clientele

Clients may recommend and promote your services or products to their friends and family

Helps you to earn more money and reach commission targets

FEATURES AND BENEFITS

Encouraging your clients to buy retail products and to try new services will be beneficial to you, the salon and, most importantly, your client.

When you promote your salon's services and products to clients, you should explain the features and the benefits to them.

The features are the **characteristics** of the service or product, such as:

- what it does
- how long it will last
- how to use it
- how much it costs
- what ingredients it contains.

Characteristics
Qualities or features

The benefits are the advantages to your client of using the product or having the service, such as:

- enhances the style
- prolongs the life of a colour
- provides **longevity** to the style
- improves the condition of the hair
- easier for your client to maintain their hair.

Longevity
Lasts longer

The following diagram shows the benefits to your clients of purchasing additional services or products.

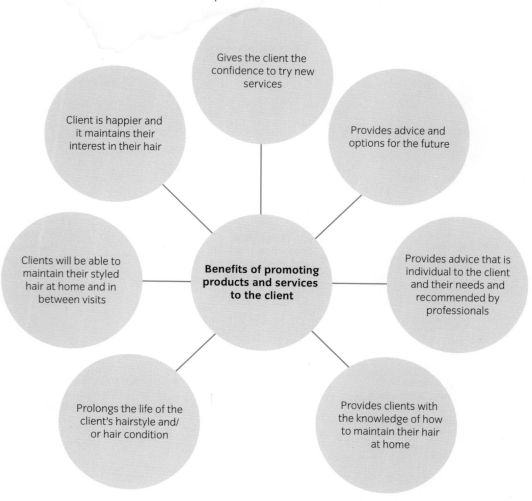

The table below shows examples of the features and benefits of some products, and additional services.

Service/product	Features	Benefits
Colour-enhancing shampoo	■ Some contain aloe vera for conditioning properties. ■ Locks in colour. ■ Returns hair to its natural pH.	■ Enhances the colour tones. ■ Prolongs the colour.
Conditioning treatment	■ Adds moisture and shine to the hair. ■ Smoothes the cuticle layer and penetrates into the cortex to aid temporary repair of the hair.	■ Hair feels smooth, looks shiny and is tangle free. ■ Hair is easier to manage and the condition is maintained.

Service/product	Features	Benefits
Root-lift mousse	▪ Supports the root area. ▪ Not sticky. ▪ Easy to remove.	▪ Hair is easier to style. ▪ Style is prolonged.
Haircut	▪ Removes the dead ends of the hair. ▪ Improves the condition. ▪ Improves the shape of the style.	▪ Hair will feel and be in better condition. ▪ The hairstyle will look better and stay in shape for longer.
Woven highlights	▪ Fine to medium weaves of hair are coloured. ▪ Clients can have more than one colour added. ▪ Less noticeable regrowth than a full-head colour.	▪ Adds texture to enhance the haircut. ▪ Can go lighter, darker or brighter.

ACTIVITY

- Andrea has a newborn baby and has very little time to spend on her hair. She wants a style and colour that will last, but will not be high maintenance. Which services and products would you recommend to her and why?

- Suzie has just had her long hair cut short, into an asymmetric style. Which services and products would you recommend to her and why?

- Angela is a new client to the salon and has very blonde highlighted hair; she would like to revert back to her natural hair colour. Which services and products would you recommend to her and why?

- Suzanne has coarse, wavy to curly hair and she struggles when blow drying to keep it straight. Which services and products would you recommend to her and why?

 SmartScreen 205 handout 4 and worksheet 3

List your salon's services and products, and describe one feature and one benefit for each of them. Note any services you are not sure about and discuss these with a colleague or your salon manager/tutor.

CONSULTATION AND COMMUNICATION TECHNIQUES

Try to spot opportunities throughout your working day when you can naturally promote additional services. If you are restyling a client's hair, think about whether your client would benefit from colour to enhance the new style, or a root perm for lift and body.

VERBAL COMMUNICATION

When you communicate with your client and make suggestions for purchasing retail products or for trying a new service, your use of language is very important. You can confuse your client if you blind them with science, or use technical jargon. Always ensure you use non-technical words and give clear, accurate advice about the benefits to your client of trying new products and services, re-using a product or repeating a service they have had before.

Pitch your tone of voice loud enough to carry above any salon noises, but be careful not to shout or come across as demanding or intimidating. Use a calming voice that delivers clear, accurate and relevant facts to help your client make an informed decision. Repeating what your client has asked of you shows you have been listening, confirms any points and gives your client confidence in the recommendations you are making.

Open and closed questioning techniques

When you are discussing new services or products with your clients, you need to give sufficient, accurate information that will allow them to make an informed decision. Use open questions that start with 'why', 'what', 'when' and 'how', to obtain lengthier answers about their requirements. Then use closed questions that require 'yes' or 'no' answers to confirm their agreement, such as the following:

Open questions

- What type of products do you currently use on your hair?
- How do you find they work for you?
- Why did you choose these products?

Closed questions

- Would you like to purchase the styling product, 'defining texture', that we discussed today?
- Shall I book you in for a restyle for your next appointment?

ACTIVITY

Identify the open and closed questions from the following five questions:

1 When did you last have your hair cut?
2 How do you get on with your current styling products?
3 Do you get on with your current finishing products?
4 If you use this heat protective spray, prior to straightening your hair, you will find it helps to maintain the condition of your hair. Would you like to buy one today?
5 Would you like to buy the serum that we discussed as well?

NON-VERBAL COMMUNICATION

Non-verbal communication includes your listening skills! You must really listen to what your client wants; this promotes confidence with your client and proves you are 'hearing' what they are saying. Repeat back to your client what has been discussed and nod regularly so she knows you are paying attention and considering her requests.

Your facial expressions and body language give away a lot of information, which can promote positive body language, but also show the tell-tale signs of negative body language. Of course this works both ways, and watching your client's body language will tell you how she is feeling too and whether or not she is interested in the services and products you are suggesting.

SmartScreen 205 worksheet 2

Positive body language signals

- smiling
- eye-to-eye contact
- open palms
- good open posture
- nodding
- leaning towards your client.

Negative body language signals

- crossed arms
- talking with your hand in front of your mouth
- scratching behind your ear or your neck
- poor posture.

Visual aids

Visual aids can really help both you and your client confirm any discussion points and clarify any areas of uncertainty. The table below shows suggested use of visual aids.

Aid	Advantage
Colour chart swatches 	Using colour chart swatches during the promotion of a colouring service can help to clarify the colours the client may like and help the client to create a mental image of what you are suggesting.
Magazines 	The same can be said for using magazines and style books when discussing changes to styles or haircuts.
Retail products 	If you are recommending any retail products, let your client see, hold, feel and smell the products you are suggesting. Manufacturers spend thousands of pounds researching what attracts clients to the visual look of the product packaging, and showing the client the actual product may help you to **close a sale**.
Equipment 	If you are suggesting that the client purchases and uses a certain item of equipment, you should demonstrate to them how the equipment works so they can see the desired result and want one for themselves.
Record cards 	The client's record card can also be a very useful visual aid for you – the stylist. This will give you a comprehensive record of the client's history, services that they have had before and may wish to revisit, or give you an indication if a particular service was not a favoured one. You may be able to see a record of previous products that have been purchased, to know if the purchasing of retail is something the client may be interested in. However, if there is no record of previous purchased services or products, do not assume your client will not be interested in new ideas. It could be that they are waiting for someone, like you, to offer these suggestions to them.

EFFECTIVE PERSONAL PRESENTATION

It is important that your appearance and personal presentation reflect the image of the salon. You should dress appropriately and always maintain your personal hygiene.

Close a sale
Successfully complete a sale

Effective personal presentation

You must always ensure you have:

 SmartScreen 205 handout 2

Dress	**Appearance**	**Personal hygiene**
Clean, ironed clothes are in line with your salon policy for uniform/dress code; suitable shoes for comfort and safety	Well-groomed hair, clean and styled. Suitable day make-up or trimmed facial hair. Minimal jewellery	A daily shower – use deodorant. Fresh breath. Clean nails.

Effective personal presentation helps to maintain and enhance the salon's image as well as your own. It also avoids offending clients and colleagues, and creates and maintains a professional working relationship.

IMPORTANCE OF GOOD PRODUCT AND SERVICE KNOWLEDGE

Some of your own continual professional development (CPD) should include training on new or forthcoming products. It is important that you ensure you are up to date with the salon services offered. To be able to sell and recommend additional or new services and products, you need to know what is available and how your clients can benefit from them. It is important that you have good product and service knowledge to ensure:

- you follow the Sale of Goods Act and the Trade Descriptions Act
- your client benefits from purchasing your recommendations
- you give accurate advice and information
- you effectively promote the products and services the salon offers.

The training you receive could be in-house, provided from your salon or manufacturer, or you could obtain training via your hairdressing supplier/wholesaler by attending trade shows. As you progress, you might wish to attend some specific training on advanced colouring or cutting techniques, for example, you can access these at Wella, L'Oréal, etc.

HANDY HINTS

Always ensure that you are confident in and knowledgeable about your products before you promote them to your clients.

 SmartScreen 205 handout 5

SERVICES AVAILABLE IN THE SALON

To identify which services are available in a salon, a good place to start is with the salon price list. The price list will contain all the services available and how much they cost. You should try to learn the salon prices and always keep a copy of the price list to hand. Ideally, as you read through the list you should be able to think of reasons your clients would benefit from these services.

PRODUCTS AVAILABLE IN YOUR SALON

You should also look at the retail product price list and ensure you are familiar with all the products available to your clients, and their costs. Check you are up to date and aware of all the shampoos, conditioners and treatments available for each hair type, and the ranges for styling and finishing products.

If you are completing a colouring or chemical service, you should recommend conditioning treatments and regular haircut appointments in the salon, and promote shampoos and conditioning treatments that your client can use at home between salon visits. For cutting and styling services, you should recommend styling products, finishing products and equipment that your client can use at home to maintain their new look.

Price list for products

Price list for retail services

ACTIVITY

List all the retail products available in your salon and identify which clients would benefit from each product and why.

STAGES OF THE SALE PROCESS

The diagram below shows the stages of the sale process.

Identify the need

Identify and recommend a product to suit the need

Explain the features and benefits of the product

Demonstrate the product

Overcome any obstacles

Close the sale

IDENTIFY THE NEED

You need to choose the most appropriate time to inform your client about additional services and products, and create opportunities for encouraging your client to try out new ideas.

Suitable times to recommend products and services are:

- when your client is booking their appointment
- during the consultation
- throughout the service
- at the end of the service.

While booking an appointment

Clients might telephone the salon and make enquiries about a service. During the telephone call, you should ask suitable questions about the service required and also ask when they last visited the salon. Try to identify what services your client usually has and suggest some alternative ideas. You can always offer your client an appointment for a consultation only, and use this time to make suitable recommendations and suggest new services.

If a client visits the salon and asks for advice on services or retail products, you should discuss with them the options available and promote new ideas that will suit their needs. If your client has already expressed an interest in a certain service for their hair and/or the need for a new look, you should maximise this situation and make suggestions to improve your client's salon experience.

Receptionist showing client the price list

During the consultation, shampoo and service

During the consultation and throughout the service are ideal times for you to communicate with your client about the service you are providing, and how to maintain their style, cut or colour at home between salon visits.

While you are shampooing and conditioning their hair, discuss the products that you are using and how your client would benefit if they used the same products at home.

When you are styling the hair or carrying out a service, again you should keep your client informed of what you are using and why.

At the end of the service

When you are finishing the completed style, revisit your recommendations and again suggest appropriate future services and retail products. When your client books their next appointment, ask them if they wish to try the new service you have suggested.

Clients who like variety and often change their image are the ideal clients to promote your retail products and additional services; this opportunity should not be missed. Equally, if you have clients who have not had a change of style or service for some time, maybe now is the time to suggest a change and promote a new image for them.

Stylist showing client retail during the consultation

INDUSTRY TIP

You should identify appropriate services or products that may interest your client by seeking information directly from them and responding **spontaneously** to client comments about their hair.

Spontaneously

Immediately and instinctively

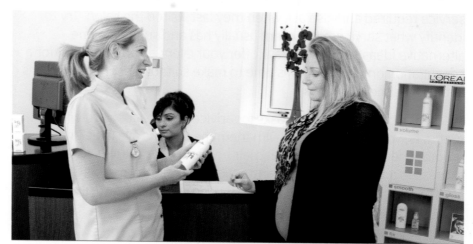

Stylist showing client retail at reception after the service

 Smartscreen 205 worksheet 4

IDENTIFY AND RECOMMEND A PRODUCT TO SUIT THE NEED

As part of your consultation and service requirements, you will naturally decide on the best products and equipment to use to achieve the desired result. When you carry out tests on the hair, if the hair feels dry then explain to your client how they would benefit from treatments and certain shampoos and conditioners, etc.

If your client has informed you that she is struggling to maintain a certain style, this would be a perfect opportunity to mention styling and finishing products that could help your client when she is styling her hair at home. You should make the most of these opportunities to advise your client on your recommendations.

EXPLAIN THE FEATURES AND BENEFITS OF THE PRODUCT

Explain to your client what the product does and what the benefits of purchasing the product will be.

DEMONSTRATE THE PRODUCT

When you are shampooing or conditioning the hair, you could suggest they feel their hair when the conditioner is on and demonstrate how wonderful the hair feels. Let your client feel, smell and see the products as you are using them. Make sure you always inform your client of the benefits of using these professional products and inform them of how much to use.

OVERCOME ANY OBSTACLES

In order to gain your client's commitment to using additional services or purchasing products, you will need to identify any factors that might influence their decision. These factors could be:

- uncertainty due to lack of knowledge
- the cost of the services or products
- manufacturers' advice
- whether they have used these types of products or services before
- the advertising material.

Overcoming client's uncertainty

If your client is uncertain about whether to commit to the service or products you are advising, then you will need to find the reason why. You should ensure that your client has a thorough understanding of why they would benefit from the products or from committing to a service. Give clear and accurate information and always give your client guidance on how to use products and maintain services, to give them the confidence to commit to them.

The cost

Always ensure you give the exact price to your client and explain any offers that are available. Your client will want to know what the cost will be when the

INDUSTRY TIP

You should suggest additional services and/or products that your client has not used before, or not used for some time.

Confused client

special offer ends and they want to continue using the product or having the service. Never assume that your client can or cannot afford the service or product; let them make the decision.

Manufacturers' advice/ingredients

Always encourage your clients to read the product labels and the manufacturers' instructions (MFIs). Your clients might wish to read the ingredients if they have any allergies, or decline purchasing the products if they have been tested on animals, contain animal products or certain ingredients. Always follow the MFIs and check for contra-indications or medical reasons why your client should or should not commit to certain services or products.

Previous experiences

If a client has already used the services you are suggesting, make sure you ask why they stopped using them. Was it for financial reasons or were they disappointed with the results? Of course, it might be that your client just wanted a change, or it could be that they were unhappy with the previous result. When you know their reasons, you will be able to offer suitable advice about how or why things might be different this time.

The advertising material

Advertising material can grab someone's attention and entice them to buy items they do not actually need. Manufacturers spend thousands of pounds on advertising, so always make sure you promote the services and products professionally and creatively in the salon.

To overcome any client concerns to committing to new services or products, ensure the service or product meets their needs. Be sure to promote the benefits to your client, clarify any uncertainties and give further guidance where necessary. Ideally, your salon should offer a varied price range of products and services.

CLOSE THE SALE

You will need to decide whether you think your client is interested or not in the service or product you are recommending. Almost every client is a potential sale; some might just re-book for their service, others might treat themselves to new products or buy them for a friend or family member, and some will want a new service. If your client does not express any interest in the service or product you are recommending, then you must close the discussion and move on to a neutral conversation. Do not make your client feel obligated to buy or commit.

Future sales will be more likely if your client has chosen to commit or make purchases for themselves, and some might return a few days later when they have given your comments some further thought. If your client expresses an interest, make sure you give the relevant information to move the conversation forward; perhaps bring the products over to the workstation from the retail stand and let your client look, feel and smell them.

You need to be able to interpret the possible buying signals, which show your client might be interested in the product or service. This could be:
- clients handling the products and reading the labels
- clients responding positively to what you are saying
- clients asking any of the following questions:
  Can I buy this product here?
  Do you offer this service here?
  How would I use the product?
  How much does it cost?
  What size is the product and how much do I need to use?
  Which of these products would you recommend for my hair?

Use closed questions towards the end of the sell, such as:
- Would you like to take both of these products away with you today?
- Shall I book you an appointment for the new service we have been discussing?

SELLING TECHNIQUES

There are good and bad ways to promote additional services and retail products. Although you might need practice to feel really confident in promoting and selling, the art to sounding confident is being confident!

To be confident you will need to know:
- what you are selling
- why you are selling it
- what the features are and how they will benefit your clients.

You will also need to believe in the product or service and articulate to your client how it will enhance their hair.

Poor selling techniques
- Avoid the **hard sell**. A good product or service, if it is right for your client, will virtually sell itself. It is your role to bring the retail item or service suggestion to your client's attention, explain the features and benefits, and then let your client decide.
- Do not fake it! If you do not know enough about a product or service, do not offer it.
  Find out what the benefits are and then suggest it.

> **HANDY HINTS**
>
> If your client would like to commit to a service that you personally did not offer, invite the relevant salon team member to join your discussion, to offer further advice and guidance. Let the person responsible for the service take over the conversation and book the client for the relevant service.

> **HANDY HINTS**
>
> Selling and making recommendations is part of good customer service; selling the wrong product or service, or trying to force a sale, is poor service and likely to result in a lost client.

 SmartScreen 205 handout 3

Hard sell
Forceful selling technique

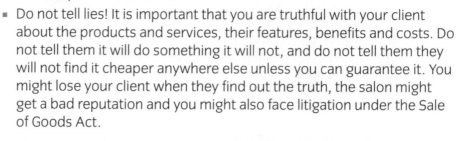

SmartScreen 205 handout 1

- Do not talk over your client. Ask your clients about their needs, listen to their answers and make suitable suggestions. You will never sell retail products or positively promote new services if you do not listen to what your client wants!

- Do not tell lies! It is important that you are truthful with your client about the products and services, their features, benefits and costs. Do not tell them it will do something it will not, and do not tell them they will not find it cheaper anywhere else unless you can guarantee it. You might lose your client when they find out the truth, the salon might get a bad reputation and you might also face litigation under the Sale of Goods Act.

Good selling techniques

- Suggest additional services and products that will enhance your client's hair and help them to maintain their style at home.

- Ensure you give an appropriate range of information and only recommend products and services that you are trained in, or know about in depth.

- When you know and understand your client's needs, be clear about the information you offer and make recommendations to suit their needs.

- Avoid jargon and speak in non-technical terms, using client-friendly language.

- Be precise, clear and accurate about the information that you give.

- Ensure your client has time to ask questions about the services or products.

- Recognise signs of negative body language, such as a lack of eye contact or frowning, and positive body language, such as smiling, eye contact and an open posture that shows interest. Remember, if your client is not interested, let it go. You can always make a note on the record card to revisit the conversation at their next appointment.
- Try not to take it personally if your advice is not taken.

ACTIVITY

In pairs, discuss occasions when you have experienced a hard sell, how that made you feel and what the outcomes were. Did you make a purchase and what were the reasons for your decision?

ACTIVITY

Design a leaflet to promote a product or service of your choice.

LEGISLATION AFFECTING SALES

When your client agrees to and books an appointment and you agree to carry out that appointment, you both enter a contract. This is a contractual agreement between you and your client. You/the salon agree to:
- carry out the service to the standards discussed
- provide the service to your client with the benefits agreed
- charge your client the agreed price.

Your client agrees to:
- attend the appointment booked
- pay the agreed price.

You and the salon are also bound by legislation and must follow these Acts to ensure the client's rights are protected:

The Data Protection Act – protecting the client's personal details by ensuring that:
- only authorised staff have access to client details
- you record the details accurately and keep them up to date
- you only use them for official use
- you destroy any out-of-date details securely
- the salon is registered with the Data Protection Registry if the details are held on a computer system.

Trade Descriptions Act 1972 – ensuring the items are described accurately.
- The quality must be as stated.
- It must be sold at the stated price.
- It must be fit for purpose.
- It must be clearly labelled as to where it was made.
- Verbal or written advertisements must be true and accurately describe the product.

The Supply of Goods and Services Act 1982 – ensuring services are provided with professional care and skill.

WHY DON'T YOU...
Practise your selling techniques on your colleagues.

SmartScreen 205 worksheet 5

HANDY HINTS
Always follow the Sale and Supply of Goods Act, the Consumer Safety Act, the Supply of Goods and Services Act, the Trade Descriptions Act and the Prices Act.

Product label

- Salon staff must be competent to deliver the service.
- Salon staff must be knowledgeable and competent to promote the products they are recommending.

The Prices Act 1974 – ensuring that the prices are accurate and displayed, so the consumer is not misled as to the value or price of the item.

The Consumer Safety Act 1978 – reducing the risk to the consumer from any products that might potentially be dangerous.

The Consumer Protection Act 1987 – ensuring safety standards of consumer goods and goods used in the workplace. Under this Act, anyone who suffers personal injury, damage to personal property or death can take legal action against:

- producers
- importers
- **own-branders**.

METHODS OF PAYMENT

When you have successfully secured the sale, you will need to determine the method of payment that your client wishes to use. Many salons will accept the following methods of payment:

- Cash – coins and notes from the Bank of England are **legal tender** for payment in England.
- Cheques – these are being accepted less and less by salons now, due to 'cheque guarantee cards' being phased out. Some salons might allow regular clients to pay with a cheque, but it is likely that the use of cheques will be completely stopped in October 2018.
- Debit cards – the salon is paid within a day or two, as the clients' money leaves their bank account immediately.
- Credit cards – credit card companies authorise payments to the salon and then request their client's payment at a later date, normally on a monthly basis.

 SmartScreen 205 handout 6

Own-branders

People who put their name to goods sold

Legal tender

Coins and notes that are legal to use as payments in the country they are being received in

THE CITY & GUILDS TEXTBOOK

- Vouchers – these are normally purchased by a consumer and given as gifts to others. The client with the voucher uses it as a cash alternative. Not all salons give change when payments are made with vouchers and often they have an expiry date. Vouchers can also be in the form of discount vouchers, entitling the bearer to a discount against the total payment due, or a special offer price voucher. The types of vouchers available will vary from salon to salon.

For further information on how to take payments and check for authenticity, refer to Unit 216 – Reception duties.

WHY DON'T YOU...
Visit a couple of salons in your area and identify the types of payments they accept and whether they sell vouchers.

SmartScreen 205 handout 7

SmartScreen 205 revision cards and sample questions

Turn to page 485 for the answers.

1 Which **one** of the following identifies the benefit to the salon of promoting products and services?
   a Increased profit and turnover.
   b Increased commission rates.
   c Increased staff turnover.
   d Increased disposable income.

2 **Statement 1:**
   When selling, it is important to show the features of a product; this means that the cost, ingredients and how to use it are explained.

   Statement 2:
   Benefits are explained by telling the client how their hair might improve by having the service.

   Which **one** of the following is correct for the above statements?

	Statement 1	Statement 2
a	True	True
b	True	False
c	False	True
d	False	False

3 Which **one** of the following identifies an ideal opportunity to sell a root perm?
   a When colouring to achieve multi-tonal effects.
   b When cutting to achieve a straight, blunt look.
   c When adding extensions to achieve length.
   d When blow drying hair to achieve volume.

4 How might the use of a colour chart support the sales process?
   a It demonstrates the stylist's knowledge.
   b It maintains a record of the discussion.
   c It creates a professional image.
   d It helps to clarify the expected result.

5 **Statement 1:**
   Taking part in relevant CPD will help to maintain up-to-date product knowledge.

   Statement 2:
   Following the requirements of the Sale of Goods Act and the Trade Descriptions Act will ensure that stylists' knowledge of services is accurate.

   Which **one** of the following is correct for the above statements?

	Statement 1	Statement 2
a	True	True
b	True	False
c	False	True
d	False	False

6 Which **one** of the following identifies the **first** in the sequence of the sales process?
   a Overcome any obstructions.
   b Demonstrate a product.
   c Identify a need.
   d Recommend a service.

7 Which **one** of the following identifies a poor selling technique?
   a Not taking offense if the client is unwilling to buy.
   b Recognising the signs of negative body language.
   c Talking over the client.
   d Avoiding jargon.

8 Which **one** of the following legislation is **not** linked to the selling of products and services?
   a The Prices Act.
   b The Consumer Safety Act.
   c The Trades Descriptions Act.
   d The Health and Safety at Work Act.

CASE STUDY: LEONARDO RIZZO

Leonardo Rizzo manages the Sanrizz salon in Guildford and heads up the Sanrizz International Artistic Team, creating beautiful photographic shoots and styles. He also acts as the group's international educator, presenting to thousands of people all across the world. Leo believes there are seven keys to successfully promoting products and services.

1 Personal recommendation – they want your professional advice

Always take the approach in retail that you are giving your professional advice just like a doctor would, so be serious and informative.

Product knowledge and confidence are vital. If you can explain why a particular product is the solution to a client's problem and explain the benefits, then the client is more likely to put confidence in not only you but the product too.

2 Great display merchandising

It is vital to make your retail displays attractive to clients. Think about promoting a product of the week or month and highlight it in a specific area of your retail section. Another good idea is to regularly change the displays to keep the retail area looking fresh, which will help attract the client's attention.

3 The salon windows are your most visible marketing tool

Using the window is a great way to entice new custom and help people make a decision to step inside. If you can show beautiful window styling, top-class products and present something of the salon experience and feel, then you are more likely to get a walk-in appointment or a retail sale.

4 Demonstrate!

Show your clients exactly how much product they need to use. Many clients use too much product and feel salon-exclusive brands are too expensive, but if you actually show them how little they need, because of the higher quality of the product, it will have a lasting impact.

5 Retail goals

Think about introducing team incentive schemes – perhaps offering prizes or gift vouchers to the stylists who sell the most. It can encourage sales, and perfection of product pitches too!

6 Plan ahead

You should plan what retail products you want to focus on over the year, ie shampoo, irons, summer/Christmas sets, and then give a clear and consistent message to your team about what you want your salon to promote by training them to push this message. Having a clear strategy enables you to see what particularly has worked and what has not.

7 Make the most of the styling stations

Use mirror stickers to promote new services or product ranges, as there is no way the client will not see this! Have take-home literature at the reception desk too, but do not go overboard – you do not want to be shouting at the client from every corner of the salon.

Mastering the art of cutting hair will give you the necessary skills to create some amazing styles, build a long-lasting client base and the foundations for a lifelong career. To start with, you need to learn the basic cutting techniques and take into consideration factors which can affect the end result. When you have gained experience in the basics of cutting hair, you can build on these skills and become more creative.

There are two learning outcomes in this unit. The learner will be able to:

- prepare for cutting hair
- provide a cutting service.

PREPARE FOR CUTTING HAIR

During this part of the unit you will learn:

- the safety considerations for cutting hair
- communication and behaviour requirements
- consultation techniques that should be used
- factors that should be considered when cutting hair.

SAFETY CONSIDERATIONS

Working safely with cutting tools is very important; you must ensure that your tools and equipment are well-maintained and fit for use. Always protect your client's clothes from hair cuttings by gowning her and using a clean towel or cutting collar to make your client comfortable throughout the service. As you have read in previous units, you must maintain your own personal hygiene. You should remove any jewellery that might get caught in your client's hair and cause client discomfort, or cause you to contract contact dermatitis. You must correctly clean and prepare your workstation in advance of your client's arrival.

The diagram below reminds you of the safe working methods that are specific to cutting.

Complete a thorough consultation

Gown and protect your client – protect your client from hair cuttings

Remove waste and hair cuttings throughout the service

Maintain an effective and safe working environment

Position your client comfortably – support their back at all times, keeping legs uncrossed

Take care with sharp tools and use them for the correct purpose

Maintain a good posture – stand with body weight evenly distributed

Clean and sterilise tools and equipment prior to and after the service

Prepare your tools, equipment and work area in advance

Maintain good personal hygiene

You must remove hair cuttings during and at the end of the service. Wet and dry hair can be slippery and cause accidents. Sweep up the hair and place it in the salon's designated hair bin.

Take care with scissors so as not to cut yourself or your client. If you do cut yourself or your client, dispose of any contaminated waste in a salon bin with a lid, cover any open wounds and take care not to cause any cross-contamination. Remember to record the details in the salon's accident book.

 SmartScreen 206 handout 2 and worksheet 1

POSITIONING OF YOURSELF AND YOUR CLIENT

The positioning of yourself and your client are most important when you are cutting hair, as the result and balance of the finished look can be affected by this.

Your body position

You must stand with your body weight evenly distributed throughout the entire cutting process. This will not only prevent fatigue and back problems, but ensure the hairstyle is balanced. Sit on a cutting stool while cutting hair short or for working on the back of your client's head. This will prevent you from bending and over-stretching and help to maintain your comfort, which is essential during the cutting service.

Your client's positioning

When gowned and protected, make sure your client sits comfortably, with her back supported by the chair, squarely in the mirror, in an upright position with her legs uncrossed and evenly balanced.

Stylist sitting on a cutting stool to cut short graduation into the nape of the neck

Good client positioning

HANDY HINTS

If your client's posture is unbalanced or she is sitting with her legs crossed, your resulting haircut may also be unbalanced as your client may have a tendency to lean to one side. Always ensure your client is sitting upright with her legs uncrossed.

COMMUNICATION AND BEHAVIOUR

As we have mentioned in previous units it is very important that you are polite with your clients and speak to them in a friendly manner. You should be clearly spoken and show positive body language at all times. When speaking with clients or your colleagues, ensure you are respectful to them and respond to their needs.

You should use client-friendly terminology and speak in a reassuring and confident manner. Make sure you really listen to what your client is asking of you and respond by nodding and maintaining eye contact to prove you are listening. Before your client arrives, it is good practice to read your client's record card and during/after the visit record any changes or update it with today's service.

ACTIVITY

List three positive body language points which show you are listening to your client.

CONSULTATION TECHNIQUES

You must always carry out a thorough consultation with your client, to identify her needs and to be able to carry out her wishes. During the consultation you should tell her how long the service could take, and how your client can maintain the look between salon visits. The consultation process continues throughout the cutting service, as you should update her on the progress of the haircut and check you are cutting to the agreed lengths.

THE CONSULTATION PROCESS

It is advisable to begin the initial consultation before you gown your client, to see her style of dress and overall image. You should ask your client about her day-to-day lifestyle and available time to commit to styling her hair. Always listen to what your client is asking of you, and be honest yet tactful with the advice you give her. You should use open questions to obtain as much information as possible and finish with closed questions to confirm what has been agreed.

During the consultation you should ask questions about how much hair she would like taken off the length and the layers. You must be specific with your questions to achieve an accurate account of her needs. Remember to use your open questions, beginning with 'what', 'why', 'how', etc, to obtain as much information as possible, before switching to closed questions. These require a 'yes' or 'no' answer to confirm you are both in agreement with what has been discussed.

Show her in the mirror how much hair you are going to remove to confirm what you assume to be the agreed lengths and amounts. Use visual aids, such as magazines, to agree on styles and shapes. Always give your client the option to try something different from her current style, and give her the opportunity to express what her vision of the finished look should be.

When you have decided on a style together, ask your client which products she currently uses to style her hair, to identify whether you need to recommend any alternative products for her new image.

HANDY HINTS

Revisit Unit 203 for more in-depth information on consulting with your client.

Check with the client how much hair to cut off

SmartScreen 206 worksheet 3

FACTORS THAT SHOULD BE CONSIDERED WHEN CUTTING HAIR

You need to consider factors that might affect the outcome of the service required. Always check the hair and scalp for any lumps and bumps that could cause discomfort to your client when you are combing through the hair. Some scalp disorders might require consideration in the style recommended, as your client might want them covered up. Always ask about scalp disorders during your consultation and check for infections and infestations which would prevent the service from being carried out. Check the head for scar tissue, and the eyebrows and ears for piercings that could cause an injury if you were to accidentally catch them with the comb.

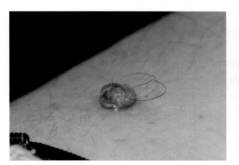

Moles or skin tags – something that a client may want her hair to cover up

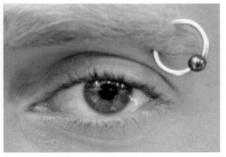

Take care with your scissors and combs, and check for piercings

FACTORS THAT MIGHT AFFECT THE SERVICE

There are many factors that could affect how you cut hair, the tools that you use and the styles that you recommend. You must consider these factors prior to and during the service. To begin with, the first factor that you must take into consideration is what your client wants! Her requirements are what your whole consultation is all about, and now you must determine whether there are any factors that might affect you achieving the desired result.

You should discuss your client's lifestyle to ensure there are no barriers preventing you achieving the desired result. Is the chosen style easy to maintain, or high maintenance? Can your client afford the time to style it?

The age of your client might also impact on the suggested style. Will the style suit your client, make her look younger, or age her? If your client is elderly, maintaining the style at home could be more difficult and you might suggest she visits the salon on a weekly basis.

Now let's look at factors outside of your client's control. The following table shows how various factors affect the service and the end result.

Factors	How they can affect the service
Hair type Curly hair Straight hair	Hair type can affect the choice of style and cutting technique. Curly hair will spring up after the hair has been cut when it is dried. Consider the amount of tension you place on the hair during the cutting service. Straight hair may not achieve the desired result, so you may need to consider products, styling tools and even a body perm to achieve the result.
Density Abundant hair Sparse hair	Density can affect the choice of style and cutting technique. You may need to thin out abundant hair to create the desired look. Consider whether abundant hair will complement the look; if not, suggest alternatives. Sparse hair will need to be blunt cut/club cut to maintain as much thickness as possible. Avoid cutting the hair too short, but equally avoid suggesting keeping fine hair long.
Texture Coarse hair Fine hair	Texture can affect the choice of style and cutting technique. Coarse-textured hair may not suit the desired look; you will need to recommend smoothing products to help achieve the result. Fine hair may also need supporting hair products and style recommendations to enhance the finish.
Head and face shape Round face Oblong face Square face Heart face Question mark shape	The head and face shape can affect the choice of style. Always aim to achieve a style which makes the face look oval shaped. For round face shapes, avoid styles that add more roundness, such as too much width or height; try to suggest styles that come onto the face. For oblong face shapes, avoid styles that come onto the face; encourage width, avoid height and suggest a fringe to shorten the illusion of a long face shape. For square face shapes, suggest softer styles, which soften the jaw-line. For heart face shapes, avoid width at the temple area and add width near the jaw-line area; try to avoid the finished length being at jaw-line level. The head shape should be considered within the overall shape of the style. The ideal head shape will look a little like a question mark from the side view. The head should be rounded from the crown to the occipital bone and then dip in slightly towards the nape.

Factors	How they can affect the service
Prominent features ![Protruding ears and strong nose/jaw features] **Protruding ears** **Strong nose or jaw features**	Facial features can affect the choice of style. For clients with **protruding** ears, suggest styles that cover the entire ear. For strong nose features or jaw-lines, avoid centre partings that encourage the eye to follow down from the parting to the nose and chin.
Hair growth patterns ![Nape whorl] **Nape whorl**	Hair growth patterns can affect the choice of style and cutting technique. For cowlicks avoid fringes; instead suggest side half fringes that work with the cowlick. For widow's peaks avoid fringes completely and suggest styles with the top area going over to one side or straight back. For double crowns suggest maintaining a little length around the crown area and ideally work the natural fall into the style. For nape whorls suggest maintaining the length at the nape area, or at least a little weight. Avoid cutting into the hairline.
Elasticity ![Elasticity test] **Elasticity test**	Elasticity can affect the cutting technique. For hair with poor elasticity you should avoid pulling with too much tension during the cutting process.

ACTIVITY

Look into a mirror and draw around your face shape using a dry-wipe pen. This will help you to understand face shapes. Ask a colleague to do the same and compare the shapes.

ACTIVITY

Draw the different face shapes and add sketches of hairstyles that will complement each one to give the illusion of an oval face.

Prominent or protruding
Sticking out

 SmartScreen 206 worksheet 4

HANDY HINTS

When checking dry hair before the service, you are looking at a styled head of hair which may have products on, or may have been styled to change the natural fall and make the hair feel thicker. Always recheck the hair type, and natural movement and fall of the hair when it has been shampooed.

PROVIDE A CUTTING SERVICE

During this part of the unit you will learn:

- the correct use and maintenance of tools and equipment
- techniques used to cut women's hair
- step-by-step guides to creating the looks
- aftercare advice that should be given to clients.

CUTTING TOOLS AND EQUIPMENT

You must always use your tools correctly. Scissors are extremely sharp and accidents can occur. Always carry your scissors with the blades closed and keep them safe from harm by storing them in a cutting case.

Your scissors are likely to be the most expensive item in your tool collection, and dropping them with the blades open or pointing downwards can be very costly and affect the position of the blades.

Care of scissors should include:

- using them only for their intended purpose – cutting hair
- not carrying them in the pockets of your clothes
- carrying them in a safe manner and storing them after use
- ensuring they are fit for purpose
- using the correct type of scissors for specific styles
- cleaning and sterilising them after use
- removing all hair cuttings and oiling them regularly
- having them professionally sharpened when required.

Care of razors should include:

- using them only for their intended purpose
- carrying them in a safe manner and storing them after use
- ensuring they are fit for purpose and using a new blade when required
- cleaning and sterilising them after use
- removing all hair cuttings
- disposing of used razor blades in a sharps bin.

You might, on occasion, use clippers. These must be maintained by removing all excess hair from the blades and oiling the blades. Adjusting the blade settings while oiling helps lubricate the entire blade area.

> **HANDY HINTS**
>
> Always clean your non-electrical tools prior to disinfecting or sterilising, using detergent with warm water. Toothbrushes or nail brushes work particularly well for removing hair cuttings and scalp debris from between the teeth of combs and clipper blades.

Sharps bin

> **HANDY HINTS**
>
> Control your tools and use them safely to minimise damage to your client's hair and scalp, to avoid accidents and maintain client comfort.

 SmartScreen 206 worksheet 2

ACTIVITY

Discuss with a colleague how you think a client would feel if you used combs, scissors or clippers with the previous client's hair still on them.

CHOOSING SUITABLE CUTTING TOOLS

For most basic cutting techniques, you will use scissors with an average blade length of 12.5 cm (or 5 inches), depending on the size of your hands. Choosing the right scissors for you to work with comfortably is important. As you become more experienced you are likely to want a selection of scissors for a variety of techniques, and you will probably buy more expensive scissors as your skill level increases.

Scissors

Although at a glance all scissors look the same, they are indeed very different. They can vary in size and weight due to the metals they are made from, and the type of cutting blade might also vary. At varying costs, you can purchase scissors that have a movable thumb area, which can make it more comfortable for you to cut baselines and achieve exaggerated angles. Scissors are available with serrated or straight blades.

Serrated scissors are most suitable when you first start cutting hair, as they aid control and grip the hair as you cut. However, if you wish to use texturising techniques and slide or slice cut the hair, these will not be suitable as they pull the hair, affecting the cut, and might cause discomfort to your client.

Straight scissors, or non-serrated blades, are the sharpest for cutting, slicing and chipping. You can use these for most techniques and can buy them from around £30 up to a few hundred pounds.

Thinning scissors are used to remove bulk at the end of the haircut and have 'teeth' or 'notches' all the way up one or both blades. Thinning scissors with notches on both blades remove less bulk than those with only one notched blade.

Texturising scissors can be used to add texture to a finished haircut. These have wider notches along the blades and remove weight from the hair section as you cut.

INDUSTRY TIP

If you are left-handed, ensure that you purchase left-handed scissors.

Thinning scissors – one blade with notches

Thinning scissors – two blades with notches

Straight edge blades

Texturising scissors

What size scissors should I buy?

To help you choose the correct size scissors, rest the scissors in the palm of your hand, starting with a 12.5 cm (5 inch) blade length. If they are slightly shorter than the length of your hand, from the tip of your middle finger to the wrist, then these should be suitable. For smaller hands, try a 10–11 cm (4–4½ inch) length, and for longer hands try a 14–15 cm (5½–6 inch) length.

The thumb and finger holes vary in size too; try them for size before buying and ensure they are comfortable, but not so loose that you could lose control over the cut.

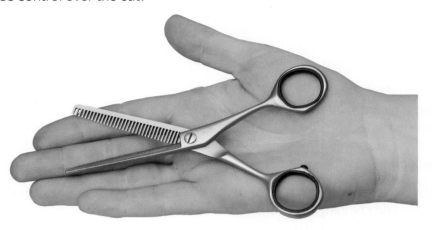

These scissors are the correct size for this hand

Store your scissors in a cutting pouch

ACTIVITY

Use the Internet to research the types of scissors available. Decide which ones would be most suitable for you and consider the following:

- How much can I afford to spend?
- What size do I need?
- What size is most suitable?
- What type of blade would I like?
- What cutting techniques do I need my scissors for?
- How am I going to store them when they are not in use?

Look at colours and styles that are available too!

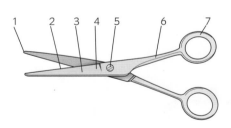

1 The points of the scissors – used for point cutting or chipping techniques and freehand.
2 The cutting blade edges – used for all club-cutting and scissor-over-comb techniques and some freehand angles.
3 The blades – outside of blade edges.
4 The heel – the strength of the scissors.
5 The pivot – an adjustable screw to loosen or tighten the movement of the blades.
6 The shanks – the length between the pivot up to the thumb and finger holes.
7 The handle – thumb and finger holes.

THE CITY & GUILDS TEXTBOOK

To help you to decide on how tight or loose your blades should be, try this simple exercise. Do not have your thumb in the hole during this exercise. Place your ring finger in the finger hole and support your scissors with your other fingers; lift and open the thumb blade and let the thumb blade drop towards the finger blade. Ideally, the thumb blade, when dropped, should stop just short of the finger blade. If the blades touch, they might be too loose; if there is a large gap between the blades, they are too tight. This can be adjusted by loosening or tightening the pivot screw.

Razors

Razors can be used when you are confident with your cutting techniques. They are used on wet hair only, to add texture or definition to your style, and to taper and remove bulk from the hair.

Razor

Clippers

Clippers can be used to blend in hair on the back of the neck, create outlines and definition, or for clipper-over-comb techniques. Trimmers can also be used to blend or remove neck hair. These are mostly used for cutting men's hair. They can be mains electrical, rechargeable or battery-operated.

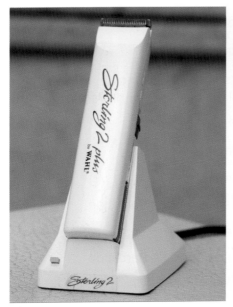

Trimmers

Clippers being used on a female client

Razor being used on wet hair

Clippers – rechargeable

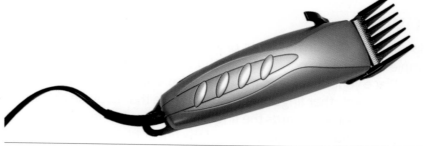

Clippers – mains electricity

STERILISING CUTTING TOOLS

The tools you are likely to use during the cutting service are:

- scissors
- thinning scissors
- razors
- combs
- sectioning clips
- clippers/trimmers.

You must disinfect or sterilise your cutting tools after every service to maintain a good reputation, ensure a professional image and prevent cross-infection and infestation. You must ensure that you protect yourself and your client from the risk of cross-contamination. Make sure all your towels and gowns are contamination free, and scissors and combs are sterile. To sterilise your tools effectively if you encounter any infections or infestations, you must boil wash all towels and gowns. Use heat, such as boiling water or an autoclave, for scissors and combs, and remember that a UV light will only maintain sterilisation, but is not an effective method of removing infections or infestations from your tools.

The table below shows the most appropriate methods of sterilising or disinfecting your tools.

Cutting tools	Appropriate method of disinfecting/sterilising
Scissors and thinning scissors	Autoclave – moist heat UV light cabinet Chemical solutions – Barbicide, wipes or sprays (oil the blades after disinfecting)
Razors	Autoclave – moist heat UV light cabinet
Combs	UV light cabinet Chemical solutions, eg Barbicide
Sectioning clips	UV light cabinet Chemical solutions, eg Barbicide
Clippers and trimmers	Chemical wipes or sprays (oil the blades after disinfecting)

CUTTING TECHNIQUES

In this part of the unit you will look at how to cut the hair using a variety of techniques, while following a guideline to achieve a range of different looks.

The looks that you will create might involve a number of techniques, including club-cutting, freehand, texturising, tapering and scissor-over-comb techniques to achieve one-length, uniform layers, short graduated- and long graduated-layer looks.

CLUB CUTTING

Club cutting is also known as blunt cutting and involves cutting the hair straight across, while holding the hair with tension between your fingers. This technique will reduce the length of the hair and layers but will retain the thickness of the hair.

FREEHAND TECHNIQUE

When using the freehand technique, you must not hold the hair with any tension, but instead comb the hair into position and cut. Use this technique when you do not require tension, such as when you are cutting fringes, or allowing for the natural fall of the hair over the ears when you are cutting hair one length.

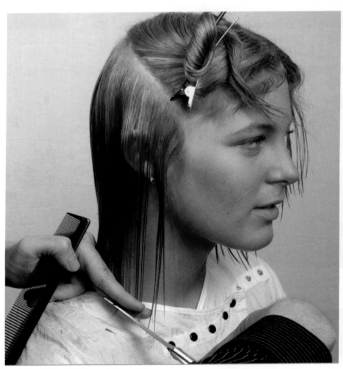

Holding the hair for club cutting

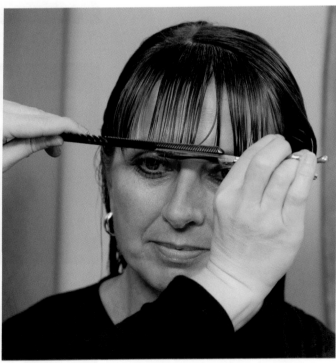

Use freehand for fringes and one-length cuts to allow for natural fall

TEXTURISING

Texturising is a method used to give the hair '**texture**'. This could mean slice cutting the hair through the mid-lengths to ends, or chipping into the hair at the tips. Scissors or razors can be used to achieve these effects.

Scissors are used on wet hair for slicing techniques, as slice cutting on dry hair would snag and cause discomfort to your client. It can also blunt your scissors. Chipping into the hair is often done at the end of the cut to remove any unwanted bulk and add 'texture' to the end result; this can be done on wet or dry hair.

Razors are used for slicing through wet hair to remove unwanted bulk and add 'texture' to the end result.

Texturising on wet hair with scissors – slicing

Texturising on dry hair with scissors – chipping into

Texturising on wet hair with razor – slicing

TAPERING

Tapering is a method used to remove the hair's bulk and reduce it to a point. It literally thins out the hair.

You can use scissors on dry sections of hair and you quickly and carefully move (slice) the scissors up and down the hair shaft with the blades open. During the process you must not close the blades, as you will cut the hair's length and the idea is to remove the thickness at the mid-lengths and ends only.

Razors can also be used on wet hair; angle the razor's blade so it can slide down the hair and as you lightly slide downwards it removes bulk. When using the razor for tapering, you can either remove just the bulk or the length too, by changing the angle of the blade. This technique helps to achieve a soft 'razored' look to a layered haircut.

Tapering on dry hair with scissors

Tapering on wet hair with a razor

HANDY HINTS

With any cutting technique you must always work with the natural fall of the hair, taking account of the weight distribution to ensure you achieve the expected shape.

SCISSOR OVER COMB

When you are using the scissor-over-comb technique, run the comb up the hair and use the comb to lift and support the hair to be cut. The hair is cut with the scissors over the comb. This technique gives a graduated effect to the cut and blends short hair into the neck.

GUIDELINES

The guideline is the most important part of the haircut. If you are cutting and lose your guideline – STOP! The guideline determines the finished length of the cut and the overall shape and balance. Without a guideline you cannot work methodically through the haircut or maintain accuracy. Even the most experienced stylists will follow a guideline.

Guidelines are the first cuts of the hairstyle. First you take an accurate clean section and then cut in a baseline length – when the length has been agreed with your client. This baseline length becomes your guideline for the overall length of the haircut.

Scissor over comb

 SmartScreen 206 worksheet 6

155

Baseline guideline (one length)

When you have agreed and cut the baseline length, you are ready to begin the guideline for the internal layers of the hair. This internal guideline will help you achieve the shape of the style. Again, agree the desired length of the layers with your client and then cut in your internal guideline to suit the angle at which the hair will be cut. You can either cut in your internal guideline from front to back and ear to ear, or work in stages, cutting the back first from crown to nape, and then working towards a front guideline.

Internal guideline crown to back

Stylist following guideline when cutting

When you have cut your guideline, every section you cut afterwards will follow this guideline to the same length, so you must hold the hair at the same angle on both sides of the head. Always ensure that your cutting sections are clean and that you take manageable size sections.

CUTTING HAIR AT DIFFERENT ANGLES

The cutting angles that the hair is held at will vary for every haircut and style.

The diagram below shows the most common angles that you use for cutting the hair for creating one-length, uniform layers, short graduation and long graduation looks.

The table below shows the angles at which the hair is cut and the cutting techniques used to achieve the look.

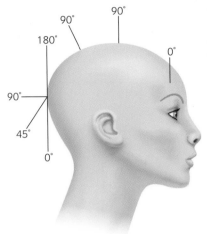

WHY DON'T YOU...
Practise sectioning and pulling the hair out at the angles described in the diagram.

SmartScreen 206 handout 3

Look	Cutting angle	Cutting angle diagram	Cutting techniques
One length below shoulder	The hair is pulled directly down at a 0° angle.	0° 0°	Club cutting Freehand
One length above shoulder	The hair is pulled directly down at a 0° angle.	0°	Club cutting Freehand

Look	Cutting angle	Cutting angle diagram	Cutting techniques
Uniform layers	Use 0° for the baseline, and for the layers the hair is pulled out at a 90° angle throughout the entire haircut.	90°	Club cutting Freehand
Short graduation	The inner layers of the hair lengths are longer than the outline shape and generally pulled out at 45°.	45°	Club cutting Freehand Texturising Tapering Scissor over comb
Long graduation	Use 0° for the baseline, and between 90° and 180° for creating the longer layer effects.	180°	Club cutting Freehand Texturising Tapering
Fringes	Often cut freehand to allow for the natural movement and fall of the hair growth patterns, but fringes can be cut under tension and pulled down to 0°.	0° 0°	Freehand Club cutting

CUTTING HAIR WITH TENSION

When you are cutting hair with tension, you must remember that wet hair stretches more than dry hair. So make sure that the end result is not shorter than you expected. You must always keep the same tension to ensure an even result. This includes keeping an even moisture balance during the cutting service so that the hair is not of mixed porosity or elasticity, which could cause tangles, damage to the hair or uneven cutting results.

HANDY HINTS

Curly hair will spring up when dry – use less tension when cutting curly hair. This can be achieved by using the wider tooth end of your comb.

HANDY HINTS

As hair only grows about 1.25 cm (½ inch) each month, it is important that you do not cut the hair too short.

CUTTING HAIR WET OR DRY

Whether you cut the hair wet or dry will affect the technique used and the end result. Hair should be checked while dry to identify the natural fall of the hair, and rechecked after shampooing.

Dry cutting

You must check the hair while it is dry to see how your client is currently wearing her hairstyle, to identify any natural hair growth patterns and to feel the density and texture of the hair. Always carry out a porosity test on dry hair prior to the service.

Freehand and scissor-over-comb cutting techniques are best carried out on dry hair. Only use thinning scissors and clippers on dry hair.

Wet cutting

When the hair has been shampooed and prepared for the service, check through the hair to identify the natural parting. On wet hair you will be able to see the hair type in its natural state, such as curly or straight, and recheck the movement of the hair.

The elasticity in the hair allows wet hair to be stretched to up to 50% of its original length, and you must consider this when you are cutting the hair wet, as the dried result could be much shorter than you or your client anticipated. Always carry out an elasticity test on wet hair. Only use razors and any slice-cutting techniques on wet hair.

THE IMPORTANCE OF CROSS-CHECKING THE CUT

It is important that your client's body position is balanced and upright throughout the haircut. If your client has her legs crossed, then the balance of the baseline cut could be uneven. Equally you must ensure that you have an even distribution of body weight too.

Cross-checking the haircut during the service and at the end ensures an accurate finish. You can cross-check the haircut at any point during the service to check for balance and even cutting lengths. Using a mirror will help you to check for balance.

For layered haircuts you can cross-check the whole cut by sectioning the hair in the opposite direction to which you cut the layers. If you cut the layers in vertical sections, then cross-check horizontally and vice versa.

HANDY HINTS

Cross-checking the cut ensures it is accurate, evenly balanced and has an even weight distribution throughout.

Cross-checking horizontally

Cross-checking in the mirror

Ensure your client is sitting straight

The final and most commonly used method of cross-checking is used as you progress through the haircut. Pull out sections of cut hair on both sides to feel if the lengths are the same. For longer hair you can pull sections forward and see if they meet evenly under the chin.

STEP-BY-STEP GUIDES TO CREATING THE LOOKS

In this part of the unit we will look at how to cut hair to create the following looks:

- one length above the shoulder
- one length below the shoulder
- uniform layers
- short graduation
- long graduation.

CREATING A ONE-LENGTH LOOK

When cutting the hair to create a one-length look, you need to take very thin sections to enable you to follow your guideline, and take into consideration the natural fall of the hair. The hair is pulled straight down at 0°.

One length above shoulders

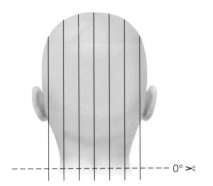
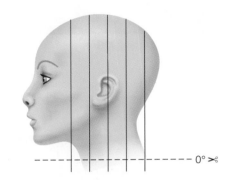

Cutting angles for one-length hair

STEP 1 – Gown the client and position the head.

STEP 2 – Use a horizontal section at the back for the guideline.

STEP 3 – Make the horizontal cut following the guideline, using a club-cutting technique.

STEP 4 – The next horizontal section.

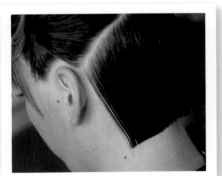

STEP 5 – Complete the back sections.

STEP 6 – Take a section from the sides to blend into the back.

STEP 7 – Blend in the side section and take a guideline.

STEP 8 – Cut the guideline.

STEP 9 – Cut the sides.

STEP 10 – Cut a fringe if required.

STEP 11 – Cross-check the cut, to ensure it is evenly balanced.

STEP 12 – The completed look.

One length below shoulders

STEP 1 – Gown the client, position the head and section the hair.

STEP 2 – Use the horizontal section at the back for the guideline.

STEP 3 – Club cut following the horizontal cut guideline.

STEP 4 – Club cut the next horizontal section.

STEP 5 – Check for balance regularly.

STEP 6 – Remove any graduation after checking.

STEP 7 – Blend in the side section and take a guideline.

STEP 8 – Cross-check the cut, pulling sections down evenly.

STEP 9 – Cut the guideline for the fringe, using a freehand technique.

STEP 10 – When balanced, apply finishing products and style the hair.

STEP 11 – The finished look.

WHY DON'T YOU...
Create a mood board of varying one-length looks and write up how to achieve one of the images.

 SmartScreen 206 worksheet 7

CREATING A UNIFORM-LAYER LOOK

When cutting the hair to create a uniform-layer look, you will need to make a guideline section for the length of the hair and one for the internal layers of the hair. The hair is cut at 90° all over.

Uniform layers

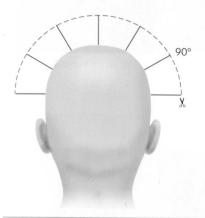
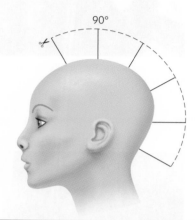

Cutting angles for uniform layers

STEP 1 – Take clean, vertical sections of hair and pull the hair up at 90°.

STEP 2 – Cut the hair in sections from the top to the back, following the head shape.

STEP 3 – Ensure you pull the hair directly away from the head, maintaining a 90° angle.

STEP 4 – Blend the length into the base guideline.

STEP 5 – Cut the internal guideline, using club-cutting techniques.

STEP 6 – Work around the back sections taking hair at 90°.

STEP 7 – Cross-check the hair using a horizontal section.

STEP 8 – Cross-check the cut, pulling sections out evenly to the sides.

STEP 9 – The completed look.

WHY DON'T YOU...
Create a mood board of varying uniform-layer looks and write up how to achieve one of the images.

 SmartScreen 206 worksheet 9

WHY DON'T YOU...
Create a mood board of varying short graduated-layer looks and write up how to achieve one of the images.

 Smartscreen 206 worksheet 10

CREATING A SHORT GRADUATED-LAYER LOOK

When you create a short graduated haircut, the hair must gradually get shorter towards the nape and neck area. The top can be cut in a similar way to the uniform layers and held out at 90°, but the sides and back of this style must be cut at 45°.

Short graduation

STEP 1 – Section the hair vertically.

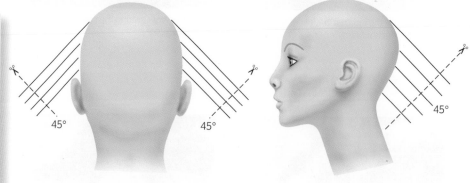

Cutting angles for short graduation

STEP 2 – Position your hands and the cutting section at a 45° angle.

STEP 3 – Take clean sections for the internal layers, and cut in your first guideline.

STEP 4 – Follow your sections around the head.

STEP 5 – Cross-check the sides horizontally.

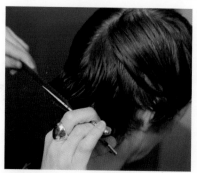

STEP 6 – Cross-check the back horizontally.

STEP 7 – Check the client is happy with the end result.

CREATING A LONG GRADUATED-LAYER LOOK

When you create a long graduated-layer look, the hair must gradually get longer. This style maintains the length of the hair. The top layers can be held out between 90° like the uniform layer and the back and sides pulled up to 135° or 180°, depending on the length of the hair and the layers.

Long graduation

WHY DON'T YOU...
Create a mood board of varying long graduated-layer looks and write up how to achieve one of the images.

 SmartScreen 206 worksheet 8

 SmartScreen 206 activity assignment and worksheet 5

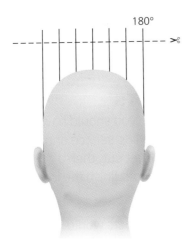
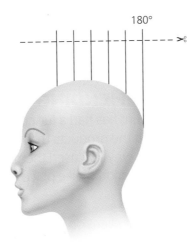

Cutting angles for long graduation

STEP 1 – Cut in the internal guideline using a club-cutting technique.

STEP 2 – Take your cutting guideline.

STEP 3 – Pull out the crown and back layers at 180°.

STEP 4 – Cut the hair using club-cutting techniques.

STEP 5 – Pull the back and side layers up to 135° or 180°.

STEP 6 – Use freehand to blend from the fringe area to maintain the length.

STEP 7 – Check the client is happy with the end result.

AFTERCARE ADVICE

You have just created a fabulous haircut for your client – when she leaves, she is an advert for you and your salon. Not only does your client want the new style to look great every day until her next visit, so do you! Every compliment your client receives about her hairstyle could be a potential new client for you or the salon. Therefore it is essential that you provide suitable aftercare for your client on maintaining the look you have created.

You should advise her on what products to use and how to use them, and what equipment would best enable your client to recreate the look at home. Suggest other services, such as a colour, that would enhance her style. Finally, suggest when to return to the salon for her next appointment and advise her how long her current style should last.

RECOMMENDING RETAIL PRODUCTS

If your client has had a full cut-and-blow-dry service, you should have discussed the products that you used during the styling service and explained why you used them. If the service was a wet cut, then a discussion should take place on how your client should finish the look herself.

Advise your client on which styling and finishing products would enhance and support her finished look. Explain how particular styling products will aid the drying and styling process, help control the hair and provide longevity to the finished result. You should advise her on how much product to use and how to apply it. If the product could cause a build-up on the hair, advise her on how to remove the product effectively.

Recommend aftercare to your clients

RECOMMENDING TOOLS AND EQUIPMENT

Throughout the styling service you should advise your client on which tools to use at home to recreate her look; and during the blow-dry service demonstrate what you are doing and why. This gives your client a thorough understanding of what she will need to do when styling her hair at home. Talk to her about how to create root lift if required, or how to prevent it. Discuss which brushes she will need and the correct sizes to use. Remember to discuss the health and safety side of styling, the use of electrically heated styling equipment on the hair and the damage it could cause.

RECOMMENDING FURTHER SERVICES

During the cutting and styling service is a good time to recommend colouring services to your clients, to enhance the image created. Adding colour and highlights to a haircut helps to add texture and definition to the shape. A modern block colour can add a striking finish to any cut. Without doubt, colour enhances and complements every look you create.

Show your client how to achieve root lift

You could recommend enhancing a haircut with subtle colours to add depth, tone and shine

Ask your client if she would like to buy any products or equipment

RECOMMENDING WHEN TO RETURN

You should advise your client on when to book her cutting service. To help guide her, explain that it depends on how quickly her hair grows. You should suggest that she returns to the salon when the style grows out of shape and when she has trouble maintaining the style, as this might indicate it is ready for a cut.

 SmartScreen 206 handout 4

SmartScreen revision cards and sample questions

Turn to page 485 for the answers.

1 Which **one** of the following describes the **best** action to take in the event of a minor cut to a client's skin?

   a Apologise and offer them a free return visit.

   b Cover the wound and enter into the accident book.

   c Call their doctor and record in the accident book.

   d Apply pressure and wait for the emergency services.

2 Which **one** of the following identifies the reason for good posture for the stylist and good positioning of the client?

   a To prevent over-stretching and client fatigue.

   b To enable the stylist to see the style in the mirror.

   c To minimise the risk of damage to the client's back.

   d To minimise fatigue and help balance the finished look.

3 **Statement 1:**
Hair growth patterns, lifestyle, piercings and scar tissue are all important factors to consider before cutting a client's hair.

  Statement 2:
Abundant hair looks very fine and fly-away and a blunt cut is needed to maintain its thickness.

Which **one** of the following is correct for the above statements?

	Statement 1	Statement 2
a	True	True
b	True	False
c	False	True
d	False	False

4 Which **one** of the following identifies the **best** way to use and maintain scissors?

   a Use only for their intended purpose and clean regularly.

   b Use only on wet hair and keep in a safe place when not in use.

   c Ensure they have been PAT tested and sterilised before use.

   d Ensure that they are sharpened and aligned once per year.

5 **Statement 1:**
Texturising scissors have notches that are narrower than thinning scissors; these remove less bulk.

  Statement 2:
Thinning scissors with notches on both blades remove more weight than those with notches on one blade.

Which one of the following is correct for the above statements?

	Statement 1	Statement 2
a	True	True
b	True	False
c	False	True
d	False	False

6 Which **one** of the following identifies the correct use and effect of using a razor?

   a Use on dry hair only to achieve a textured look.

   b Use on wet hair only to achieve a blunt look.

   c Use on wet hair only to achieve a textured look.

   d Use on dry hair only to achieve a blunt look.

7 Which **one** of the following identifies the effect of tapering?

   a Removes bulk and reduces the hair to a point.

   b Removes weight and leaves a blunt look.

   c Increases curl and density to the hair.

   d Increases movement and retains thickness.

8 Which **one** of the following describes a short graduated hairstyle

   a Hair is held at 0° and bulk is retained at the nape.

   b Hair is held at 45° and inner layers are longer than outer layers.

   c Hair is held at 90° and outer layers are longer than inner layers.

   d Hair is held at 180° and bulk is retained at the crown.

CASE STUDY: BARRIE STEPHEN

Barrie Stephen runs four successful salons in Leicestershire. His team is passionate about hair, loves to be creative and takes care that every single cut reflects commitment to the client. He has four important cutting messages for you.

1 Consultation is key; find out how your clients want to feel

Listening to the client is the most important aspect of an appointment. Nine times out of ten, business is lost because people complain that their last stylist did not listen to them properly. Gain information about their lifestyle, their time constraints and about what they want to achieve from their style. The goal is to decide on a personalised style for them.

Ask how open to change they are as well. If they bring in pictures, you might have to manage their expectations too and suggest a different cut which will better suit their hair texture and face shape.

A new cut always looks amazing with a new colour, so promote colour services too. The thing to remember is that clients want to feel they are getting a professional service where you take control.

2 Your mirror is your best friend!

Do not be afraid to check the client's silhouette, the outline of the cut, the levels of hair on each side, the way it looks from profile and move the chair around to check all the angles so you ensure a good-looking style.

3 Involve the client at all stages of the cut; work with commentary

Talk through what you are doing, for example: 'I'm going to cut this much off now', 'We talked about cutting in a sweeping fringe – how would you like this angle?' Reaffirm back to them what you both discussed in the initial consultation. Hair is such a massive part of a person's appearance, especially a woman's, and they need to know that you understood them and that you are not just going to do your own thing.

4 Show the client how to use the products

While blow drying and finishing the style, let the client have the inside know-how about how to recreate the look at home. You will be reinforcing the professional brand you are working with, encouraging retail sales and helping the cut look good for longer, which will be a great walking advert for your skills and the reputation of the salon.

COLOUR AND LIGHTEN HAIR

Colouring the hair adds texture, style and creativity to individualise every look, for both men and women of all ages. For the stylist, colouring is one of the most exciting, creative, profitable and challenging services in hairdressing. The service you offer and the skills you develop in colouring will be among the most important you learn. Your knowledge of colouring will be useful throughout your hairdressing career, so maximise your potential by mastering these colouring skills.

There are two learning outcomes in this unit. The learner will be able to:

- prepare for colouring hair
- provide for colouring services.

PREPARE FOR COLOURING HAIR

During this part of the unit you will learn:

- safety considerations and working practices required
- the correct way to communicate and behave
- consultation techniques
- about colouring and lightening products available for use
- tools and equipment available for use
- factors that must be considered prior to colouring hair
- about hair tests and the consequences of not carrying them out
- the principles of colour selection and basic science
- the effects colour products have on the hair's structure.

SAFETY CONSIDERATIONS

The client's first impression of the salon and the staff will last, so make it a positive one! You have already looked at your professional and salon/stylist image in Unit 202, but let's revisit these areas specifically for the colouring service.

ARE YOU READY FOR YOUR CLIENT'S ARRIVAL?

Poor standards of health and hygiene can offend your clients, spread germs and cause cross-contamination. Always seek guidance from your manager before going to work if you have a potentially infectious condition.

ACTIVITY

List four ways to maintain your personal hygiene. List five things about your appearance that are important. Discuss your answers with your supervisor or tutor.

HANDY HINTS

Always cover and protect any cuts or open wounds to prevent cross-contamination and further harm.

HANDY HINTS

PPE is *your* personal protective equipment, not your client's!

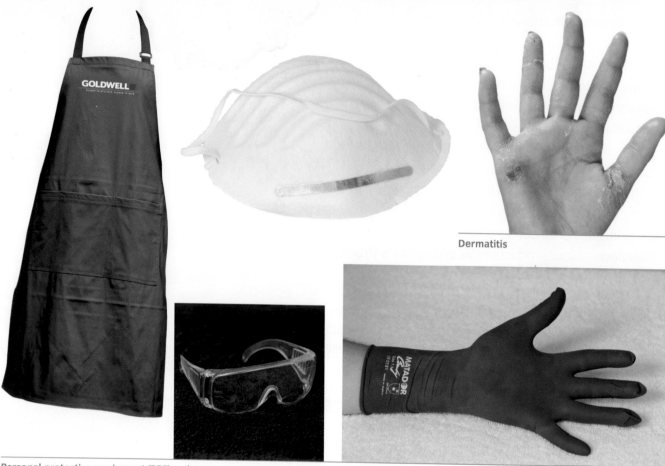

Dermatitis

Personal protective equipment (PPE) – gloves, apron, particle mask and eye protection

HANDY HINTS

Be safe – look after your hands and protect yourself from occupational contact dermatitis. You should rinse, dry and moisturise your hands after every service.

HANDY HINTS

Depending on the nature of the equipment, clean with detergent and water, sterilise in an autoclave, sanitise in an ultraviolet light cabinet or disinfect with chemical liquids, such as Barbicide solution.

Barbicide

Protecting your hands and clothes

It is important to protect your hands from contact dermatitis and to protect your clothes from damage when colouring. Always wear PPE.

PPE for the stylist and assistant includes:

- non-latex gloves to protect your hands from chemicals and staining
- aprons to protect your clothes from chemical damage
- eye protection for mixing colours and bleach powders, to prevent chemicals from entering the eyes.

If you suffer with asthma or allergies, you should:

- wear a particle mask when mixing or using colours and bleach powders, to prevent inhaling substances.

IS YOUR WORK AREA READY FOR YOUR CLIENT'S ARRIVAL?

A clean, well-prepared workstation will help you to consistently provide a hazard-free area and prevent cross-contamination, work efficiently and maintain a professional image. Report any problems with tools and equipment to a senior member of staff, and inform the relevant person of any products which need re-ordering.

Protecting your client

When your client arrives, sit them comfortably at your workstation and after the consultation, protect them suitably for the service.

Client protected for a colouring service

Always use:

- a fresh clean towel
- a fresh clean gown
- a plastic/disposable cape or another fresh clean towel (this might vary depending on your salon requirements).

A client must wear a gown during a chemical service to protect their clothes.

POSITIONING OF SELF AND CLIENT

Colouring services can involve long periods of time standing for the stylist and sitting for the client, so comfort is very important.

Your posture and positioning

You must position your trolley to your preferred side of working. If you are right-handed, your trolley should be positioned to your right and vice versa if you are left-handed. This will prevent you from over-stretching and causing you back problems. While you are applying colour, stand with your body weight evenly distributed and your feet slightly apart. When you are ready to remove the colour, position yourself comfortably at the basin area. Poor body position, over-stretching and twisting can cause back problems and fatigue.

Your client's positioning

During the colour service, ensure your client sits straight, with their legs uncrossed and with their back supported by the chair. At the end of the

HANDY HINTS

Powder lighteners can be dangerous if breathed in, especially for suffers of asthma. Take extreme care when mixing these products; wear particle masks and mix in a well-ventilated area. If you should get any product in your eyes, rinse immediately with cold water using an eye-bath, repeating as necessary. Consult your GP if symptoms persist.

HANDY HINTS

SHUD – what you **SHOULD** do when using chemicals.

SmartScreen 207 handout 2

Accelerators

Electrical appliances used to provide heat, accelerating development

HANDY HINTS

Refer to Unit 202 for a full recap on health and safety, the Acts and maintaining effective and safe methods of working.

SmartScreen 207 worksheet 1

service, support your client's neck as they lean back towards the basin; adjust the basin height and ensure their back is supported throughout the colour removal process and shampoo service.

SAFE USE OF SUBSTANCES

Colouring and lightening products are strong chemical substances that can cause you and your client harm. You must follow the Control of Substances Hazardous to Health Regulations (COSHH) 2003 when you are mixing, using and applying colours. Always ensure you follow:

- the manufacturers' instructions (MFIs)
- local by-laws
- your salon's policies and procedures.

This includes wearing PPE and applying the following best practices:

Store chemicals and substances correctly.

Handle chemicals and substances correctly.

Use chemicals and substances correctly.

Dispose of chemicals and substances correctly.

SHUD is derived from the rules of COSHH.

SAFE USE OF ELECTRICAL EQUIPMENT

Before using electrical items, such as **accelerators**, rollerballs or climazones, check them visually for any cracks in the main body or plug. Check that the wires are tangle free and not frayed. If you identify any problems or faults with electrical equipment, remove it from the salon, label it as faulty and report it to a senior member of staff. Remember to carry out your responsibilities under the Electricity at Work Act.

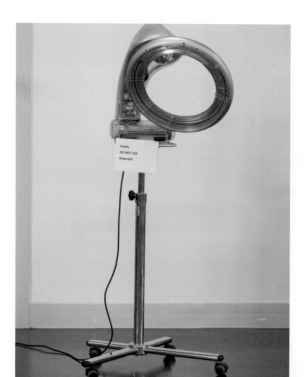

Label faulty equipment

DISPOSAL OF WASTE

At the end of the service, immediately remove waste products and dispose of them in the dedicated salon waste bin with a lid. Rinse any unused chemicals down the sink with plenty of cold water, following local by-laws and MFIs.

COMMUNICATION AND BEHAVIOUR

The following diagram indicates how you should communicate with your client.

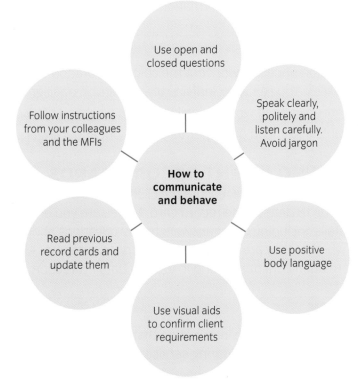

- Use open and closed questions
- Speak clearly, politely and listen carefully. Avoid jargon
- Follow instructions from your colleagues and the MFIs
- **How to communicate and behave**
- Use positive body language
- Read previous record cards and update them
- Use visual aids to confirm client requirements

CONSULTATION TECHNIQUES

To complete an effective consultation for colouring services you will need to discuss your client's requirements, identify any barriers to the service and carry out tests on the hair as required.

- Identify client requirements
- Identify factors that may affect the service
- Carry out relevant hair tests
- Decide on the most suitable service to carry out
- Select suitable tools and equipment
- Choose suitable products
- Choose the correct peroxide or developer strength

SmartScreen 207 handout 4 and worksheet 2

At the end of the consultation, you and your client should be confident that the desired result is achievable. Before making a start, inform your client of the likely cost and duration of the service. This should include the development time and confirmation of the expected result.

ACTIVITY

Using your salon price list, work out the cost and duration of Suzie's and Barry's services. You can work individually, in pairs or small groups.

- Suzie wants half-head woven highlights, with a cut and blow dry.
- Barry wants a full-head quasi-permanent colour and a finger dry.

COMPLETING CLIENT RECORD CARDS

During and after the service, ensure the client details are correct, easy to read and up to date on the record card. Make sure you enter all of the service details, including client answers to any questions about their hair, and whether they are happy with the service outcome. Always keep client information confidential and follow the Data Protection Act.

ACTIVITY

In small groups, discuss the information that should be detailed on a client record card after a colouring service. Compare your answers.

COLOURING AND LIGHTENING PRODUCTS

You must choose the most suitable products for your client's requirements. The products you choose to colour your client's hair will depend on the reason they are having their hair coloured.

WHY PEOPLE COLOUR THEIR HAIR

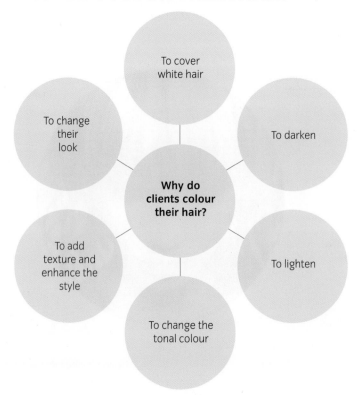

HANDY HINTS

You may need the record card if the client is unhappy with the service, or wants to take legal action. The record card provides evidence to support any defence, and shows that professional standards were met. For more information on the Data Protection Act, refer to Unit 202.

SmartScreen 207 handout 3

ACTIVITY

Can you think of other reasons why client's colour their hair?

The following table shows which products are most suitable for your client's requirements.

Colouring product	Lasting effects	Coverage of white hair	Levels of lift achievable
Temporary colour	1 shampoo	Blend only	None – adds tone only
Semi-permanent colour	6–8 shampoos	Blend only	None – darkens or adds tone only
Quasi-permanent colour	12–24 shampoos	50% as a guide	None – darkens or adds tone only

Colouring product	Lasting effects	Coverage of white hair	Levels of lift achievable
Permanent colour	Permanent	100%	Depending on the natural depth of hair and peroxide strength, lifts up to three shades. Also darkens and deposits tone
High-lift tint	Permanent	Blend only	Depending on the natural depth of hair and peroxide strength, lifts up to four to five shades. Also deposits tone
Lightening products (bleach)	Permanent	Blend only	Depending on the depth of hair and peroxide strength, lifts up to six shades. Also removes tone

NON-COMMITMENT COLOURING SERVICE

Temporary and semi-permanent colours are referred to as non-commitment colours. They only affect the cuticle layer of the hair and do not involve the use of chemicals.

Temporary colouring products

Temporary colouring products	Reasons to have temporary colour	Reasons not to have temporary colour
You apply these products directly to the hair before or after styling. They are available as mousses, lotions, gels, sprays, rinses, creams and even hair mascaras. They stain the hair and are used in the same way as styling products. Mousses, gels, lotions, rinses and creams are usually applied to wet hair, with sprays and hair mascaras being applied to dry hair. Temporary colours are usually removed from the hair with the next shampoo.	■ No commitment ■ Lasts only one shampoo ■ Adds shine ■ Adds tone ■ Neutralises unwanted tone ■ Chemical free ■ Enhances current look ■ Introduction to colour ■ Quick fashion effect ■ No development time	■ Lasts only one shampoo ■ No lift possible ■ Colour might be uneven or last longer in porous hair

Always follow the MFIs when you are using colouring products, and wear PPE to prevent staining the skin and damaging your clothes.

HANDY HINTS

Hair mascaras are used to paint colour onto the hair, to add texture and create a highlighted effect.

Semi-permanent colouring products

Semi-permanent colouring products	Reasons to have semi-permanent colour	Reasons not to have semi-permanent colour
These generally come in liquid or cream form and can be applied directly to pre-shampooed hair. Apply them either from the bottle or by measuring the product into a bowl and applying with a sponge or brush. Semi-permanent products are rinsed from the hair after the development time and conditioner is applied in the normal way.	■ No commitment ■ Introduction to colour ■ Full-head coverage ■ No regrowth ■ Lasts only six to eight shampoos ■ Adds shine, tone and depth ■ Neutralises unwanted tone ■ Can be used for colour correction services ■ Chemical free ■ Mostly allergy free ■ Enhances current look and refreshes existing colour ■ Quick service and fashion effect ■ Blends up to 20% of white hair	■ Lasts only six to eight shampoos ■ Vibrancy of colour gradually fades with each shampoo ■ No lift possible ■ Colour can only blend white hair ■ Colour might be uneven or grab in porous hair

Temporary colour – perfection rinse

Semi-permanent colour

Quasi-permanent colour

COMMITMENT COLOURING SERVICES

Quasi, permanent and lightening products are alkaline, therefore they lift the cuticle during development and affect the cortex. As these colours have a long-lasting effect on the hair, they demand a commitment to colour. These colours introduce a developing agent or peroxide to the colour.

Quasi-permanent colouring products

Quasi-permanent colouring products	Reasons to have quasi-permanent colour	Reasons not to have quasi-permanent colour
Quasi-permanent colouring products are mixed with a developer (mild or weak peroxide) to pre-shampooed hair and can be applied either straight from an applicator bottle or with a bowl and brush/sponge.	<ul><li>Adds depth and tone</li><li>Covers up to 50% white hair</li><li>Lasts between 12–24 shampoos, gradually fading out</li><li>Introduction to permanent colour</li><li>Weaker chemicals used</li><li>Used for colour correction</li><li>Fashion colours</li><li>Refreshes faded colours</li></ul>	<ul><li>No lift possible</li><li>Overuse can lead to a regrowth area</li><li>Contains chemicals</li><li>Colours gradually fade</li></ul>

Permanent and high-lift colours

Permanent and high-lift colours	Reasons to have permanent/high-lift colours	Reasons not to have permanent/high-lift colours
Permanent and high-lift colours are generally supplied in 60 ml tubes, and are always mixed with peroxide. You apply them to clean, dry hair using a bowl and brush.	<ul><li>Adds depth and tone</li><li>Lightens by up to three shades for permanent colours</li><li>Lightens by up to four or five shades for high-lift colours</li><li>Permanent colours cover 100% white hair</li><li>Used for fashion effects (foils)</li><li>Permanent result</li><li>Used for colour correction</li><li>Fashion/vibrant colours</li><li>Change of image</li><li>Adds texture</li><li>Covers regrowth</li></ul>	<ul><li>The result is permanent</li><li>Contains chemicals</li><li>Vibrant tones gradually fade</li><li>Committed to colour</li><li>Regrowth occurs every 4 to 6 weeks</li></ul>

Permanent and high-lift colour

> **INDUSTRY TIP**
>
> Tint does not lift tint! If your client has tint on her hair and wants to go lighter, you will need to use a lightener.

> **INDUSTRY TIP**
>
> Clients who have had henna tattoos are more likely to develop an allergy to hair colours. Always ask your client if they have had a henna tattoo, or suffered from any other allergic reaction. Record their responses on the client record card.

Lightening products

Although normal tints and high-lift tints lighten the hair, they are not lightening products. When referring to lightening products, we are referring to bleach products. These products come in many varieties.

Lighteners can be a bleach powder or a gel, and they are always mixed with peroxide. You apply them to clean, dry hair using a bowl and brush.

Bleach powder

Bleach powder can be a blue or white powder and is most commonly used for highlighting methods and off-scalp techniques. However, some lightening powders can be used on the scalp, but always read the manufacturers' instructions to be sure.

Lightening powders

Lightening powders are normally mixed to a preferred **consistency** rather than measured. Add lightening powder to a bowl and mix with the peroxide to make a paste.

Bleach gel/creams

Gel bleaches or creams are normally used for scalp applications. This thicker type of lightener contains a booster or activator which is pre-mixed with the gel and the peroxide to obtain maximum lift while limiting the harm to the hair's condition. There are many varieties available, so you must refer to the MFIs for methods of mixing and applying the products.

Consistency
Density or thickness

Lightening products

 SmartScreen 207 activity 2

Hydrogen peroxide
The solution that activates the colouring product to allow the colouring process to take place

Reasons to use a lightener	Reasons not to use a lightener
<ul><li>Lightens by up to six shades</li><li>Removes depth</li><li>Removes tone</li><li>Removes tint from the hair</li><li>Fashion effects (foils)</li><li>Permanent result</li><li>Change of image</li><li>Adds texture</li><li>Covers regrowth</li></ul>	<ul><li>The result is permanent</li><li>Contains strong chemicals</li><li>Committed to colour</li><li>Regrowth occurs every 4 to 6 weeks</li></ul>

Lightening products do not have a set development time. You must regularly check the hair and carry out a strand test to visually check development, to see whether the desired result has been achieved.

ACTIVITY

List three reasons why it is important to use products economically.

HYDROGEN PEROXIDE/DEVELOPERS

Hydrogen peroxide and developers are mixed with quasi, permanent or lightening products and can be used to lighten or darken the hair depending on the strength used.

HANDY HINTS

Take care with powder lighteners – **inhaling** substances can cause **respiratory problems**.

Inhaling
Breathing in

Respiratory problems
Breathing problems

HANDY HINTS

Remember not to mix your lightening product too thinly as it will seep out of the foils or through the holes in the cap. If the lightener is too thick it will dry out too quickly. Try to mix it to a cream that will just about support your tint brush in an upward position without you holding it.

WHY DON'T YOU...
Carry out a survey on ten clients to identify the reasons for colouring their hair. Compare their answers to the examples listed in the tables.

Ammonia and hydrogen peroxide

Ammonia is a key ingredient in quasi-permanent and permanent hair colours. At room temperature ammonia is colourless with a pungent smell. It can be highly irritating to the skin and respiratory system. Ammonia, which is mixed with the tint, activates the **oxidation** process. Ammonia swells the cuticle of the hair, allowing penetration of the hair colour into the cortex.

Hydrogen peroxide is often written as H_2O_2. It is a colourless liquid, made of water (H_2O) and oxygen (O_2). Hydrogen peroxide therefore contains concentrated oxygen. Hydrogen peroxide is an acid, about pH 3–4. It is the most common chemical used in hairdressing to provide oxygen.

Its purpose is to lighten the natural and artificial colour pigments, and to develop the colour of oxidation tints.

When peroxide is mixed with the ammonia in the tint, the oxidation process begins to work. The ammonia swells the cuticle and the peroxide provides the oxygen to oxidise the hair's colour pigment inside the cortex.

Strengths of peroxide

Peroxide comes in varying strengths; some weaker strengths are referred to as developers. Peroxide strengths are expressed as volumes or percentages. Volume strengths of peroxide describe the parts of free oxygen that might be given off during development. For example, 20 volume gives off 20 parts of free oxygen. When expressed as a percentage, it describes the percentage of pure peroxide. For example, in 6% peroxide, 100 grams of solution would be made up of 6 grams of pure peroxide and 94 grams of water. So:

- 10 volume strength is equal to 3% solution
- 20 volume strength is equal to 6% solution
- 30 volume strength is equal to 9% solution
- 40 volume strength is equal to 12% solution.

Ammonia

An alkaline gas

Oxidation

A chemical process that combines a substance with oxygen

HANDY HINTS

The stronger the peroxide, the more oxygen present, and therefore the more lift/lightening is achievable. Hydrogen peroxide is a very strong chemical and you must take care when using these products.

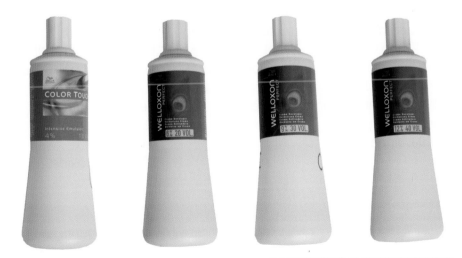

4%, 6%, 9% and 12% peroxide strengths

Using peroxide

The table below shows the different strengths of peroxide and their uses.

Percentage of peroxide	Volume of peroxide	Uses
1.9%, 3%, 4%	As a guide, we refer to these weak solutions as 10 volume and developers	To darken, to add tone and mixed with quasi-permanent colours
6%	20 volume	One shade of lift, to darken, to add tone, to cover 100% white hair
9%	30 volume	Two shades of lift with a normal tint, or three shades of lift with a high-lift tint
12%	40 volume	Three shades of lift with a normal tint, or four to five shades of lift with a high-lift tint

For quasi colours we use a developer and these generally come in varying strengths. As a guide, 3% (10 volume) is used by most manufacturers. However, some also offer 1.9% or 4% strengths. The benefit of 1.9% developers is that the colour is more subtle and will not last as long, giving your client freedom to change their colour more often. Using 4% developer will give a longer-lasting effect, and red/violet tones will be more vibrant. To decide on the developer strength, consider the vibrancy of the depth and tone required and how long your client wants the colour to last.

Mixing peroxide

Tubes of colour and tint generally come in 60 ml size tubes. A minimum quantity of a ¼ tube is usually used.

Quasi-permanent colours are mixed at a 1:2 ratio of colour to developer. Therefore, 15 ml (¼ tube) of tint would be mixed with 30 ml of developer.

Normal tints are mixed at a 1:1 ratio of tint to peroxide. Therefore, 15 ml (¼ tube) of tint would be mixed with 15 ml of peroxide.

High-lift tints (those that give maximum lift for blonde colour results) are generally mixed at a 1:2 ratio of tint to peroxide. Therefore, 15 ml (¼ tube) of tint would be mixed with 30 ml of peroxide.

HANDY HINTS

To help you mix your tint accurately, most colouring tubes are clearly marked along the sides, to show every quarter of a tube.

ACTIVITY

How much developer or peroxide would you need for the following:

- ½ of a tube of quasi-permanent colour
- a full tube of high-lift tint
- ¾ tube of normal permanent colour?

Diluting peroxide

Liquid peroxide can be diluted to a weaker strength by introducing distilled water. It is easier to refer to volumes of peroxide when diluting. For example, to obtain 30 volume peroxide from 40 volume: 30 volume peroxide is ¾ as strong as 40 volume. Therefore, ¾ of the solution must be 40 volume peroxide, and the remaining ¼ must be water. This gives you a ratio of 3:1 – 40 volume peroxide to water (see the first row of the table below).

HANDY HINTS

Always follow the MFIs when using colouring products to prevent damage to your client's hair or skin, to achieve the correct result and to avoid any legal action.

Peroxides diluted by volume strength

Required solution strength	Solution to be diluted	Fraction of peroxide required	Fraction of distilled water required	Ratio of peroxide to distilled water
30 volume	40 volume	$\frac{30}{40} = \frac{3}{4}$	$\frac{1}{4}$	3:1
20 volume	40 volume	$\frac{20}{40} = \frac{2}{4} = \frac{1}{2}$	$\frac{2}{4} = \frac{1}{2}$	1:1
20 volume	30 volume	$\frac{20}{30} = \frac{2}{3}$	$\frac{1}{3}$	2:1
10 volume	30 volume	$\frac{10}{30} = \frac{1}{3}$	$\frac{2}{3}$	1:2
10 volume	20 volume	$\frac{10}{20} = \frac{1}{2}$	$\frac{1}{2}$	1:1

Peroxides diluted by percentage strength

Required solution strength	Solution to be diluted	Fraction of peroxide required	Fraction of distilled water required	Ratio of peroxide to distilled water
9%	12%	$\dfrac{9}{12} = \dfrac{3}{4}$	$\dfrac{1}{4}$	3:1
6%	12%	$\dfrac{6}{12} = \dfrac{1}{2}$	$\dfrac{1}{2}$	1:1
6%	9%	$\dfrac{6}{9} = \dfrac{2}{3}$	$\dfrac{1}{3}$	2:1
3%	9%	$\dfrac{3}{9} = \dfrac{1}{3}$	$\dfrac{2}{3}$	1:2
3%	6%	$\dfrac{3}{6} = \dfrac{1}{2}$	$\dfrac{1}{2}$	1:1

ACTIVITY

18% or 60 volume peroxide can be purchased and diluted to weaker solutions. Using the tables above, can you dilute 18% or 60 volume to the following strengths:

- 12% (40 volume)
- 9% (30 volume)
- 6% (20 volume)
- 3% (10 volume).

SmartScreen 207 handout 9

ANTI-OXIDANT CONDITIONERS

After all chemical services, an **anti-oxidant** conditioner should be used to stop the oxidation process: this is called creeping oxidation. Anti-oxident conditioners close the cuticle and return the hair to its natural state of pH 4.5–5.5. It prevents colours from fading, the hair from becoming dry/brittle and causing damage to the cuticle or cortex.

Anti-oxidant

A substance that stops the oxidation process

Anti-oxidant conditioner

The following table shows a guide to pH values of colour and lightening products. These can vary considerably from manufacturer to manufacturer.

Product	pH value
Temporary colours	Acid pH 4.5–5.5 – the same as the hair and skin, therefore does not affect the cuticle or cortex and does not require an anti-oxidant conditioner.
Semi-permanent colours	Mild acid pH 6.5–6.9, which raises the cuticle scales very slightly to allow the colour to penetrate just inside/under the scales. Because hydrogen peroxide has not been used, an anti-oxidant conditioner is not required, but the hair would benefit from a pH-balancing rinse.
Quasi colours	Alkaline pH 7–9, which raises the cuticle scales and allows penetration into the cortex layer. A mild hydrogen peroxide/developer is used with these products and an anti-oxidant conditioner is required.
Bleach powders	Alkaline pH 8–9.5, which raises the cuticle scales and allows penetration into the cortex layer. Hydrogen peroxide is used with these products and an anti-oxidant conditioner is required.
Permanent tints	Alkaline pH 8–9.5 which raises the cuticle scales and allows penetration into the cortex layer. Hydrogen peroxide is used with these products and an anti-oxidant conditioner is required.
Hydrogen peroxide	pH 3–4 – although hydrogen peroxide is an acid, the fact that it is mixed with the alkaline colouring and lightening products and it contains oxygen, means an anti-oxidant conditioner is required after all chemical services.

ACTIVITY

Using litmus paper or an electronic pH tester, test the pH values of the products used in your salon or college and note any variations.

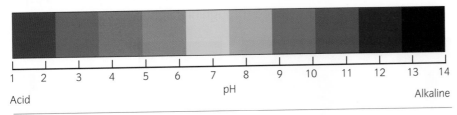

| 1 | 2 | 3 | 4 | 5 | 6 | 7 | 8 | 9 | 10 | 11 | 12 | 13 | 14 |

pH

Acid   Alkaline

The pH scale showing acid through to alkaline

Damaged cuticle layer

TOOLS AND EQUIPMENT

The tools and equipment you will need will vary depending on the chosen colouring service.

For regrowth and full-head applications you will need:

- a brush – to brush through your client's hair and remove tangles prior to the application
- a wide-tooth comb – to section the hair during the application
- section clips – to section and secure the hair and to secure the towel around your client
- a tint bowl and brush – for the application of products
- weighing scales – if you weigh tint and peroxide in your salon
- a measuring jug – to measure the peroxide solution
- a timer – to time the development process accurately
- an accelerator – to reduce development time.

For highlighting applications you will need all of the above, and:

- a tail comb – to weave the hair if you are completing woven highlights
- either foils, meches, wraps or cling-film for woven highlights, or a cap, spatula, gun or cups for pulled-through highlights.

MAINTENANCE

At the end of the service you must ensure that you wash your tint-measuring jug, bowls and brushes properly. Ensure the water runs clear from the brush's bristles, otherwise any colour deposits from the brush will be transferred to the next client. Make sure you get the entire colour out from the teeth of any used combs and clean thoroughly any section clips that have been placed into coloured hair.

FACTORS THAT MUST BE CONSIDERED

You need to look at the following **factors** during your consultation. These can affect the service outcomes and products, tools and equipment:

- client requirements
- lifestyle
- hair length and density
- hair condition/results of hair tests
- existing hair colour and previous services
- skin tone
- percentage of white hair
- temperature
- **contra-indications**.

Factors
Any details that may affect the service

CLIENT REQUIREMENTS

The most important factor to be considered – what does your client want? The consultation process is a very important part of the service. You should identify your client's requirements: what they are hoping for and their vision of the end result. You should use visual aids, such as colour charts or magazines, to clarify that you both have the same vision. This will enable you to choose the most suitable products, techniques, tools and equipment to achieve their desired result.

Contra-indications
Any reason that prevents a service or treatment from being carried out

LIFESTYLE

You will need to identify whether your client's lifestyle fits with their chosen colour service. You will need to ask personal questions about home and work life. Check whether they can afford the time and money to maintain the colour. Busy mums might not find the time to have a high-maintenance colour service, but could have an alternative colour that fits their needs just as well. Check whether the colour requirement fits well with their job. Some jobs might restrict high-fashion colour techniques, but equally encourage a well-groomed image. Outdoor living can also play havoc on hair colours; sunlight and swimming in chlorine/salt water can cause colours to fade and the condition of the hair to deteriorate.

HAIR LENGTH AND DENSITY

The length and density of your client's hair will determine which techniques you use, how much product is required and how long the service might take to complete. You might need to adapt the size of your sections or weaves. Fine weaves in dense hair result in a subtle colour and thick weaves on finer hair could create a heavily highlighted effect, which might not suit your client's requirements.

HAIR CONDITION/RESULTS OF HAIR TESTS

Hair in a porous and/or weak condition will restrict your choice of products, as lightening products might cause damage. Resistant, non-porous hair might require longer development times for permanent hair colouring products. Uneven porosity might result in an uneven colour, so you need to consider what products and services will be suitable. You should always carry out any relevant tests on the hair, and take the results into consideration.

EXISTING HAIR COLOUR/PREVIOUS SERVICES

You must consider the existing hair colour to identify the following.

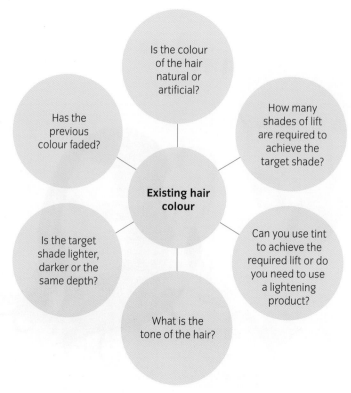

THE CITY & GUILDS TEXTBOOK

SKIN TONE

You need to check that your client's chosen hair colour will complement their skin tone. To help identify whether a client's skin tone is warm or cool, you should look for some tell-tale signs. In general, people who are natural redheads, or whose hair is reddish golden brown, deep brown and golden blonde have warmer complexions. Their skin might be paler with pink, peach, copper or gold undertones. People from Latin America, Africa or Europe with freckled complexions generally have warm tones. Depending on the hair's depth, colours such as caramel, copper and yellow–gold suit warm skin tones.

For cooler skin tones, with skin that is pale to dark without any undertones or cheek colour, look for hair colours that are naturally bluish-black, dark brown or medium ash blonde.

True olive skin, such as Mediterranean, suits cool red colours, for example burgundy, as the hair is naturally dark. Naturally lighter hair would require lighter cool ash shades.

PERCENTAGE OF WHITE HAIR

This is important because the percentage of white hair can affect the products used and services available to your client.

Covering white hair

Clients with high percentages of white hair tend to find that colour coverage can be less effective – white hair is often resistant to the colour because of the tightly compacted cuticle. To overcome this you might need to pre-soften the hair.

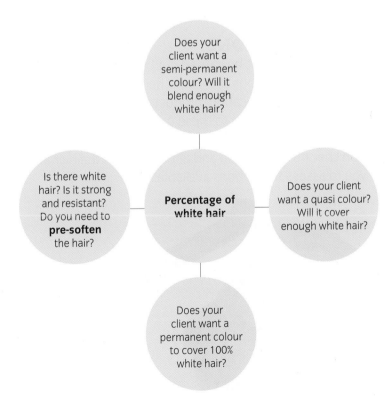

Pre-softening

A technique where liquid 6% peroxide is applied to the hair before the tint application to open the cuticle

INDUSTRY TIP

Some manufacturers have an 'intensive colour' range, which is designed to be used on white hair, without the need to pre-soften the hair.

The technique involves applying neat (undiluted) 6% liquid peroxide to the hair, prior to the colouring service. It can be used prior to a full-head or regrowth application.

- Apply the liquid peroxide to clean, dry hair, using a bowl and brush.
- Using either a hand-held hairdryer, or by placing your client under a hood dryer, dry the solution into the hair.
- Do not rinse out the solution and when dry, continue with the application process as normal.
- Record the process on the client's record card.

This technique uses added heat from the hairdryer to open the cuticle, allowing the peroxide to enter the cortex, ready for the colouring process.

TEMPERATURE

Warmer or cooler temperatures can have an effect on colouring development times. Warmth speeds up development times and lightening products develop more quickly under heat. Cooler temperatures, on the other hand, increase development time.

Accelerators generate heat, adding to the heat naturally arising from the head. If you are completing a full-head colouring service, you might need to start your application at the mid-lengths and ends of the hair, because these are furthest away from the source of heat (ie the head).

After allowing the mid-lengths and ends to develop for 20 minutes, start the root application so that the whole head colour develops evenly. Accelerators reduce development time by about 50%, but always read your MFIs to ensure they state that additional heat can be applied.

HANDY HINTS

Cool temperatures increase colour development time.

Warm temperatures reduce colour development time.

CONTRA-INDICATIONS

Sometimes a service cannot be carried out because of contra-indications. You must ask your client whether they have had any **adverse reactions** to medication, products or services in the past. You must clearly write any answers to these questions on the client's record card in case of any future legal action that might take place. During the consultation check the condition and appearance of the hair and scalp to allow you to assess the options available.

Adverse reaction

An unfavourable response

Accelerator

Use the table below to identify how to find out about clients' contra-indications.

Contra-indication	How can you find out?	What else could you do?
History of previous allergic reaction to colouring products	Ask your client if they have ever had an allergic reaction to colour before, including home colours or professional products.	Carry out a skin test following the MFIs.
Other known allergy	Ask your client if they have any allergies, such as a nut allergy. Some products contain almond oils so you would not be able to use these on a client who is allergic to nuts.	Carry out a skin test following the MFIs.
Skin disorder	Ask your client if they suffer from any skin problems, such as eczema or psoriasis.	Visually check the scalp, looking for skin disorders, infections, infestations and any cuts or abrasions.
Incompatible products	Ask your client about their previous hair services and treatments, in and out of the salon, as they might react with professional products.	Visually check the hair for any signs of hair discolouration, and if in doubt, carry out an incompatibility test.
Medical advice or instructions	Ask your client if they are taking any medication, or have been given medical advice that might affect the service result or the condition of the hair.	Visually check the hair to see if it appears healthy. Is there any new hair growth or damage?
Evident hair damage	Ask your client what they do to their hair on a daily basis, eg using straightening irons or curling tongs.	Visually check the hair for damage. Carry out porosity and elasticity tests.

Incompatible
Unsuitable

Evident
Easily seen

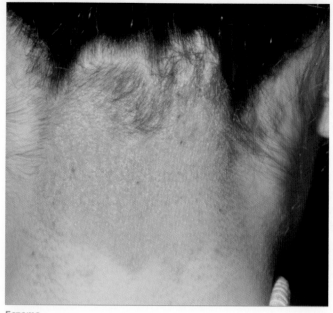
Eczema

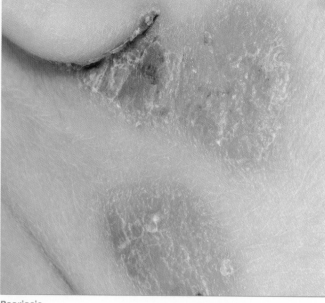
Psoriasis

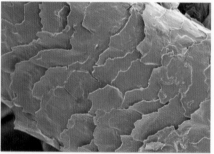
Damaged cuticle

ACTIVITY

In pairs or small groups list the types of question you could ask the client to identify contra-indications and discuss how you would record them.

ACTIVITY

Any concerns regarding contra-indications must be reported to the relevant person. Which contra-indications would you need to refer and who would you refer them to in your salon?

HAIR TESTS

During the consultation and the service itself you will need to conduct some hair tests to confirm that your client's hair is suitable for the service. You must follow the MFIs and adhere to health and safety procedures. The results of these tests must be recorded on the client record card, and if any adverse reactions occur you must seek guidance from the relevant person. Remember to work within the limits of your authority and report all adverse reactions.

Record cards must be completed for the following reasons:

- to record the service carried out
- for future reference
- to provide evidence in case of any future legal action
- to maintain the professional image of the salon.

The following table shows the hair tests before and/or during the service.

Tests	When to carry out the tests	How to carry out the tests	Why carry out the tests?	Expected results of the tests	Consequences of not carrying out the tests
Porosity test	Before any service on dry hair	Take a few hairs and slide your fingers up the hair shaft in the direction of point to root.	To test the cuticle layer to identify if the cuticles are smooth or rough	Hair cuticles should feel smooth if the hair is non-porous and feel rough or raised if the hair is porous.	Damage to your client's hair might occur or the desired outcome might not be achieved.
Elasticity test	Before any service on wet hair	Take one or two hairs and mist them slightly with water, then stretch the hair a couple of times between your finger and thumb.	To test the strength of the cortex	Wet hair should stretch about 30% more than its original length and then return when released.	Damage to your client's hair might occur or the desired outcome might not be achieved.
Incompatibility test	Before chemical services, if you suspect metallic salts are present in the hair	Take a small cutting of your client's hair and place it in a solution of 20 cc liquid 6% peroxide and 1 cc of perm solution (or a solution of 20:1 liquid peroxide and ammonium hydroxide). Leave for up to 30 minutes.	To test the hair to identify if any metallic salts are present, which would react with professional chemical products	If metallic salts are present the hair might change colour, the solution might bubble and fizz and/or give off heat.	Damage and/or disintegration of your client's hair could occur.

Tests	When to carry out the tests	How to carry out the tests	Why carry out the tests?	Expected results of the tests	Consequences of not carrying out the tests
Skin test For quasi and permanent colours – products that are mixed with a developer or peroxide	24–48 hours before a colour	Always follow MFIs as these might vary. As a guide you must clean an area in the inner elbow or behind the ear. Then apply your client's chosen colour, mixed with peroxide, to the area, and leave it exposed to dry.	To test for an allergic reaction or sensitivity to the product/ para-dyes	A positive reaction is red skin and/or sore areas that might weep and itch. A negative reaction is no change to the skin area.	Allergic reaction, anaphylactic shock, contact dermatitis or damage to your client's skin could occur.
Skin test for semi-permanent and temporary colours	24–48 hours before a colour	Always follow MFIs as these might vary. As a guide you must clean an area in the inner elbow or behind the ear. Then apply your client's chosen colour to the area, and leave it exposed to dry.	To test for an allergic reaction or sensitivity to the product	A positive reaction is red skin and/or sore areas that might weep and itch. A negative reaction is no change to the skin area.	Allergic reaction, anaphylactic shock, contact dermatitis or damage to your client's skin could occur.
Colour test	Before a colour or lightening service	Apply the chosen colour to a section of the hair (either a test cutting or on the head).	To see if the desired result is achievable	The desired result should be achieved, or further development might be required.	Damage and/or disintegration of your client's hair could occur. The desired outcome might not be achieved.

Tests	When to carry out the tests	How to carry out the tests	Why carry out the tests?	Expected results of the tests	Consequences of not carrying out the tests
Strand test	During the colouring or lightening service	Wipe off the colour or lightener from a few strands of hair.	To see if the colour result has been achieved, or if the lightener development is sufficient	If permanent colour is developed, then the desired result should be achieved. If the bleach is regularly checked, the level of lift should be achieved without damage to the hair. Further development might be required if the colour result has not been achieved.	Damage and/or disintegration of your client's hair could occur if over-developed.\n\nThe desired outcome might not be achieved if underdeveloped.

ACTIVITY

List three tests carried out before a chemical service and state their purposes. List one test carried out during a chemical service and state its purpose. Discuss your answers with your supervisor.

HANDY HINTS

If the test results show any signs of damage or breakage to the hair, do not proceed with the service. Report this to a senior member of staff and advise your client to have penetrating conditioning treatments. Retest the hair a few weeks later.

HANDY HINTS

Results from the hair tests could prevent colouring services from being carried out, and affect your choice of products. Not carrying out the tests could result not only in client dissatisfaction, but also in significant harm and possible legal action.

HANDY HINTS

You must record every test result on the record card. This will provide accurate information for future services and in the event of any adverse reaction, you have documented proof that the tests were carried out, in case of litigation.

SmartScreen 207 worksheet 3

WHY DON'T YOU...
Practise porosity, elasticity, incompatibility, skin and colour tests on a colleague.

Record the outcomes accurately on a record card and keep this for future reference. Did your tests achieve the expected outcomes?

PRINCIPLES OF COLOUR SELECTION AND BASIC SCIENCE

Now that you have completed a full colouring consultation, you must be desperate to start colouring! Before you can colour the hair you need to understand the principles of colouring and the basic science:

- the colour star
- how natural and artificial colours affect the hair
- how the International Colour Chart (ICC) works with depths and tones
- the effects of colour products on the hair.

THE COLOUR STAR

The colour star is made up of the three primary colours: red, yellow and blue.

Primary colours

Primary colours cannot be made by mixing other colours together. However, by mixing the primary colours together, we can make secondary colours. All other colours are made by mixing primary and/or secondary colours together.

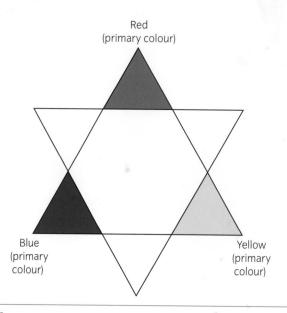

Primary colours

Secondary colours

Primary colours are mixed together to form the three secondary colours: orange (created by mixing red and yellow), green (created by mixing yellow and blue) and violet (created by mixing blue and red).

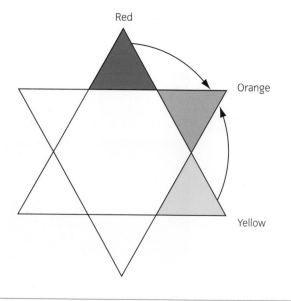

Secondary colour orange

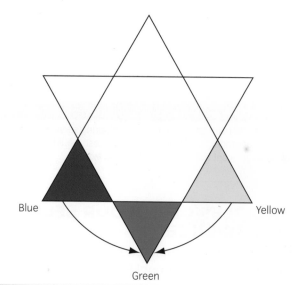

Secondary colour green

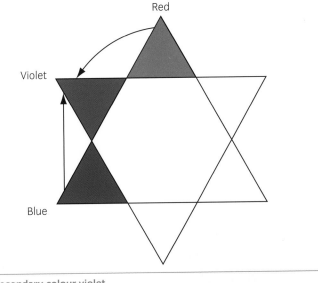

Secondary colour violet

SmartScreen 207 worksheet 11

To help you remember the order of the colour star, try to memorise:

Richard Of York Gave Battle In Vain.

Richard – Red
Of – Orange
York – Yellow
Gave – Green
Battle – Blue
In – Indigo
Vain – Violet

The colour star is used by artists and anyone else who mixes or uses colour. The principles of colour are the same for painting a picture as for colouring the hair.

Our hair is made up of natural **pigments** containing primary and secondary colours. When you add artificial colour to the hair, you rely on your understanding of the colour star.

NATURAL AND ARTIFICIAL HAIR COLOUR

The cortex contains all the natural and artificial colour pigments of the hair. It is the layer of the hair where all chemical action takes place. You can see the hair's colour through the transparent cuticle.

Natural hair colour varies from person to person, depending on the colour pigments. The pigments are called **melanin** and consist of two types.

Eumelanin is made up of black to light-brown colour pigments. These are large colour molecules with varying amounts of all three primary colours, but predominately contain blue and red pigments.

Pheomelanin is made up of blonde colour pigments. These are tiny molecules of colour spread throughout the cortex, with varying amounts of red, yellow and orange colour molecules, but predominately contain yellow pigments.

Pigment
The substance that colours our body tissue (hair and skin)

WHY DON'T YOU...
Paint your own colour star and compare your secondary colours with those of your colleagues.

INDUSTRY TIP
In hairdressing we refer to yellow as gold, orange as copper and indigo as violet.

Melanin
Pigments that give colour to the hair and skin

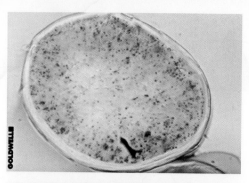

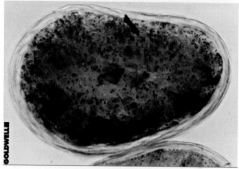

Colour molecules in the cortex

SmartScreen 207 handout 12

If you looked at two heads of hair, one dark brown and one light brown, both would have the same amount of colour pigment, but the amounts of blue, red and yellow melanin would vary. These different combinations give us depths and tones.

THE INTERNATIONAL COLOUR CHART

The International Colour Chart (ICC) is the numbering system that all manufacturers follow. Everyone uses the same numbers to describe a colour's depth. When you refer to your client's hair colour, you look at the depth and the tone of the hair. The depth is how light or dark the hair is, and the tone is the colour you see. If you describe someone as a redhead, you are describing their tone. If you describe someone as bleached blonde, you are referring to the depth of the hair.

Depths of hair

The natural depths of hair range from 1 (black) to 10 (lightest blonde).

The range of depths, from lightest to darkest, is as follows:

- 10 lightest blonde
- 9 very light blonde
- 8 light blonde
- 7 medium blonde
- 6 dark blonde
- 5 light brown
- 4 medium brown
- 3 dark brown
- 2 darkest brown
- 1 black.

ACTIVITY

WHY DON'T YOU...
Work with a colleague to try to identify each other's natural hair depth.

Lexi would like a depth 9 and is currently a natural depth 7. How many shades of lift are required? What strength peroxide would you use?

Megan would like a depth 7 and is currently a natural depth 6. What colour would you suggest? What strength peroxide would you use?

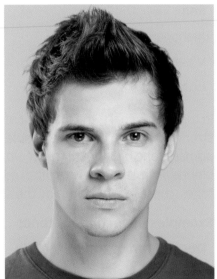

Matt would like a depth 6 and is currently a natural depth 8. What strength peroxide would you use?

Owen would like a very light blonde colour and is currently a natural depth 6. What strength peroxide would you use?

What colour are you aiming for? Would you use a permanent, high-lift or bleach colour? What strength peroxide would you use? Would you suggest a full-head colour or a highlight technique?

Tones in the hair

Sadly, manufacturers do not follow the same numbering system when describing tones. They all use a different number system, which you will need to learn. When you have mastered the ICC, it will be easier to learn the tonal colours that your salon uses. You will need this understanding throughout your hairdressing career, but you can always refer to the colour chart.

The tone numbering system describes the colour you see. All manufacturers use a similar description of the tone, but the numbering system will vary. Depths and tones are usually written in numbers for the stylist's use, and given descriptive names for your client's benefit. For example: the description for depth 8 (light blonde) might be written as 8/0, 8–0, 8.0 or 8N, depending on the manufacturer. The 0 refers to the tone.

Examples of primary tones

Description of tone	Wella	L'Oréal	Goldwell
Natural	/0	.0	N – natural
Ash	/1 or /9	.1	A – ash
Blue ash	/8	.1	BV – blue violet
Green ash	/2	–	–
Gold	/3	.3	G – gold
Red	/4	.6	R – red
Mahogany	/5	.5	RB – red brown
Violet/mauve	/6	.2	V – violet
Brunette	/7	–	B – brown

In the colour chart, the first digit after the depth is the primary or stronger tonal colour. For example, 8/3 is depth 8 (light blonde) with a primary tone of 3 (gold): this could be described as a light golden blonde. Primary tones are often mixed together to create secondary tones: these are indicated by the second digit.

Examples of secondary tones

Description of tone	Wella	L'Oréal (as a guide)
Natural ash	/01	/01
Natural gold	/03	/03
Copper (gold and red)	/34	/4 or /43 or /34
Copper (red and gold)	/43	/4 or /46 or /44 or /64
Violet red	/64	/26
Mahogany red	/54	/54
Golden brown	/73	/35 or /53

With Wella, for example, 6/43 is depth 6 (dark blonde) with a tone of /43 (red and gold). This colour could be called dark red gold blonde or dark copper blonde. If the mixed tone was more gold than red, it would be shown as 6/34. This would still be a dark copper blonde, but the copper tone created would not be as vibrant as 6/43.

Colour tones

In hair, red, gold and copper colours are known as warm tones; blue, green and violet are known as cool tones.

By mixing more or less of each primary colour we create different shades. For example, if you mix red with yellow you make orange (copper). If you add more red than yellow, the resulting tone would be a brighter copper than if you mixed more yellow than red. The various possible shades of copper can be seen on any colour chart.

Neutralising unwanted tones in the hair

The principles of the colour star not only work to create colours and various shades, but also to **neutralise** any unwanted tone in the hair.

Colours opposite each other on the colour star will neutralise each other. For example:

- red neutralises green
- green neutralises red
- yellow neutralises violet
- violet neutralises yellow
- orange neutralises blue
- blue neutralises orange.

If a colour result has a green tone, you would need to add a red toner to neutralise it. If highlight results are a little too gold (yellow), you would neutralise the tone with a violet toner. When highlighting naturally copper (orange) toned hair, you should use a high-lift tint with a blue tone. Neutralising tones work by mixing all three primary colours. When you are neutralising unwanted golden tones, use a violet toner because **yellow** is a primary colour and when you add violet (which is made with **red** and **blue** primary colours) all three primary colours have been mixed together, creating a neutral tone.

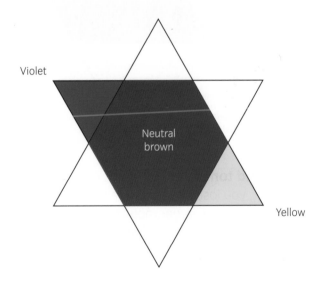

Neutralising golden tones

WHY DON'T YOU...
Work with a colleague to try to identify each other's tones. Is the colour warm or cool?

Variations of copper/orange colours

Neutralise
To make neutral or balance each other out

WHY DON'T YOU...
See how many shades of orange you can make.

 SmartScreen 207 activity 1

Unwanted green tones are neutralised in the same way. Green is a secondary colour made up of **yellow** and **blue** primary colours. When neutralised with **red**, all three primary colours have been mixed together to create a neutral tone.

This same principle works for neutralising orange tones. Orange (**red** and **yellow**) mixed with **blue** creates a neutral tone.

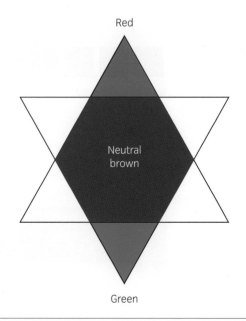

Neutralising green tones

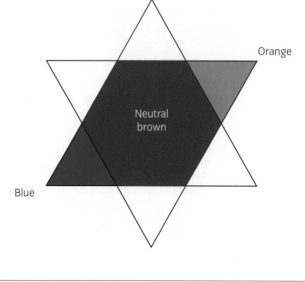

Neutralising orange tones

WHY DON'T YOU...
Mix the three primary colours together.

Did you get a neutral brown? Compare the results with those of your colleagues.

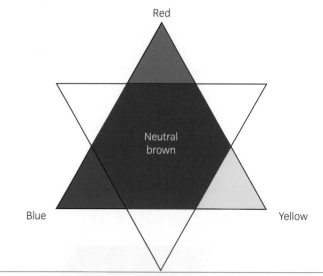

When you mix all the primary colours together you create a neutral brown colour

Removing depths and tones

When you lighten hair, you lose pigments in a certain order: red, orange and then yellow. Red tones are larger molecules, and therefore can be removed from the hair more quickly. Yellow tones are tiny molecules and it can take much longer to remove these. The yellow pigments from depths 8, 9 and 10 are the hardest to remove. If you remove too many yellow pigments, you risk breaking and damaging the hair.

Tones		Depths	
Very pale yellow		10	Lightest blonde
Pale yellow		9	Very light blonde
Yellow		8	Light blonde
Yellow/orange		7	Blonde
Orange		6	Dark blonde
Orange/red		5	Light brown
Red		4	Brown
Red		3	Dark brown
Red/blue		2	Darkest brown
Blue red		1	Black

The diagram shows the tones in the depths of hair

ACTIVITY

- If you lighten the hair colour from depth 5 to depth 8, what colour pigments (tones) would you remove? What tones would your client be left with?
- If you lighten the hair from depth 7 to depth 9, what colour pigments (tones) would you remove? What tones would your client be left with?
- If you darken the hair from depth 5 to depth 3, what colour pigments (tones) would you have added?

Factors that affect depths and tones

Many factors affect natural and artificial hair colour, causing the colours and tones to fade from the hair. Make sure you consider these factors when you add colour, as they determine the types of product, service and technique you might use. These factors include:

- porosity
- elasticity
- age of the hair and client
- length of hair
- density of hair (Is it thick or sparse?)
- texture of hair (Is it fine or coarse?)
- previous chemical treatments
- lifestyle of your client (Do they swim? Chlorine can affect hair colour and cause fading.)
- environment (Is your client out in the sun regularly? Do they often walk in windy weather?)
- heat damage (Do they regularly use electrical heat appliances on their hair?).

All of these factors can affect the hair by damaging the cuticle and the inner cortex. The cuticle must be smooth and in good condition to be able to sustain further chemical treatments. The cuticle is opened during chemical services to allow the colour to penetrate into the cortex. If the cuticle is rough and raised the hair is porous, which could affect the colouring result or cause further damage to the hair.

HANDY HINTS

Red or flushed complexions will look redder if you colour the hair with red or warm tones. Pale complexions will look even paler if you colour the hair with darker tones.

WHY DON'T YOU...
Compare colour swatches in natural and artificial light and discuss your findings with colleagues and your tutor.

EFFECTS OF ARTIFICIAL AND NATURAL LIGHT ON THE HAIR

The salon's lighting system is very important to enable your client to see their colour result accurately, effectively and in the best possible light. Natural daylight is the ideal way to show the hair's true colour. Natural light is referred to as white light, but it is made up of all the colours of the spectrum – red, orange, yellow, green, blue, indigo and violet. If you see white, that is because all seven colours are being reflected to your eyes from the object you are looking at. If you see one colour, such as red, the other six colours are being absorbed. If you see black, then no colour is being reflected into your eyes and all are being absorbed.

Electric bulbs can make the hair look warmer in appearance and neutralise blue or ash tones because of the yellow tinge given off by the bulb. Fluorescent/tungsten tubes can make the hair appear more ash in tone as they give off a bluish tinge and remove the warmth from the hair.

Hair under electric bulbs

Hair in natural daylight

Hair under fluorescent bulbs

HOW COLOUR AFFECTS THE HAIR'S STRUCTURE

Clients might choose partial- or full-head colour, or a highlighted effect. Whether you are colouring the hair with a temporary colour, a permanent colour or using lightening products, it is essential that you understand their effects on the hair's structure.

EFFECTS OF TEMPORARY COLOUR

Temporary hair colours are not such a popular service as permanent colours, but they can be quickly applied for a short-term look.

Temporary colours contain large colour molecules that coat the outside of the cuticle and stain the hair shaft. If the hair is porous and the cuticle is raised, the colour might grab and coat the cortex, which can cause the colour to last longer, and/or an uneven colour result.

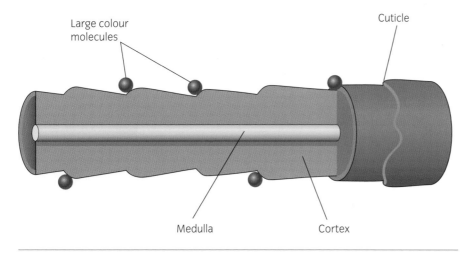

Large colour
molecules

Cuticle

Medulla

Cortex

SmartScreen 207 handout 5

Effects of temporary colour molecules on the hair

EFFECTS OF SEMI-PERMANENT COLOUR

Semi-permanent colours are a great way to introduce colouring services to your clients and can be used as a toner on bleached hair. They are quick and easy to apply and develop, and your client is not committed to the colour.

Semi-permanent colours contain large and small colour molecules. The larger colour molecules coat and stain the outside of the cuticle, whereas the smaller molecules coat the inside of the cuticle and the outer layer of the cortex.

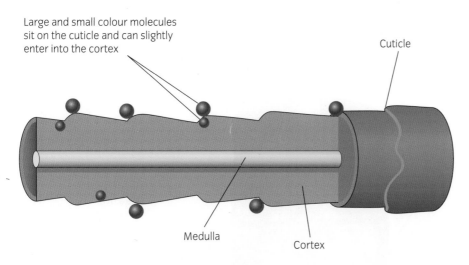

Large and small colour molecules
sit on the cuticle and can slightly
enter into the cortex

Cuticle

Medulla

Cortex

SmartScreen 207 handout 6

Effects of semi-permanent colour molecules on the hair

EFFECTS OF QUASI-PERMANENT COLOUR

Quasi-permanent colours are popular services in salons. When used effectively, the colour is not permanent so there is a minimal commitment.

Quasi-permanent colours contain small and medium-sized colour molecules. The small molecules coat the cuticle and lie in the cortex, whereas the medium colour molecules penetrate into the cortex. The weak developer, when mixed with the quasi-permanent colour, oxidises and swells the cuticle slightly, allowing the deposit of depth and tone into the cortex.

HANDY HINTS

If quasi-permanent colours are used too regularly, a more permanent colour effect can occur and definite regrowth can be seen at the roots.

 SmartScreen 207 handout 7

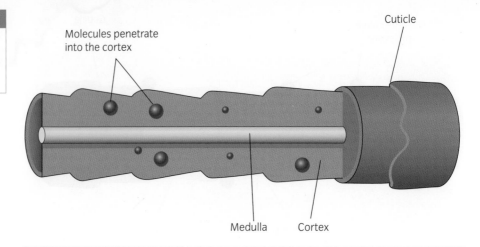

Effects of quasi-permanent colour molecules on the hair

EFFECTS OF PERMANENT AND HIGH-LIFT COLOUR

Permanent and high-lift hair colours are the most popular colour treatments in salons. They can be used to create many effects and variations, such as regrowth and full-head colour services, and highlighting and lowlighting effects. Combinations of these services can be used. For example, you can combine half-head woven highlights with full-head colour in between the packets.

These products can be used to lighten or darken the hair, depending on the strength of peroxide used. The stronger the peroxide used, the higher the lift, and the greater the effect on the cortex of the hair.

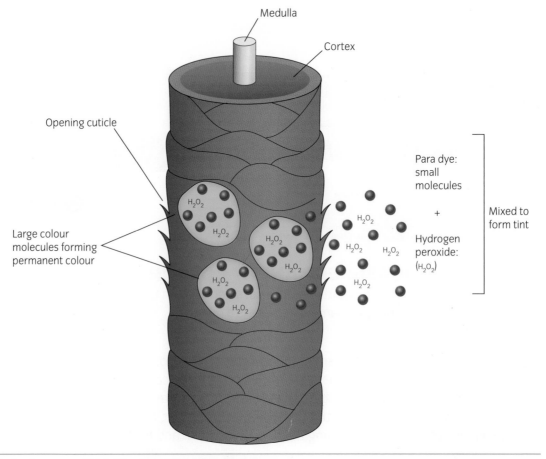

Effects of permanent/high-lift colour molecules on the hair

They contain small colour molecules that expand and join together during the development process. The peroxide, when mixed with the ammonia from the tint, swells the cuticle and allows the small molecules to enter the cortex. This allows the tint to deposit the required depth and tone.

The products must be fully developed to allow the colour to reach its desired depth, deposit the tonal colours and neutralise – colour molecules need time to swell and join in the cortex to become permanent.

EFFECTS OF LIGHTENING PRODUCTS

Lightening products enable clients to achieve the lightest blondes and lighten artificial colour in the hair. They can be used to create varying effects, including regrowth, partial and full-head colour services, and highlights.

These products can be used with any strength peroxide for off-scalp techniques, such as highlights. Peroxide with a strength of 6% must be used for on-scalp techniques, such as regrowths. Lightening products can achieve up to five or six shades of lift.

The lift achievable and development time vary greatly, depending on the peroxide strength and the depth of your client's hair in relation to your target shade. Lightening products affect the hair by oxidising the natural and artificial colour pigments in the cortex. These products are alkaline and contain ammonia. Ammonia, when mixed with peroxide, releases oxygen; the oxidisation process causes the melanin to become **oxy-melanin**.

SmartScreen 207 handout 8

Oxy-melanin
A colourless molecule

SmartScreen 207 handout 10

HANDY HINTS

Take extra care when using lightening products on previously chemically treated hair. Ensure your application is not overlapped, as this will cause greater porosity, damage to the hair's condition and potentially uneven colour results.

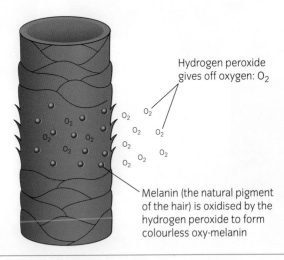

Hydrogen peroxide gives off oxygen: O_2

Melanin (the natural pigment of the hair) is oxidised by the hydrogen peroxide to form colourless oxy-melanin

Effects of lightening products on the hair

PROVIDE FOR COLOURING SERVICES

During this part of the unit you will learn:
- colouring and lightening techniques
- the types of problems that can occur and how to remedy them
- about aftercare advice you should provide to clients.

COLOURING AND LIGHTENING TECHNIQUES

Now you are armed with all the product knowledge and understand the principles of colour, you are ready to carry out the colouring service. The colouring services you need to be able to carry out are:

- the application of temporary, semi-permanent, quasi-permanent, permanent and lightening products
- colour and lightening techniques – regrowth, full-head, pulled-through and woven techniques.

Your four final observation assessments must cover the following: Regrowth, full-head, pulled-through AND woven technique

| Application of a semi- or quasi-permanent colour | Application of a permanent colour or a lightening product | Application of a permanent colour | Application of a lightening product |

SmartScreen 207 worksheet 4

You must prepare your materials in advance (for example, pre-folding foils). If you are completing a full-head colour/lightening service and it is your salon policy to use barrier cream, ensure that the hairline is completely covered. Make sure that you have not coated the hair itself, as the colour will not take.

When you are mixing the chemicals and products, always wear your PPE and mix in a well-ventilated area. Remember to follow COSHH and SHUD, and safely measure your peroxide and other liquids at eye level to ensure accurate measurements.

Barrier cream being applied to the client's hairline

HOW TO CARRY OUT A TEMPORARY COLOURING SERVICE

Gown and protect your client for the service and wear PPE. Apply the colour mousse to pre-shampooed/conditioned hair, and comb the product through to ensure an even application.

HOW TO CARRY OUT A SEMI-PERMANENT COLOURING SERVICE

Temporary colour application

STEP 1 – Gown and protect your client and shampoo their hair.

STEP 2 – Apply the semi-permanent colour evenly, direct from the applicator bottle.

STEP 3 – Sit client comfortably for the development time, add water to emulsify, then rinse thoroughly and condition the hair.

 SmartScreen 207 worksheet 5

HOW TO CARRY OUT A QUASI-PERMANENT COLOURING SERVICE

STEP 1 – Confirm with the client the choice of colour; gown and protect the client.

STEP 2 – Apply Paul Mitchell The Colour Shine Amethyst 3V evenly using the brush and bowl technique.

STEP 3 – After the development time, add some water, emulsify and rinse thoroughly.

STEP 4 – Shampoo and condition the hair.

STEP 5 – The finished result.

SmartScreen 207 worksheet 6

Quasi-permanent colours must be rinsed off the hair at the end of the development time, followed by a shampoo. An anti-oxidant conditioner should then be used to return the hair to pH 4.5–5.5.

INDUSTRY TIP

A quasi-permanent colouring service takes about 45–50 minutes to complete in a salon.

INDUSTRY TIP

Watching a stylist carrying out the colouring services helps you to learn the best techniques to use, and improve your skills and timings.

HOW TO CARRY OUT A REGROWTH COLOURING SERVICE

Permanent and high-lift products can be used for regrowth and full-head colouring services.

STEP 1 – Gown and protect your client and apply barrier cream.

STEP 2 – Section the hair cleanly into four sections (hot cross bun).

STEP 3 – Apply the colour evenly and cleanly to the root area.

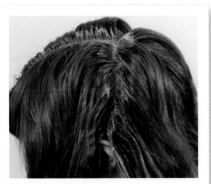

STEP 4 – Follow your section pattern for a thorough coverage.

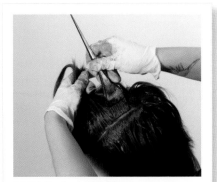

STEP 5 – Cross-check your sections to ensure even coverage.

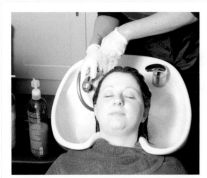

STEP 6 – After development and checking of the colour, rinse, **emulsify**, shampoo and condition.

INDUSTRY TIP

Tint removes tint from the skin. If you encounter any staining of colour around the hairline and ears, you can apply some tint from the bowl and massage gently into these areas prior to the colour removal process.

Emulsify

The mixing of a small amount of water with the colouring product

INDUSTRY TIP

A permanent colouring service takes about 1½ hours to complete in a salon.

Tinting products must be thoroughly removed from the hair at the end of the development time using the following methods:

1 Apply a small amount of water to the hair.

2 Emulsify the product into the moistened hair using a rotary massage technique.

3 Rinse the emulsified product until the water runs clear.

4 Shampoo the hair, using a shampoo for coloured hair.

5 Condition the hair using an anti-oxidant conditioner.

SmartScreen 207 worksheets 7 and 8

Lightening products used for regrowth and full-head services must be thoroughly removed from the hair at the end of the development time using the following method:

1 Apply a small amount of water over the hair.

2 Gently emulsify the water into the lightening product, using a gentle rotary massage technique.

3 Rinse the emulsified hair until the water runs clear.

4 Gently shampoo the hair, using a shampoo for coloured hair.

5 Condition the hair using an anti-oxidant conditioner.

INDUSTRY TIP

Be gentle with your massaging when shampooing off lightening products because the hair will be in a delicate state, and the scalp may be tender.

HOW TO CARRY OUT HIGHLIGHTING TECHNIQUES

Permanent, high-lift and lightening products can be used for creating highlighting and lowlighting effects. These techniques are useful when clients want to see a proportion of their natural hair colour or an additional colour, alongside a lighter highlight. The techniques available are pulled-through or woven highlights. Always consider the hair's length, density and texture before you make your choice.

Pulled-through highlighting techniques

Pulled-through techniques are not as popular as woven techniques, but can be used to achieve quick, effective methods of highlighting. There are several methods that you can use.

Cap highlights can be used if only one additional colour is required, and the hair is short. Always remember to add talcum powder to the inside of a cap before you pull it onto the head, otherwise it can cause discomfort for your client.

You should pull the hair through the holes to achieve the desired thickness of highlights.

At the end of the service rinse the product from the cap and apply conditioner to the hair to gently ease the cap from the head. Shampoo the colour from the hair and apply an anti-oxidant conditioner.

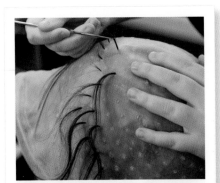

STEP 1 – Place the cap on the head and pull through the hair. The thickness will depend on your client's requirements.

STEP 2 – Apply the colour/lightener.

STEP 3 – Add water to remove.

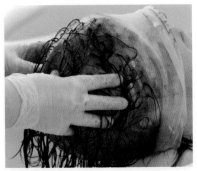

STEP 4 – Add conditioner and gently remove the cap. Shampoo and condition the hair.

 SmartScreen 207 worksheet 10

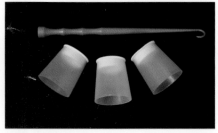

Colour cups

Colour cups can be used to create a number of multi-coloured highlighting effects. This method is ideal on short to medium-length hair.

Decide with your client where to place the colour cups, and attach them in place. The colour is then added inside the cups and left to develop, following the MFIs. At the end of the service, detach the cups and remove the product from the hair.

STEP 1 – Section the hair, place the base of the colour cup at the root area and gently pull through the required thickness of hair.

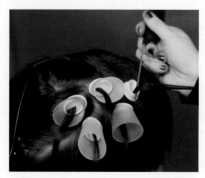

STEP 2 – Attach the cup on top of the base and pull the hair through.

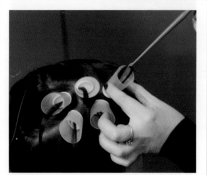

STEP 3 – Continue to work around the head, placing the cups to complement the style.

STEP 4 – Apply Paul Mitchell dual-purpose lightener with 6% developer, to lighten the natural colour to an orange undercoat.

STEP 5 – Shampoo off the lightener and dry the hair, then apply Paul Mitchell Inkworks Neon-Red to pre-lightened areas.

STEP 6 – The finished style.

Spatula highlights can be a quicker way of creating a woven highlighted look. These are more suitable for one colour highlighting on longer hair. Only permanent and high-lift tints can be used with this method, as bleach products swell and would create an uneven, patchy result.

At the end of the service, rinse the product from the hair until the water runs clear, shampoo and then use an anti-oxidant conditioner.

STEP 1 – Section the hair and weave a small section.

STEP 2 – Place the spatula at the root area and apply the product onto the spatulla.

STEP 3 – Slowly pull the spatula away from the root area.

STEP 4 – Gently lay the coloured hair onto the non-coloured hair.

STEP 5 – Continue with your next weave.

STEP 6 – Apply the colour carefully.

STEP 7 – Work neatly through the sections to the top of the head.

STEP 8 – The finished look.

INDUSTRY TIP

Spatula highlights use woven and pulled-through methods. As hair is woven first, the colour is applied onto the spatula and the spatula is pulled through the hair.

A **L'Oréal colour gun** can give a highlighted effect on medium to long hair. You can combine several colours, ranging from fine to thick highlighting effects. Colour is applied directly from the gun onto the hair by placing the gun at the root area and moving it along each section of hair from root to point, squeezing the trigger to release the colour. Remove the product from the hair as you would when using a spatula.

Woven highlighting techniques

Woven highlights are produced using foils, meches or wraps. They are suitable for any hair length. It is very important to consider your client's requirements and expected results, and the density and texture of the hair, when deciding on the quantity of hair to be woven.

The woven technique is very flexible as you can use various colours and products alongside partial or whole-head colouring techniques. T-bar and half-head sectioning patterns are commonly used in salons for quick, cost-effective highlighting.

If you are using lighteners, some meches might need to be removed while others are still developing. To do this, secure the meches that are still developing and ensure they do not move and cause seepage. Apply water over the meche's seals, or unfold the foils to loosen them. Remove the meches or foils carefully from the hair and thoroughly rinse the area. At the end of the service, carefully remove all remaining meches or foils from your client's hair without causing discomfort. When you remove the materials from the hair, remove the product in the usual manner.

SmartScreen 207 worksheet 9

HANDY HINTS

When sectioning and weaving the hair you need to secure and control the hair effectively. This enables you to work methodically and achieve an even colour result.

STEP 1 – Divide the hair to be coloured into manageable sections, and weave your section.

STEP 2 – Apply the product evenly without overloading the root area.

STEP 3 – Work in a methodical manner, towards the top of the head.

STEP 4 – When you have completed all the hair, leave it to develop.

STEP 5 – The finished look.

ACTIVITY

Case study 1

Katie would like light blonde highlights, but your test results show metallic salts are present in the hair. What action should you take? Would you proceed with the service? What further services would you recommend for Katie?

INDUSTRY TIP

A highlighting colouring service takes about 1½–2½ hours to complete, depending on the service.

Case study 2

Hannah has heavily bleached hair, and the porosity and elasticity tests show the cuticle is rough and the cortex is weak. She would like to return to a medium brown colour. Which service would you recommend for Hannah?

Case study 3

Marek would like a whole head colour and this is his first colouring service. His hair is in good condition but he has psoriasis and very sensitive skin. What tests would you carry out and, depending on the results, which services would you recommend for Marek?

Choose one of the client case studies and prepare a trolley with the tools and equipment you would need to carry out the appropriate service.

Katie

Hannah

Marek

SOLVING COLOURING PROBLEMS

You might encounter some problems when you are colouring the hair. The table below shows the causes and remedies to common problems.

Colouring problem	Cause of problem	Remedial action
Result too dark	■ Underdeveloped/ overdeveloped ■ Peroxide strength was not strong enough ■ Wrong colour/product choice ■ Did not consider present colour on the hair – tint does not lift tint	■ Use a lightener to lift the hair

Colouring problem	Cause of problem	Remedial action
Result too light	■ Overdeveloped ■ Peroxide strength was too high ■ Wrong colour/product choice ■ Did not consider depth of natural hair colour ■ Porous hair	■ Use a quasi-permanent colour to darken the hair
Hair is too yellow	■ Underdeveloped ■ Peroxide strength was not strong enough ■ Wrong colour/product choice ■ Did not consider tones present in the hair	■ Use a violet toner ■ Re-bleach if hair condition allows
Uneven colour result	■ Poor mixing of product ■ Uneven application ■ Porous hair prior to application ■ Incorrect selection of colour for white hair ■ Underdeveloped ■ Overlapping of colour	■ Apply a quasi-permanent colour if suitable ■ Spot tint/bleach uneven areas
Poor coverage on white hair	■ Resistant hair ■ Did not pre-soften ■ Incorrect choice of colour ■ Incorrect strength of peroxide used ■ Lack of base shade colour used	■ Pre-soften hair in future ■ Reapply product if hair condition allows
Skin staining	■ Poor application ■ Dry skin/hairline ■ Did not use barrier cream	■ Use a stain remover ■ If not too late, emulsify colour at the back wash
Scalp irritation	■ Product too strong ■ Allergy to product ■ Possible cuts or abrasion ■ Products not removed properly	■ Remove product immediately ■ Rinse with cool water ■ Refer to GP if required

Colouring problem	Cause of problem	Remedial action
Over-processed result, or deterioration of hair condition	■ Overdeveloped ■ Peroxide too strong ■ Too much heat used ■ Overlapped previous colour	■ Remove product immediately ■ Apply conditioning treatment to the hair
Product seepage	■ Poor application ■ Incorrect mixing of product ■ Incorrect use of foils or meche	■ Spot tint to cover seepage of product

 SmartScreen 207 worksheets 12 and 13

AFTERCARE ADVICE

After every colouring service you should provide your client with effective aftercare advice. Your advice should include suggestions for suitable products to maintain the hair's colour and condition between salon visits. Use positive body language together with open and closed questions to identify your client's needs.

You might need to recommend lifestyle alterations to your client, to ensure both the colour and condition of the hair are preserved. This might include advising wearing a hat on sunny or windy days, or warning about the effects of chlorine on hair colour. Chlorine can cause hair to dry out and become brittle, the colour to fade and even a colour reaction. You might recommend shampoos that remove chlorine from the hair, and additional shampoo and conditioning products that will enhance the colour and improve durability.

Excessive use of electrical heat appliances will also cause the colour to fade and the hair to lose condition. You should advise your client appropriately and suggest regular conditioning treatments.

 SmartScreen 207 handout 11

SmartScreen 207 revision cards

Finally, you should advise your client when to return to the salon for additional services, or for their next colouring service. Explain how long they should expect the current service to last, and advise them on what to look for as a guide for when they should return. This might include white hair becoming noticeable around the hairline, a visible regrowth or colour fade.

When you are giving your client effective aftercare advice, maintain eye contact and speak politely and clearly.

WHY DON'T YOU...
Identify the products available in your salon that you could recommend to clients after a colouring service.

INDUSTRY TIP

Suggest that your client books their next appointment while they are still in the salon. This helps the salon to maintain regular trade and revenue, and also allows your client to look forward to their next appointment.

Turn to page 485 for the answers.

1 Which **one** of the following describes the **best** reason for the workstation to be kept clean and tidy?

  a To prevent cross-contamination and reduce hazards.

  b To prevent hazards and minimise offense to staff and colleagues.

  c To maintain a professional image and increase retail sales.

  d To maintain a hazard-free environment and reduce loss of stock.

2 **Statement 1:**
If you are left-handed, position the trolley on your left-hand side to prevent over-stretching and inefficient working.

Statement 2:
When you are rinsing the colour at the end of the service, position your client and the height of the basin so that the colour can be removed effectively.

Which **one** of the following is correct for the above statements?

	Statement 1	Statement 2
a	True	True
b	True	False
c	False	True
d	False	False

3 Which **one** of the following legislation requires that colouring products should be kept in a safe and secure area in the salon?

  a HASAW Act.

  b COSHH Regulations.

  c PPE Regulations.

  d PUWER Regulations.

4 Which **one** of the following is referred to as 'non-commitment' colours?

  a Temporary and quasi-permanent.

  b Semi-permanent and permanent.

  c Temporary and semi-permanent.

  d Permanent and quasi-permanent.

5 **Statement 1:**
Gel or cream bleach is specifically designed for maximum lift for on-scalp applications.

Statement 2:
Powder bleach can be used on the scalp as long as you follow the manufacturers' instructions.

Which **one** of the following is correct for the above statements?

	Statement 1	Statement 2
a	True	True
b	True	False
c	False	True
d	False	False

6 Which **one** of the following describes the effects of using a 9% (30 volume) hydrogen peroxide?

  a Two shades of lift with a normal tint, or three shades of lift with a high-lift tint.

  b Three shades of lift with a normal tint, or up to five shades of lift with a high-lift tint.

  c One shade of lift to darken, to add tone, to cover 100% white hair.

  d To darken, to add tone and mixed with quasi-permanent colours.

7 Which **one** of the following identifies the tests that should be carried out before a colour?

  a Skin, porosity, strand, elasticity and incompatibility.

  b Skin, elasticity, colour-test and porosity.

  c Skin, strand, porosity and incompatibility.

  d Skin, porosity, strand, elasticity and colour test.

Jo Hansford's hair colour salon in the UK is globally renowned for exceptional colour correction work, and is the salon of choice for many leading celebrities. Successful colour correction demands honesty and patience on both sides. If this scenario is handled skilfully and sympathetically, you will be left with a loyal client for life. Here, Jo Hansford MBE shares with you her top tips for the perfect colour change.

- Consultation – always be aware of your client's emotional state. It is often a knee-jerk reaction to change hair colour in a crisis and clients should always be encouraged to make the decision when they are not feeling too emotional.

- Always complete a strand and skin test to check for allergies and reactions. Assess your client's eye colour, face shape, skin tone and condition of their hair. It might not be possible to create the look they want and it might not be suitable for their own colouring – all of these factors have to be taken into consideration.

- Advise a trip to the wig department in a department store first to check if they will be happy with the look. It is amazing how many clients will change their minds or get more confidence from this exercise! It helps them manage expectations, too, so you do not give them a huge shock on the day.

- Look at their haircut – it usually needs to be changed to complement the colour change and should be discussed and booked in simultaneously to get the real wow factor from the appointment.

- Ensure that the products recommended for the aftercare are the right ones – often they need a change to suit the new hair and this can make or break the success of the appointment long term.

- Do not be afraid to say no – it is not about money, it is about client retention and recommendation. You want your client to look and feel great, to be a walking advertisement for your salon and to come back again and again!

208
PERM AND NEUTRALISE HAIR

Curly and fuller body styles are making a come-back! Perming the hair can give the client soft curls, waves, root lift or tight curls, creating a variety of different looks. Perm winding can be creative and improves your dexterity skills, but understanding the basic science behind it is extremely important, as you are working with strong chemicals and do not want to damage your client's hair. This process permanently changes the structure of the hair.

There are two learning outcomes in this unit. The learner will be able to:

- prepare to perm and neutralise hair
- perm and neutralise hair.

PREPARE TO PERM AND NEUTRALISE HAIR

During this part of the unit you will learn:

- safety considerations and working practices required
- consultation techniques
- perming and neutralising products available for use
- tools and equipment available for use
- factors that must be considered prior to perming hair
- hair tests and the consequences of not carrying them out.

SAFETY CONSIDERATIONS

When perming and neutralising the hair, you will be using some very strong chemicals that can cause harm to yourself and your client. It is therefore important that you work safely throughout this service and ensure that both you and your client are effectively protected.

WORK AREA AND PREPARATION FOR THE SERVICE

Before your client arrives, ensure you are prepared to carry out the perm service. Keep your work area clean and tidy to avoid potential hazards and risk of injury, to ensure the salon looks professional and to minimise the risk of infection, infestation and cross-contamination. Prepare your trolley with the tools and equipment required, and clean and sterilise your tools before and after use.

ACTIVITY

Which tools can be sterilised using the following methods:

- autoclave
- UV light cabinet
- chemicals?

HANDY HINTS

Clean your tools and work surfaces with detergent and water to remove oil, products, hair and debris. Disinfect with chemical solutions or wipes, sanitise using a UV light cabinet or sterilise in an autoclave.

INDUSTRY TIP

Most salons allow 45 minutes for a stylist to perm wind the hair; the average time in the salon for completing a perm service, including a cut and blow dry, is around 2½ hours. During your training this may take up to 3 hours to complete.

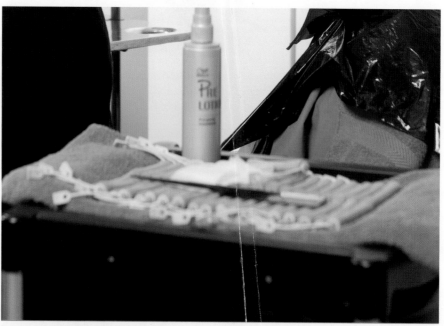

Prepare your trolley in advance of the service

PERSONAL HEALTH AND HYGIENE

You must maintain your personal health and hygiene throughout the service by showering daily, wearing clean clothes, using deodorant and carefully covering and protecting any cuts or open wounds. Always check that your body odour and breath are fresh, as you are working in close proximity to your client and colleagues.

You will be standing for long periods of time, so you must wear sensible, flat-soled, closed-in shoes. Always wear personal protective equipment (PPE) to protect your clothes and skin from the chemicals.

HANDY HINTS

Stand with your feet apart and your body weight evenly distributed. Avoid over-stretching or bending too much to prevent fatigue and back problems.

INDUSTRY TIP

Keep your trolley to your preferred side of working; the right-hand side for right-handed stylists and vice versa for left-handed stylists.

ACTIVITY

Research contact dermatitis and list three ways in which you can help prevent it.

HANDY HINTS

Poor standards of hygiene can cause offence to your clients, give a poor salon image and cause cross-contamination.

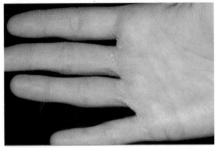

Dermatitis

SmartScreen 208 handout 2

WORKING WITH ELECTRICAL EQUIPMENT

Your equipment must have a yearly portable appliance test (PAT) by an electrician to ensure it is safe and fit for use. Every time you use a piece of electrical equipment, you must check it visually by looking at the power cable, plug and main body to ensure that it is in good working order. This will prevent harm and risk of injury to you and others. While carrying out a perm service you might use accelerators – equipment to speed up the perm process. Always carry out your responsibilities and follow the rules of the Electricity at Work Regulations.

ACTIVITY

What visual checks must you carry out before using an accelerator? If it was faulty, what would your responsibilities be under the Electricity at Work Regulations? List three responsibilities.

WORKING WITH CHEMICAL SUBSTANCES

During a perming service you will use shampoo, pre- and post-perm conditioner, perm lotion, neutraliser and styling products. All of these are substances that could be hazardous to your health, through **absorption**, inhalation or ingestion. Always follow the Control of Substances Hazardous to Health (COSHH) guidelines and follow the manufacturers' instructions (MFIs) and your salon policy. Wear PPE, eg gloves, apron, eye protection and mask (particularly if you are asthmatic), and mix the chemicals in a well-ventilated area.

Absorption
Soaking up

Wear gloves to protect your hands from dermatitis

Barrier cream

PROTECTING YOUR CLIENT

You must always ensure that your client is comfortable; periodically ask about their comfort and offer refreshments. You must protect your client's clothing with a gown, towel and a shoulder cape to ensure they remain dry and to avoid getting chemicals on their clothes. Ask your client to sit upright, with their back against the back of the salon chair and their legs uncrossed. Before you apply the perm lotion or neutraliser, you should apply a barrier cream and dampened cotton wool around your client's hairline to protect the skin from the chemicals. When you neutralise the hair at the basin, support your client's head and neck when positioning them down to the basin and, again, lifting their head and neck after the neutralising process. You must take particular care to avoid getting lotion in your client's eyes. If you splash any perm lotion or neutraliser in your eye, use an eye-bath and rinse thoroughly with cool water. If irritation persists, visit a GP.

Protect your client

SALON WASTE

Remove any used cotton wool after the perm or neutralising process. This will aid client comfort and prevent perm lotion coming into contact with the skin for long periods, which might cause chemical burns to the hairline area. Dispose of all salon waste in the designated waste bin with a lid, and rinse any excess perm lotion or neutraliser down the sink with plenty of cold water. This will ensure that chemicals are diluted. You should work within your salon policy, following the MFIs and local by-laws. If, during the service, you identify any stock shortages, you must report this to the relevant person, who will add these products or resources to the stock order list.

CONSULTATION TECHNIQUES

To identify the type of perm that is best suited to your client's requirements and to achieve the desired result, you should ask a series of questions. Whether your client is new to perming or not, ask the same questions. Regular clients might want a change of curl, but even if a repeat service is required, you need to check if anything has changed with the condition of the hair, their lifestyle and their health.

The types of open and closed question you should ask are:

- What do you want your perm to achieve?
- What is your vision of the end result?
- What type of curl would you like?
- What size curl would you like?
- How much time do you have available to spend on your hair?
- Have you had a perm before?
- When was your last perm?
- Have you had any previous problems with a perm?
- What chemical products do you currently have on your hair, if any?
- Do you have any colour on your hair, and if so what type of colour service did you have?
- Do you have any contra-indications, eg allergies?
- Do you have recent scar tissue?

You must always listen carefully to your client's responses and write them on the record card. You should ask your client to sign the record card to confirm that what has been written is accurate and true.

RECORD CARDS

If you are going to carry out a perm service on a regular client, refer to their previous record card to check the service details, and make sure that the last perm service was to their satisfaction. Whether you are repeating the same service or changing it, you will need to add the details to the record card. For every client, regular or new, always ensure that their details are correct: check the client's name, address and contact details. Record the date, type of service, stylist's name, products used and the result, and the development time, ensuring that the card is completed accurately and is easy to read. You must also record any relevant tests that were carried out, the results and any questions that you asked, including the client's responses. This will ensure that:

- the correct service is carried out
- the records are available for future services
- you maintain a professional image
- you have documented evidence, in case of **litigation**.

 SmartScreen 208 handout 6

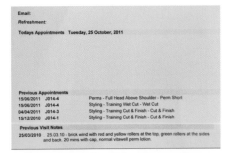

Completed record card for perm service

Litigation

Legal action

 SmartScreen 208 handout 17

PERMING AND NEUTRALISING PRODUCTS

To perm the hair, you will need to know about the types of pre-perm shampoos, pre-and post-perm conditioners and types of perm lotions and neutralisers that are available for use.

PRE-PERM SHAMPOO

A pre-perm shampoo should be used prior to perming. This type of shampoo has a neutral pH (pH 7) and therefore slightly opens the cuticle layer to allow the perm lotion to penetrate the cortex layer, where the changes during the perming process take place. A pre-perm shampoo contains no additives; it helps to remove any dirt, products and oil residue from the hair that might coat the cuticle layer, and create a barrier to the perm lotion.

PRE-PERM CONDITIONER

A **pre-perm conditioner treatment** should be used on the mid-lengths and ends of the hair if you identify that the hair has an uneven porosity. A pre-perm conditioner can be sprayed (or sprinkled directly from a **phial**) on the hair before sectioning or winding the hair with the rods. It is important that you avoid spraying on hair that has good porosity and aim it directly onto the porous and uneven areas of the hair. These conditioners even out the porosity and allow the perm lotion to penetrate evenly into the cortex layer.

PERMING PRODUCTS

Perming products are available in varied forms, such as acid and alkaline perm lotions, and come in varied strengths to suit all hair types.

These might be shown as:

- 0 or R – for resistant hair types, or hair that is difficult to perm (such as coarse hair)
- 1 or N – for normal hair types
- 2 or T – for tinted or coloured hair that is porous.

Strengths of perm lotion: '0' or 'R' – resistant, '1' or 'N' – normal and '2' or 'T' – tinted

---

WHY DON'T YOU...

Ask your manager if you can look at a client's perm record card so that you can see examples of the details recorded.

Pre-perm conditioner treatment

A spray-in conditioner that evens out the porosity of the hair

Phial

Small bottle

When deciding whether to use an acidic or an alkaline perm lotion, you should consider all of the following:

- what movement your client would like
- the condition of the hair and what products are already on the hair
- the texture, density and hair length
- whether your client wants a soft or long-lasting curl result.

Acid perms

Acid perms are pH 6–7 and are therefore less damaging to the hair than alkaline perms. Acid perms either require heat or a heat activator to help open the cuticle layer of the hair. The heat activator either comes in a separate bottle, or can be 'hidden' in the screw cap of the perm lotion bottle. When the cap is twisted, it pierces the seal and the activator mixes with the perm lotion, activating it. Whether you add a separate activator or activate the product from the cap, when the two products mix, mild heat is generated – these perms are called exothermic acid perms.

The heat helps to open the cuticle layer to allow the perm lotion into the cortex layer. You must activate acid perm products when the hair is wound and ready to be damped. If you activate them too early, the product strength will weaken. Therefore, acid perms can be used only for post-damp applications. Acid perms are most suitable for sensitive hair, fine hair and softer curl requirements, but they are available in varying strengths for resistant, normal and tinted hair.

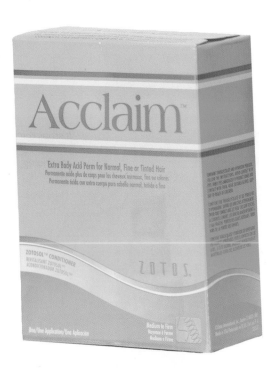

Alkaline perms

Most alkaline perms are pH 8.5–9.5, but some can be much lower, around pH 7.1. The lower the pH, the milder the lotion and therefore the less damaging it is to the hair. Alkaline perms give firmer curls and are

Pre-damp

Winding with lotion already applied to the hair.

most suited to resistant, strong, oily and white hair. Most perms are wound up and then the lotion is added; some alkaline perms allow you to **pre-damp**, but always read the MFIs.

NEUTRALISERS

You should always use the neutraliser that comes with your chosen perm lotion, as the manufacturer will have designed the two products to work together. Neutralisers are pH 3–5 and can be applied in different ways; refer to the MFIs. Some products must be applied directly from the bottle on the rinsed rods; others might be diluted in a large applicator bottle and sprinkled over the rinsed rods. Another way to apply neutraliser is to pour the contents into a bowl and 'foam' it with a sponge. The neutraliser is then applied to the rods with a sponge and left to develop.

POST-PERM CONDITIONER

After every perm service, use a pH-balancing conditioner. We refer to these as post-perm conditioners. A post-perm conditioner has special properties, shown in the following diagram.

Creeping oxidation

When chemicals are left in the hair and they carry on working and cause damage

 SmartScreen 208 handout 13 and worksheets 3, 5 and 6

It closes the cuticle layer and stops the hair from losing moisture and becoming brittle

It stops the chemical processing from continuing

It returns the hair back to its natural pH of 4.5–5.5

It stops **creeping oxidation**

TOOLS AND EQUIPMENT

Your trolley should be prepared with the items in the table below, before your client arrives.

Fish hooks

Buckled ends from poor winding technique

Tools/equipment	Reason for use
Apron and gloves	To protect your clothes and skin from the chemicals.
Pintail comb	To section the hair during the winding process. A metal pintail comb cannot be used when winding with lotion (pre-damp technique).
Section clips	To hold longer hair in sections, to aid methodical working. Section clips are also used for sectioning a nine-section perm wind.
Untangling comb/wide-tooth comb	To untangle the hair. This wide-tooth comb will prevent damage to the hair and minimise discomfort for the client.
End papers	To be used on the ends of the client's hair when winding the hair down the rod, enabling you to control the ends of the hair and wind without causing **fish hooks**.

Tools/equipment	Reason for use
Band protectors	Plastic sticks, which keep the perm bands off of the hair and prevent breakage.
Barrier cream	To be applied around the hairline before the dampened cotton wool is applied. This prevents the perm lotion coming into contact with the scalp and skin, thereby avoiding discomfort or chemical burns.
Cotton wool	To be placed around the client's hairline when the perm lotion or neutraliser is being applied. Make sure the cotton wool is replaced if it becomes saturated with perm lotion, or it might hold the chemicals against the client's skin.
Water spray	To be used during winding. Wound hair should be misted all over with the water spray to maintain an even moisture balance.
Plastic cap	To be placed over the wound head of hair once the perm lotion has been applied, to keep in the natural heat from the head and aid development.
Timer	To time the development of the perm and the neutralising process.

When you have completed your consultation, relevant hair tests and decided which rod sizes are required to achieve the desired result, you will be able to add the following items to your prepared trolley/work area.

Tools/equipment	Reason for use
Perm rods, small to medium	These are generally used when a client requests tighter curls, but can also be used to achieve medium curls on dense hair. Longer hair might also require a slightly smaller rod, as the weight of the hair might pull the curls down, making them a little looser.
Perm rods, medium to large	Provide a looser curl for softer-looking curls.
Bendy rods	Bendy rods come in different sizes and can be used to produce spiral curls, tight curls and loose curls. This will depend on the hair length, density, chosen wind and size.
Accelerator	An accelerator can be used to speed up the development process of the perm (check the MFIs).

When you have completed the perm and the neutralising process needs to take place, you will need two more items at the basin area.

Tools/equipment	Reason for use
Bowl 	To contain the neutralising product (if you are applying the neutraliser with the bowl and sponge technique).
Sponge	To froth/foam the neutraliser in the bowl before applying the neutralising product.

SmartScreen 208 worksheet 1

ACTIVITY

After reading the lists on the previous pages, go and prepare a trolley for a perm service. Leave your list/textbook behind and set up from memory. Afterwards, check with your lists and note down anything you had forgotten.

FACTORS THAT MUST BE CONSIDERED

To help you decide on the best rod/roller size and lotion choice and strength, you need to analyse your client's hair. By analysing the hair you can identify any potential problems that might occur. You should feel the hair and visually check it to identify the factors in the diagram below; a pre-perm test curl can be carried out to confirm the curl results if need be.

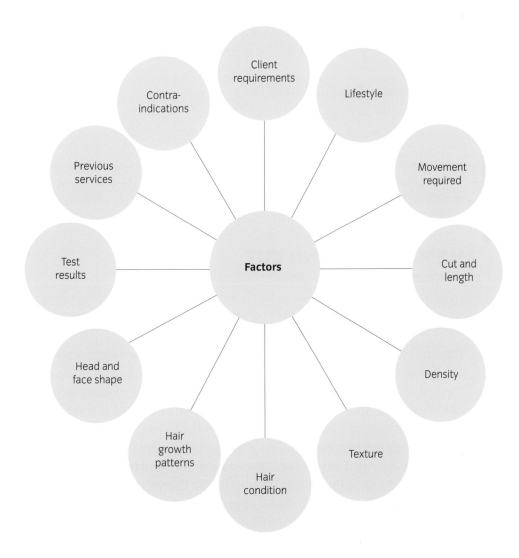

CLIENT REQUIREMENTS

During your consultation you should have discussed with your client what their requirements are. This is your starting point for considering the other factors. Now you know what they would like, you need to identify if their lifestyle and hair and scalp will enable the desired look to be achieved.

LIFESTYLE

Having your hair permed can be an easy way of maintaining a curly style. Some clients confuse set styles with permed styles. When you have confirmed that the service required is a perm, you need to consider the client's lifestyle and how they will be able to maintain the style. Remember to discuss work life, home living and fitness regimes, as all of these can impact on the maintenance of the hair.

- Work life – Does your client have to get up early for work or work long hours? Will having a perm make the time spent on their hair longer or shorter? Will the style suit their job and its image requirements?

- Home living – Has your client got a family life that is time demanding? Do they enjoy outside activities or spend lots of time in the sun, which could have a detrimental effect on the condition of her hair?

- Fitness regime – Does your client go to the gym and wash his/her hair every day? Do they enjoy swimming, where the chlorine could affect the condition of their hair?

Soft perm result – movement required

When you have established that your client's lifestyle is suited to the chosen service, you should look at the hair and scalp.

MOVEMENT REQUIRED

How much curl does your client require?

How much body does their hair already have?

If the hair is naturally very straight, you might need to use a stronger perm lotion, smaller rollers or develop for longer. For hair with some natural movement, remember that the perm could develop quickly and the result might be curlier than desired, so you should use a slightly larger rod.

HAIR LENGTH AND CUT

How long is your client's hair?

What is the current style?

Does the hair need to be cut before the perm?

For longer hair you will need more time for the wind, more lotion to coat the hair and you might also need to consider your winding technique. If the hair is long and in good condition you might decide to wind with lotion – a technique called pre-damping. This ensures that all the hair is covered with lotion through to the ends, as the lotion might not penetrate through to the ends if it is applied after winding. Longer hair will go around a rod more times than shorter hair and therefore create more movement. Although you might decide to use larger rods because of this, you must remember that the weight of long hair can pull the curls looser, so you must consider the density of the hair before making your final decision on rod size.

DENSITY

How much hair does your client have?

When checking the density of the hair, you are identifying whether the hair is sparse, medium or abundant. For sparse hair, you will need to be careful with your wind and avoid too much tension. Avoid winds that create roller section marks, use less lotion than normal, and use a product that is milder on the hair. For abundant hair, you will need more rods, more lotion and smaller sections when winding, so allow yourself sufficient time to wind the hair. Use larger rods on thick, abundant hair, as smaller rods might result in frizzy curls.

TEXTURE

How thick is each individual hair?

When checking the hair's texture, you are identifying whether the hair is fine, average or coarse. Perms on fine hair will develop more quickly than on coarse hair, and will require a softer perm lotion. Coarse hair will take longer to develop, depending on its condition, and larger rods might be required. You are likely to need more lotion for coarse hair.

CONDITION

How porous is the hair (results of porosity test)?

You must always carry out a porosity test to identify if the cuticle layers are open or closed and if the hair is porous, non-porous or even resistant. Porous hair will need protecting from the chemicals and you might need to use a pre-perm conditioner. Resistant hair requires more lotion, longer development time, smaller rods and you might need to pre-dampen the hair with lotion prior to winding.

How strong is the hair (results of elasticity test)?

You must also carry out an elasticity test to check the strength of the cortex layer. If the hair is weak, alternative services must be recommended instead of a perm, or suggest a series of conditioning or penetrating treatments for a few weeks before retesting the hair's strength. If the hair is normal or strong, then consider the lotion strength required.

ACTIVITY

Feel the different hair textures and densities of the people in your salon. Look at their hair lengths and natural movement and identify which perm lotion would be most suitable. Do not forget to consider the hair's condition and what products have already been used. Ask each person to give you an indication of what sort of curl result they would like, so you can also choose the rod size.

HAIR GROWTH PATTERNS

Has your client got a double crown, a cowlick or a widow's peak?

Hair growth patterns cause more of a problem on shorter hairstyles, particularly a double crown. You need to consider the growth patterns to help you choose your winding technique. A directional perm wind might help disguise the growth pattern and overcome the problem.

HEAD AND FACE SHAPE

What is the face shape of your client?

Are their any prominent features?

As you know, ideally we want to create the illusion of an oval face shape, so for round faces you would need to avoid round curly styles. However, for a square face or a strong jaw-line, a round curly style would help to soften the jaw-line. For pointed noses or chins you should avoid centre partings that draw attention to the sharp feature and opt for a directional perm wind, over to one side.

Round face   Oblong face   Square face   Heart face

TEST RESULTS

You must carry out all the relevant tests on the hair and consider all the results before perming. See the chart on page 245.

PREVIOUS SERVICES

What products are on your client's hair?

Along with the relevant hair tests, you must identify what chemicals, if any, are already on the hair. Is there a previous perm on the ends? Does this need to be cut off first or can you use a pre-perm conditioner on the ends?

Is there colour on the hair? Is it even and over the whole head or are there highlights, which might give an uneven porosity? Is there bleach on the hair?

Hair that has been highlighted and tinted can often be permed with a perm lotion, especially for highlighted hair, but a course of penetrating treatments might be required before perming. Hair that has been bleached must not be permed.

SmartScreen 208 handout 12 and worksheet 4

CONTRA-INDICATIONS

Ask appropriate questions to check whether your client has ever had any of the problems in the diagram below.

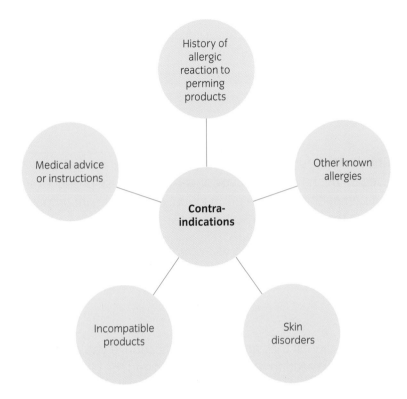

Contra-indication	Why you must consider these contra-indications
Depending on the results, you can either proceed with the perm, carry out further tests or stop and do not proceed with the service, but suggest a suitable alternative.	
History of previous allergic reaction to perming products 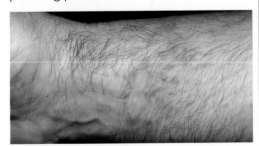	If your client has had an allergic reaction to perming products before, you must carry out a skin test using your chosen perm lotion prior to starting the wind. If you are unsure DO NOT PERM, recommend an alternative service and ask the client to get medical advice before continuing with the service.
Other known allergies 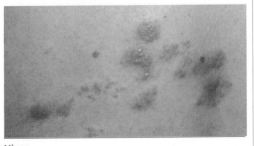 Hives	Ask your client what their allergies are, check the ingredients in the perm lotion and neutraliser and carry out a skin test with the chosen product. If you are unsure DO NOT PERM and recommend an alternative service.

Contra-indication	Why you must consider these contra-indications
Skin disorders 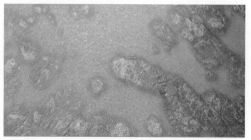 Psoriasis	If your client has a skin disorder on the scalp, check if it is open or weeping. If it is, DO NOT PERM. If it is not open, sore or weeping and you can protect it, proceed with care. Check that the disorder is not infectious or an infestation, if it is, DO NOT PERM.
Incompatible products  Split ends	Check with your client regarding products that have already been used on the hair. If you have concerns that these products are not compatible with the perm lotion, carry out an incompatibility test on the hair. If the result is positive, DO NOT PERM.
Medical advice or instructions 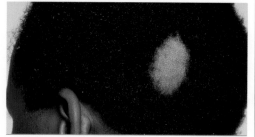 Alopecia areata	Ask your client if they are on any medication. If you are unsure as to the likely reaction of the medications and the client's health with regard to perming the hair, DO NOT PERM; refer your client to their GP for further advice and follow medical instructions.

 SmartScreen 208 handout 7

208 PERM AND NEUTRALISE HAIR

HANDY HINTS

For every question you ask about contra-indications, you must record every answer on the record card and ask your client to sign the record card as confirmation of what has been said and recorded. This will provide accurate information for future services and in the event of an adverse reaction you have documented proof of your client's responses in case of litigation.

INDUSTRY TIP

Always seek guidance from the relevant person (a manager/senior stylist) if you are unsure of what to do about a contra-indication.

HAIR TESTS

Always carry out porosity and elasticity tests on the hair to identify whether the cuticle layers are porous or non-porous, and to test the strength of the cortex layer. If you think the hair might have products on it that are incompatible with your salon products, carry out an incompatibility test on the hair. Refer to Unit 203 for further guidance.

If your client has a history of allergic reactions, you must carry out skin tests prior to perming, following the MFIs.

If you are unsure which lotion or rod size to use, you can carry out a pre-perm test.

For every perm service, you must carry out a development test curl to identify whether the perm has fully developed.

Use the table on the next page to find out how, when and why you should carry out these tests. Always follow the MFIs in relation to these tests.

Tests	When to carry out the tests	How to carry out the tests	Why carry out the tests?	Expected results of the tests	Consequences of not carrying out the tests
Perm skin test	Prior to a perm service	Always follow MFIs as these may vary. As a guide you must clean an area in the inner elbow or behind the ear. Then apply the chosen perm product to the area and leave it exposed to dry for 24 hours.	To test for an allergic reaction or sensitivity to the product	A positive reaction is red skin and/or sore areas that may weep and itch. A negative reaction is no change to the skin area.	Allergic reaction, contact dermatitis or damage to the clients' skin could occur. Legal action.
Pre-perm test curl	Before the service	Weave the hair and wind a roller section on the head. Protect the rest of the hair and complete the full perm process on one or two rods. Or: Take a cutting of hair and complete the perm process on the hair cutting.	To identify if the rod size and perm lotion choice are suitable to achieve the desired result	The curl should be suitable and as expected. If too tight, you need a larger rod, too loose you need a smaller rod, and if too dry or frizzy you need a weaker lotion or a pre-perm conditioner.	Result may be too loose, too tight or the hair condition may be too dry or damaged. Legal action.
Development test curl	During the development process of a perm	Unwind a perm roller partially and push the hair back towards the root area. Do this in 3–4 areas around the head.	To check if the perm development time has been sufficient	A positive result shows an adequate 'S' bend in a similar size to the roller. A negative result will be either a weak 'S' bend, meaning the development time is insufficient or a too tight 'S' bend meaning the hair is overdeveloped.	Damage and/or disintegration of the clients' hair or skin, could occur if overdeveloped. The desired outcome may not be achieved if underdeveloped. Legal action.

These test results could prevent the service from taking place. DO NOT PERM if a client has a positive reaction or if breakage occurs during a test. Offer advice for penetrating conditioning treatments and suggest alternative services. Always seek guidance from your manager if you are unsure what to do about the result of a hair test.

You must record every test carried out and its result on the client's record card.

 SmartScreen 208 worksheet 2

PERM AND NEUTRALISE HAIR

During this part of the unit you will learn:

- basic science of the perming and neutralising process
- effects that perming and neutralising products have on the hair's structure
- perming techniques
- types of problems that can occur and how to remedy them
- aftercare advice you should provide to clients.

BASIC SCIENCE

The hair is made up of amino acids and peptide bonds, which originate in the hair follicle. The many amino acids and peptide bonds form the polypeptide chains (coils), which are held together by permanent and temporary bonds inside the cortex layer of the hair.

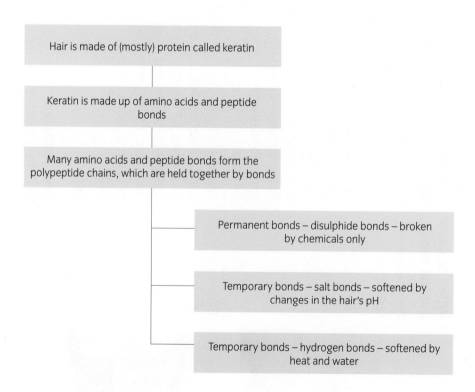

HOW PERMING PRODUCTS AFFECT THE HAIR'S STRUCTURE

The perm and neutralising process goes through three stages: softening, moulding and fixing. The perm lotion (with the addition of heat) starts the softening stage, the development process is the moulding stage and the neutraliser fixes the hair in its new shape.

The diagram on the right shows a single hair from the cuticle layer to the cortex layer. The polypeptide chains (coils) are found inside the cortex.

When you are blow drying, setting or styling with heated equipment, the temporary bonds are softened by the water and heat, and temporarily set into their new shape. When hair is permed, we are permanently changing the bonds with the use of chemicals. These bonds are called **disulphide bonds** (permanent bonds).

The temporary bonds hold the polypeptide chains in place along the length of the coils.

Temporary bonds

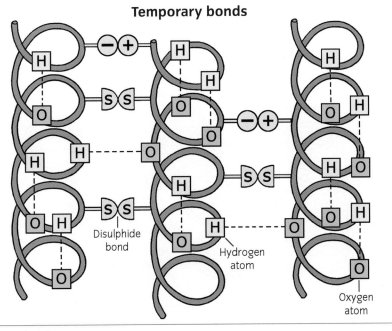

Temporary bonds

Detailed hair structure

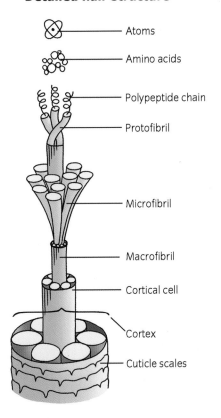

- Atoms
- Amino acids
- Polypeptide chain
- Protofibril
- Microfibril
- Macrofibril
- Cortical cell
- Cortex
- Cuticle scales

Disulphide bonds

Two sulphur atoms bonded together

Disulphide bonds before perming process

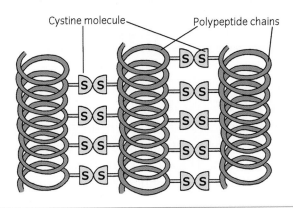

Disulphide bonds holding the polypeptide chains together

 SmartScreen 208 handout 8

247

The bonds that we change during perming are the disulphide bonds that hold the polypeptide chains in position across the coils from left to right. A disulphide bond is also known as a cystine molecule, and is shown in the diagram on page 247.

THE SOFTENING STAGE

When you add perm lotion to the hair, it uses either the heat generated from the exothermic acidic perm lotion or additional heat, to open the cuticle layer; or the pH of an alkaline lotion causes the cuticle layer to open. As the cuticle layer opens, the perm lotion penetrates the cortex layer and begins to soften the disulphide bonds that hold the polypeptide chains together.

When you apply the perm, it adds hydrogen to the hair and the hydrogen breaks down some of the disulphide bonds* as shown in the following diagram.

Hair during the perming process

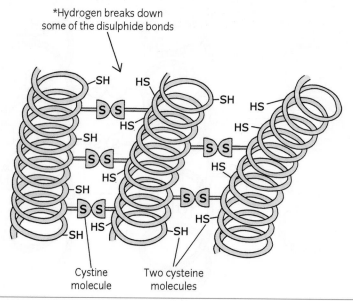

The softening stage

> **HANDY HINTS**
>
> During the development process, about 25–30% of the disulphide bonds should be broken. Any more than that and the hair could become frizzy – the hair structure will be permanently damaged. The development process can take 5–20 minutes, depending on the hair's condition.

THE MOULDING STAGE

As the disulphide bonds are broken by the hydrogen, the *cystine* molecule is reduced into two *cysteine* molecules, as shown in the diagram above. The softened hair then starts to take on the shape of the perm rod, and is beginning to mould into its new shape.

THE FIXING STAGE

The neutraliser stabilises the hair and permanently fixes it in its new shape. The neutraliser is an oxidising agent, and therefore contains oxygen. When you add the neutraliser, the oxygen combines* with the hydrogen in the *cysteine* molecules, so there are now two hydrogen molecules and one oxygen molecule on the hair. This is also known as H_2O** – the chemical formula for water, as shown in the following diagram.

SmartScreen 208 handout 10

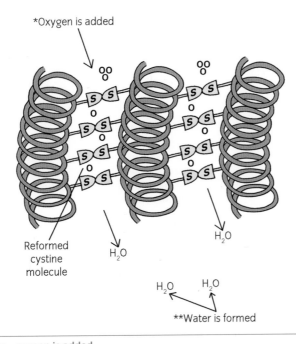

The fixing stage – oxygen is added

The oxygen bonds with the hydrogen, which leaves the *cysteine* molecules. This allows the recreation of one *cystine* molecule. The hair is now in its newly formed, permanently bonded shape, as shown in the following diagram.

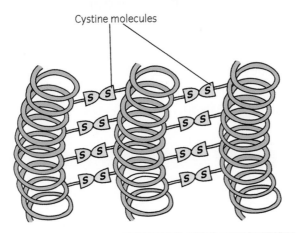

Cystine molecules re-joined

HANDY HINTS

Perm lotion is also known as a reducing agent, as it reduces the *cystine* molecules to *cysteine* molecules. Neutraliser is also known as a fixing agent as it fixes the hair into its new shape. To help you remember the order for cystine and cysteine, use the number of 'e's from each word. There is one 'e' in cystine for one molecule, and two 'e's in cysteine for two molecules.

The following diagram summarises what you have just learnt.

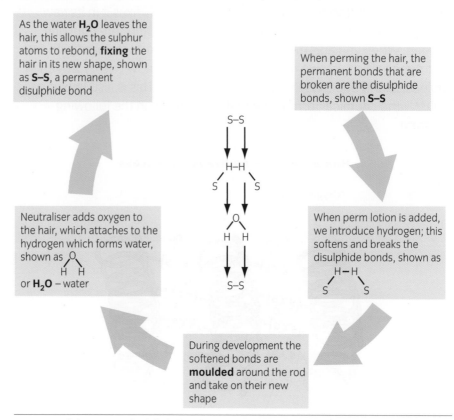

As the water **H₂O** leaves the hair, this allows the sulphur atoms to rebond, **fixing** the hair in its new shape, shown as **S–S**, a permanent disulphide bond

When perming the hair, the permanent bonds that are broken are the disulphide bonds, shown **S–S**

Neutraliser adds oxygen to the hair, which attaches to the hydrogen which forms water, shown as H H or **H₂O** – water

When perm lotion is added, we introduce hydrogen; this softens and breaks the disulphide bonds, shown as H–H S S

During development the softened bonds are **moulded** around the rod and take on their new shape

Summary of changes to disulphide bonds

HOW TEMPERATURE AFFECTS THE PERM PROCESS

As you have just learnt, acid perms/exothermic perms need an activating ingredient which produces heat, or additional heat to enable the cuticle layer to open and the perm to penetrate into the cortex layer. Alkaline perms naturally open the cuticle layer because of their higher pH value.

When you process the perm, you need to ensure that the environment is warm enough. Cold salons will increase the development time, as cool air slows down the development process. A warm salon or additional heat, such as an electronic accelerator, will decrease the development time. If a client is sat by an open window, then the resulting curl might be uneven, due to the temperature differences and speed of development.

To decrease the development time, you can use a rollerball, a climazone, a hood dryer, or even just a disposable cap, as this will keep in natural heat generated from the head.

Accelerator

INDUSTRY TIP

If you are using a hood dryer to develop the perm process, you must take care to prevent the dryer from drying out the perm lotion. Always ensure you use a plastic cap to contain the moisture.

ACCURATE TIMING

You must always follow the MFIs in relation to the suggested development times. These will give you a guideline, but the timing will also depend on:

- hair texture – remember white hair can be misleading
- hair density
- hair type
- hair length
- temperature of the salon
- winding method. If you wound with lotion (pre-damped) then the development time will be decreased when all the rods are in place. If you applied the lotion after the wind (post-damped) then the perm might take longer to develop.

If the perm lotion is underdeveloped, an insufficient number of bonds will break and the hair will not take on the new shape. If the neutraliser is underdeveloped, the curl will not be fixed in its new position. Either way, the curl is likely to drop and produce an unsatisfactory result.

If the perm lotion is overdeveloped, too many disulphide bonds are broken (over 25–30%) and the hair might become frizzy. If either the perm lotion or the neutraliser are overdeveloped, the hair condition can deteriorate and the hair's structure might be weakened.

You must always carry out a development test curl and check the S-bend, to see if the perm has sufficiently developed.

Development test curl

RINSING THE HAIR

When the perm lotion is developed and the development test identifies that about 25–30% of the disulphide bonds are broken, the hair must be thoroughly rinsed to remove all traces of perm lotion. Perm lotion and neutraliser react together and can cause chemical burns to the hair and scalp, so you must rinse the hair, not only to stop the perm lotion from continuing to work, but to prevent chemical burns when you apply the neutraliser.

When you have thoroughly rinsed the perm lotion, **blot dry** the hair to prevent diluting the neutraliser and apply the fixing agent/neutraliser.

When developed, thoroughly rinse the neutraliser from the hair to prevent over-processing, which damages the hair's structure.

Blot dry
Soak up excess water using cotton wool, without rubbing the hair

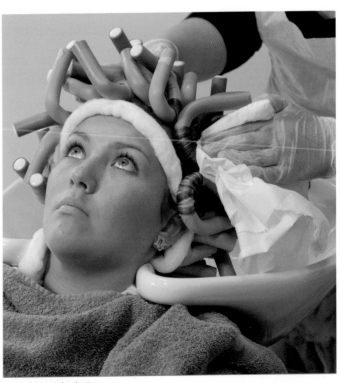
Blot drying the hair

ACTIVITY

For the purpose of research, and under the supervision of your manager/tutor, mix a small amount of perm lotion with an equal amount of neutraliser. Feel the container and note how hot the two products become when they are mixed together. Remember to wear PPE! Now think how your client would feel if this was put on her head! Now remember to always rinse the perm lotion thoroughly from the hair, before applying the neutralising agent.

THE IMPORTANCE OF WATER TEMPERATURE

When you shampoo the hair in preparation for the perm, you should use warm water to help cleanse the hair, removing products, oil and dirt. Warm water will also aid the opening of the cuticle layer, ready for the lotion to be applied. When you rinse the perm lotion from the hair, again use warm water to keep the cuticle layers open, ready for the neutraliser to fix the hair in its new shape. Remember that the scalp might be sensitive from the chemicals, so consider your client's comfort and ensure the water is not too hot.

> **INDUSTRY TIP**
>
> Always rinse the perm lotion and neutraliser thoroughly from the hair to ensure the products are removed and to prevent the hair from over-processing.

PERMING TECHNIQUES

In this section you will learn about the perm process from start to finish, looking at:

- whether to choose post-damp or pre-damp
- how to securely and evenly section the hair
- how to ensure the sections are on base or off base as required
- choosing the most suitable technique and carrying out the process.

POST-DAMP OR PRE-DAMP?

Post-damping is winding the hair around the rods and then applying the perm lotion to each rod, one after the other. Pre-damping is applying a weak perm lotion to the hair prior to winding. For pre-damping, you will need to wind the hair quickly to avoid over-processing the hair.

Remember to wear PPE to avoid allergic reactions or contact dermatitis from the chemicals.

> **INDUSTRY TIP**
>
> If the water is too hot, then your client may suffer discomfort or scalp irritation, and the perm may process more quickly than expected. But if the water is not warm enough, the cuticle layer will not be sufficiently opened to allow the chemicals to penetrate the cortex layer, which could slow down the development process.

When deciding whether to use post-damping or pre-damping, you need to consider the following:

- the sequence of the winding technique – particularly for pre-damping
- MFIs – post-damping is the only option for some perms
- the hair length – you might decide that pre-damping is the best option to ensure that you thoroughly cover the hair
- the hair texture and condition – never pre-damp fine or porous hair types, but consider the benefits to coarse, resistant hair or hair that is difficult to wind.

 SmartScreen 208 handout 14

SECTIONING THE HAIR

When you have decided which winding technique and rod size to use, you can begin to wind. Each section of hair must be about the size of your rod choice – width and depth. If you are using varied sizes, then your section sizes must vary too.

If the section size is too large for the rod, the curls might be uneven or too loose. If the section size is too small, you might struggle to get all the rods on the head and your resulting curls might be too tight.

SmartScreen 208 handout 4

SECURING THE HAIR

To secure the hair in place as you wind, you must use an end paper. These are used on the ends of the hair to keep all the hairs in place and prevent buckled ends or fish hooks.

Incorrectly wound-in end paper

Correctly wound-in end paper

INDUSTRY TIP

You must ensure that you maintain the tension from root to point when winding the hair, or the end result may be uneven.

When you have wound the hair around the rod, secure it with a perm band. This band must go straight across the hair, without any twists. Bands that are twisted or secured too closely to the root area can break the hair.

WINDING ON BASE OR OFF BASE

When you are winding the hair, your rods should ideally be wound to sit on their own base. But, as with setting, you can wind on base to achieve maximum root lift, or wind off base to prevent root lift.

On-base perm winding

INDUSTRY TIP

Keeping the hair misted with water while winding makes it easier to control.

> **INDUSTRY TIP**
>
> Ensure that the completed wind is not too tight, as this can cause scalp irritation and damage the hair.

Off-base perm winding

> **INDUSTRY TIP**
>
> Make sure you decide whether you are winding on base or off base before you begin. If your aim is to wind on base and you create root drag as you wind, the resulting curl will be similar to that of off-base winding, and no root lift will be achieved.

CHOOSING YOUR TECHNIQUE

When you have completed the following, you should be in a position to decide which winding technique to use.

1 Consult with your client and confirm the curl result required.

2 Analyse your client's hair.

3 Identify any contra-indications and factors that could affect the desired result.

4 Carry out the relevant hair tests.

Directional wind

A directional wind is similar to that of a directional set; you wind the hair in a directed manner to suit the style requirements. The benefits of a directional wind are:

- the roots are wound in the direction that the style will be worn
- the hair is wound to suit the partings worn
- it is suitable for any hair length.

Directional winding

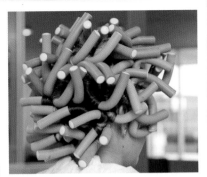

STEP 1 – Complete the whole area to be wound.

STEP 2 – Apply perm lotion to the hair, following the MFIs.

STEP 3 – Use an accelerator to decrease the development time.

STEP 4 – Carry out a development test curl.

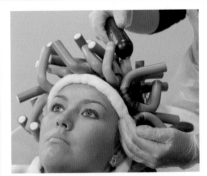

STEP 5 – Rinse the hair thoroughly at the basin to remove all traces of perm lotion.

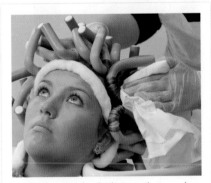

STEP 6 – Blot dry the hair, so that you do not dilute the neutraliser.

STEP 7 – Using fresh towels and cotton wool, apply the neutraliser following the MFIs.

WHY DON'T YOU...
Watch the stylists in your salon wind a directional perm and then practise on a head block.

INDUSTRY TIP

You may notice that qualified stylists in the salon complete a post-damp 'nine-section' perm wind using just five sections. They may wind:

- section 1 – from top to back
- section 2 – a back-side section
- section 3 – a front-side section and
- sections 4–5 – repeated on the other side of the head.

This is ok, when you are qualified, and only if you are completing a post-damp application.

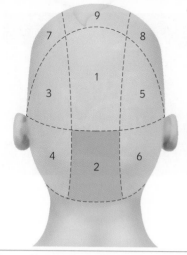

Nine-section wind sections

Nine-section wind

Winding a nine-section perm helps you to control longer hair lengths and work in a methodical manner.

When pre-damping, you must start at the crown, section 1, leaving section 9, the top and front hairline, until the end.

- Sections 1 and 2 are from the crown down to the back of the nape.
- Sections 3 and 4, and 5 and 6 are on either side of sections 1 and 2, going from the top of the head to the back of the ear and down to the nape, splitting these sections in two – from the ear to the occipital bone.
- Sections 7 and 8 are the two front side sections.
- Section 9 is the top front section.

The benefits of a nine-section perm wind are:

- methodical winding
- easier to control the hair length.

WHY DON'T YOU...
Watch the stylists in your salon wind a nine-section perm and then practise on a head block.

HANDY HINTS

If you are pre-damping you will need to consider the sequence in which you wind the hair. In a nine-section perm you wind the hair in the following order, 1–6, and finish with 7, 8 and 9 – as per the diagram. You do this to avoid overdeveloping the front hairline, where the hair is weakest. You could damage the weak hair if you wind with lotion starting from the top, because this section might already be overdeveloped by the time you complete the wind over the rest of the head.

STEP 1 – Divide the hair into nine sections.

STEP 2 – Wind from the top front section, or the crown, down towards the nape section.

STEP 3 – Complete the nape section and start on the side sections.

STEP 4 – Complete the whole head wind, maintaining tension throughout.

STEP 5 – Develop the perm then rinse the hair. Neutralise using a bowl and sponge technique.

STEP 6 – The completed perm and desired result.

Brick wind

A brick wind perm has the same winding pattern as a brick wind setting technique. Wind the hair following a brick-style pattern, offset to the row above. The benefits of a brick wind perm are that:

- it avoids partings
- there are no rod/roller marks.

Brick wind perming

Brick wind – winding sections

STEP 1 – Wind the crown area, maintaining even tension throughout.

STEP 2 – Start at the top of the head using a brick winding technique.

STEP 3 – Work down towards the nape area.

STEP 4 – Ensure your bands are not twisted or too tight.

STEP 5 – Apply perm lotion, being careful not to flood the scalp.

STEP 6 – Apply a post-perm treatment after neutralising.

WHY DON'T YOU...
Watch the stylists in your salon wind a brick wind and then practise on a head block.

SmartScreen 208 handout 5

THE PERM PROCESS

When you have wound a full head of rods, you need to prepare the client fully for the perm lotion application.

Applying the lotion

1 Protect your client with a gown, towel and a waterproof cape.
2 Apply barrier cream around the hairline.
3 Attach misted/damp cotton wool around the hairline.
4 Mist the hair with water to ensure even porosity.
5 Activate and prepare the perm lotion of your choice.
6 Apply a few drops to each rod, starting from the back and working towards the front (the resistant areas to the weaker areas).
7 After the initial application, thoroughly coat each rod a second time, without flooding the scalp with lotion.
8 Change the cotton wool if the lotion drips.
9 Place a disposable cap on the client's head.
10 Use heat if suitable.
11 Offer your client refreshments and explain the development process and roughly how long it will take.

Applying the lotion

Developing the perm

1 Leave the perm to develop without disturbing the hair for at least 5–10 minutes, depending on the MFIs, hair condition, texture, etc.
2 Complete a development test curl.
3 If the hair requires further development, leave it for another 5 minutes and then check every 2–3 minutes until the development test curl produces an S-bend that resembles the size of the rod.
4 When the development test curl is positive, escort your client to the shampoo area.

THE CITY & GUILDS TEXTBOOK

Developing the perm

Rinsing and neutralising

1. Ensure your client is adequately protected.
2. Rinse the hair, ensuring all rods are rinsed, for at least 5 minutes, depending on the MFIs and the hair length, taking care with the water temperature, flow direction and pressure.
3. Carefully blot dry the rods with a towel to prevent diluting the neutraliser, and reapply cotton wool to the hairline.
4. Apply the neutraliser either from the applicator bottle or foam it in a bowl and apply with a sponge.
5. Leave the hair to develop for about 5 minutes, depending on MFIs, and then either remove the rods and gently reapply the neutraliser to the unwound hair, or leave the rods in place and reapply the neutraliser.
6. Leave the hair for a further 5 minutes, depending on MFIs, and then remove the rods if you have not already done so.
7. Remove all the cotton wool from the hairline.
8. Thoroughly rinse the hair and apply a pH-balancing or post-perm conditioner.
9. Leave the conditioner on for a few minutes, depending on the MFIs, and thoroughly rinse the hair.
10. Towel dry the hair and gently comb through progressively from points to roots, with a wide-tooth comb.
11. Escort your client back to the workstation for the following service.
12. Your desired look should have been achieved. Check that your client is happy with the result.

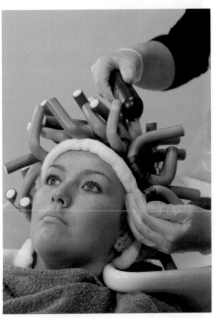
Rinsing the hair

SmartScreen 208 handout 16

SOLVING PERMING PROBLEMS

As with all services, problems can occur. Problems with perming can often be overcome, when you know what has caused them.

The following table shows the types of problems that can occur, their likely causes and how they can be remedied.

Type of problem	Cause of problem	Remedy action required
During the perm and neutralising process you notice:		
Scalp irritation	<ul><li>Lotion on the scalp</li><li>Allergic reaction to the lotion</li><li>Tension or rods too tight</li></ul>	<ul><li>Rinse the hair and scalp with cool water</li><li>Refer to GP if required</li></ul>
Rods fall out during the rinsing stage	<ul><li>Water pressure to high</li><li>Hair too short</li><li>Rods wound too loosely</li></ul>	<ul><li>Lower water pressure</li><li>Use a hairnet to secure in place</li><li>Re-wind the rods</li></ul>
The perm process is slow	<ul><li>The salon is too cold</li><li>Insufficient lotion used</li><li>Lotion too weak</li></ul>	<ul><li>Add heat and use an accelerator – check MFIs</li><li>Add more lotion</li><li>Add stronger lotion</li></ul>
After the perm process has finished you notice:		
Fish hooks	<ul><li>Poor wind, the hair has been buckled or bent during the wind</li></ul>	<ul><li>Trim the ends of the hair</li></ul>
Some straight pieces	<ul><li>Sections too large</li><li>Rod size too large</li><li>Poor wind – too loose</li><li>Uneven application of lotion</li><li>Rods loosened during rinsing</li></ul>	<ul><li>Re-perm the straight pieces if the hair condition allows</li></ul>
Hair is frizzy	<ul><li>Rod size too small</li><li>Wind too tight</li><li>Lotion too strong</li><li>Overdeveloped</li></ul>	<ul><li>Conditioning treatments</li><li>Regular trims</li></ul>
Hair breakage	<ul><li>Poor wind – bands are twisted or positioned too close to the root</li><li>Rods are too tightly wound</li><li>Incompatible products</li><li>Lotion too strong</li><li>Overdeveloped</li></ul>	There is no remedy but the following may help prevent further breakage:<ul><li>Conditioning treatments and restructurants</li><li>Regular trims</li></ul>

Type of problem	Cause of problem	Remedy action required
Discolouration of hair	▪ Incompatible products ▪ Neutraliser has faded recent colour service	▪ Use a semi-permanent or temporary colour to tone the hair colour
The curl is too tight	▪ Rod size too small ▪ Sections too small ▪ Overdeveloped	▪ Deep conditioning treatments ▪ If condition allows, you could re-perm on larger rods or relax the hair
The hair is straight	▪ Barrier on the hair ▪ Resistant hair ▪ Incorrect perm choice – too weak ▪ Underdeveloped ▪ Faulty lotion	▪ Re-perm the hair if the condition allows
The curl is uneven	▪ Sections too large ▪ Poor wind – uneven ▪ Incorrect rod size ▪ Uneven product application ▪ Rods loosened during rinsing	▪ Re-perm if condition allows

After a couple of days the client returns and states:

The curl has dropped	▪ Uneven tension when winding ▪ Insufficient lotion ▪ Uneven application of product ▪ Underdeveloped	▪ Re-perm if hair condition allows

HANDY HINTS

In some cases, the salon's insurance company may need to be notified if the client is dissatisfied or if there is damage or breakage to their hair or skin.

WHY DON'T YOU...

Find out from your salon manager which of these problems you can deal with yourself and which ones you should refer to your manager.

 SmartScreen 208 worksheet 9

AFTERCARE ADVICE

It is important that you provide your client with aftercare advice following a perm because of the strength of the chemicals. They need to know how to maintain the curl and their hair condition.

You must provide your client with the following advice:

- what equipment they should use
- which products to use
- when to return to the salon for future services.

Always give clear, accurate and constructive advice and consider your client's time constraints in relation to maintaining their hairstyle. If your client has an active lifestyle and/or enjoys swimming, make sure that you consider this and recommend suitable products. Explain to your clients that they should not wash their hair for 24–48 hours after a perm, and avoid excessive tension on the hair, as this can cause the curls to loosen. When you are making your recommendations, maintain eye contact and use positive, open body language to promote trust and a good client–stylist relationship.

EQUIPMENT

Always clearly explain to your client which tools, such as brushes and combs, they should use, and which to avoid. Inform your clients that they should always use a brush on dry hair and a wide-tooth comb on wet hair. Promote the use of a diffuser to maintain the curls without disturbing or separating them or causing the hair to look fluffy or frizzy. Explain that excessive use of heated styling equipment will increase the porosity and reduce elasticity, causing damage to the hair.

PRODUCTS

You must advise your clients which shampoos and conditioners they should use to maintain moisture levels and the condition of the hair. Suggest regular deep-penetrating conditioning treatments, which can either be used at home or carried out in the salon.

Future colouring services might need to be suggested or avoided, depending on the condition of the client's hair. If a colour has faded slightly during the perming process, you might need to recommend a semi-permanent or a temporary colour to brighten the faded colour. The perm service carried out might, however, restrict your client to certain colour services in the future, and you must make your client aware of this.

You should make recommendations to your clients about the use of styling and finishing products. Advise them which styling products to use when the hair is wet, to avoid the hair looking frizzy, and which finishing products to use to hold the curls in place. Show your clients how much of the product to use, depending on their hair length, and how to use it with their styling tools.

Recommend products suitable for permed hair

FUTURE SERVICES

Recommend to your clients when to return to the salon for a trim, and make them aware of the signs that indicate that their hair needs to be cut and styled again.

Make suggestions for future colouring services and conditioning treatments, and tell your clients how long the perm should last. It is ideal if your clients book their next appointment while they are still in the salon, when your advice is clear in their mind.

SmartScreen 208 handout 18

SmartScreen 208 revision cards

Turn to page 485 for the answers.

1   Which **one** of the following **best** describes how to sanitise tools and work surfaces?

   a   With disinfectant chemicals or wipes.

   b   With an autoclave.

   c   With a solution of water and soap.

   d   With a UV cabinet.

2   **Statement 1:**
   Perming and neutralising products are a risk to health as they can be absorbed through the skin; wearing gloves will minimise the risks.

   Statement 2:
   Risks to health can be minimised by following the manufacturers' instructions and wearing correct PPE.

   Which **one** of the following is correct for the above statements?

	Statement 1	Statement 2
a	True	True
b	True	False
c	False	True
d	False	False

3   Cotton wool used when applying the perm solution must be:

   a   Removed and replaced immediately to minimise chemical burns.

   b   Removed at the end of the service to stop the product entering the eyes.

   c   Disposed of in a covered bin and incinerated at the end of the day.

   d   Disposed of and replaced with a plastic cap to catch any drips.

4   A pre-perm conditioner is used to:

   a   Allow the lotion to process on the ends first.

   b   Ensure the perm lotion is the correct pH for the hair.

   c   Break the hydrogen bonds at an even rate.

   d   Even out porosity and absorption of the perm lotion.

5   **Statement 1:**
   Perming products come in various strengths such as 'normal', 'tinted' and 'resistant'.

   Statement 2:
   An acid perm is stronger than an alkali and can damage fragile hair.

   Which **one** of the following is correct for the above statements?

	Statement 1	Statement 2
a	True	True
b	True	False
c	False	True
d	False	False

6   Fish hooks can be avoided by using:

   a   Weaker perm lotion.

   b   End papers.

   c   Even tension.

   d   Stronger perm lotion.

7   **Statement 1:**
   Open skin abrasions are a contra-indication to perming and care should be taken when applying the lotion.

   Statement 2:
   An incompatibility test will identify any products that may react with the perm lotion or neutraliser.

   Which **one** of the following is correct for the above statements?

	Statement 1	Statement 2
a	True	True
b	True	False
c	False	True
d	False	False

8   Which **one** of the following identifies the changes to the hair structure when perming?

   a   Disulphide bonds are broken, cystine changes to cysteine and hair is softened.

   b   Disulphide bonds are broken, cysteine changes to cystine and hair is softened.

   c   Hydrogen and salt bonds are broken and reformed and hair is hardened.

   d   Hydrogen and oxygen is added to the salt bonds and hair is hardened.

CASE STUDY: KARINE JACKSON

Karine Jackson was born to be a star hairdresser. From starting her career in her parents' salon in the small Australian town of Wollongong, to excelling at Charles Worthington, to setting up her own Covent Garden salon, to winning London Hairdresser of the Year in the 2007 British Hairdressing Awards and becoming a finalist for Men's Hairdresser of the Year in 2009, Karine's huge talent and enthusiasm has always shone through. Along with Karine's fantastic work, she has also appeared on *The One Show* and in publications such as *Marie Claire* and *The Observer Magazine*.

Here are Karine's top tips for perming and neutralising:

1 Decide whether the hair is coloured, bleached, porous... we use the wet stretch test. Does it need a treatment prior to perming? Choose the correct solution for the hair type – if it is glassy the cuticles are shut tight and will be more resistant, so use stronger lotion. Check the perm after 10 minutes by unwinding one rod and seeing if it goes into a ribbon. When it does that, rinse. Smell as you are going along, it will take about 10 minutes.

2 Put a towel over and blot dry, then put the hairdryer on as you blot; do not disturb the rollers. Apply neutraliser and only leave on for 10 minutes from the second you start, not from when it is all on.

3 Do not do a heavy blow dry, use a light conditioner (no shampoo or treatments) and tell the client not to shampoo for 48 hours.

4 I think jumbo curlers are best, and freshly trim hair before you perm it.

5 The neutralising is one of the most important parts of a perm; to successfully blot dry a perm we recommend putting a towel over it and then using a hairdryer while blotting.

6 Make sure when you are rinsing that you rinse and smell – if you can still smell lotion it is not rinsed enough.

7 Perms are a great way to update a style. Bobs look fantastic with a perm; they can be worn washed and go, or straightened to give the versatility of a different look every day.

8 Ammonia-free perming systems are easy to use and are just as effective as the traditional chemical versions. They are really gentle on the hair and they drop out after about 8 weeks, dependant on hair type. This means there is no regrowth for the client to worry about.

9 A root perm will give the hair volume and lift without causing any kinks in the hair; use it at the roots of stubborn, limp, flat hair.

209
THE ART OF DRESSING HAIR

The 'art' of dressing hair – the title says it all! The styling and dressing skills that you will learn in this unit will enable you to complete a finished look, complement a haircut, enhance colour and produce a work of art! The basic science facts that you will learn will enable you (and the client) to maximise the longevity of these great-looking styles.

There are two learning outcomes in this unit. The learner will be able to:

- prepare for dressing hair
- provide a dressing hair service.

PREPARE FOR DRESSING HAIR

During this part of the unit you will learn:

- safety considerations for styling and dressing hair
- communication and behavioural requirements
- consultation techniques used
- basic science and effects that styling and heat have on the hair.

SAFETY CONSIDERATIONS

Working safely, cleanly and tidily minimises risk of harm and injury to yourself and others and prevents cross-contamination. It gives the client an image of professionalism while their hair is being styled.

MAINTAIN EFFECTIVE AND SAFE METHODS OF WORKING

You must keep your work area clean and tidy at all times. Make sure that your trolley and workstation are prepared for the required styling service, and that you are ready for the client to arrive.

You must always protect your client during the styling service with a fresh, clean gown and towel. You should wear gloves when applying styling and finishing products, to prevent dermatitis and maintain healthy hands, and an apron to protect your clothes.

Professional salon ready for styling a client

HANDY HINTS

Always ensure you follow the manufacturers' instructions (MFIs) for the products and electrical appliances you will use. Follow the health and safety Acts and your salon policies too.

Client protected and gowned

HANDY HINTS

Remember to remove accessories/jewellery such as rings or bracelets, that may cause discomfort to the client by snagging the hair. If products or moisture collect inside or around the jewellery, you increase your chances of contracting contact dermatitis.

To ensure the comfort of your client, sit them upright with their back supported against the chair. When you are styling their hair, make sure that your body weight is evenly distributed, standing with your feet slightly apart.

Sterilise your styling tools and equipment to ensure they are hygienic and ready for use. Clean your workstation and surfaces with detergent and water, disinfect your tools with suitable chemical disinfectants, sanitise using a UV light cabinet, or sterilise in an autoclave. Place your trolley on the correct side to avoid over-stretching; this will prevent neck and back problems and fatigue. It will also minimise the risk of injury and help you to work methodically, enabling the salon to run on time.

Barbicide

HANDY HINTS

Poor standards of health and hygiene can cause cross-contamination, offence to others and present a poor salon image.

HANDY HINTS

You should refer to Units 202 and 203 for a full recap on health and safety, and consultation.

 SmartScreen 209 handout 1

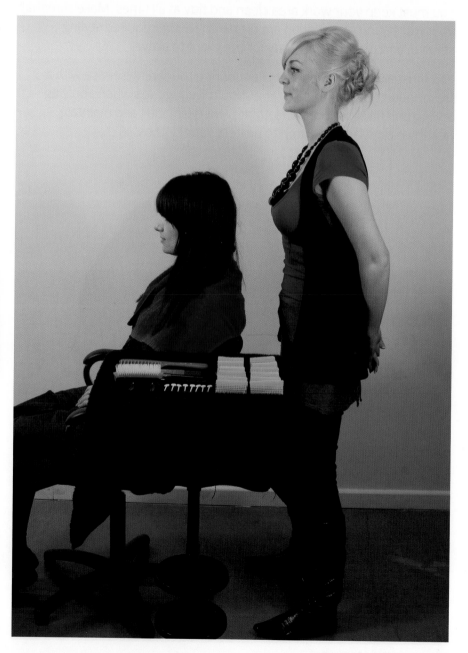

The following diagram offers helpful hints on how to maintain an effective working environment.

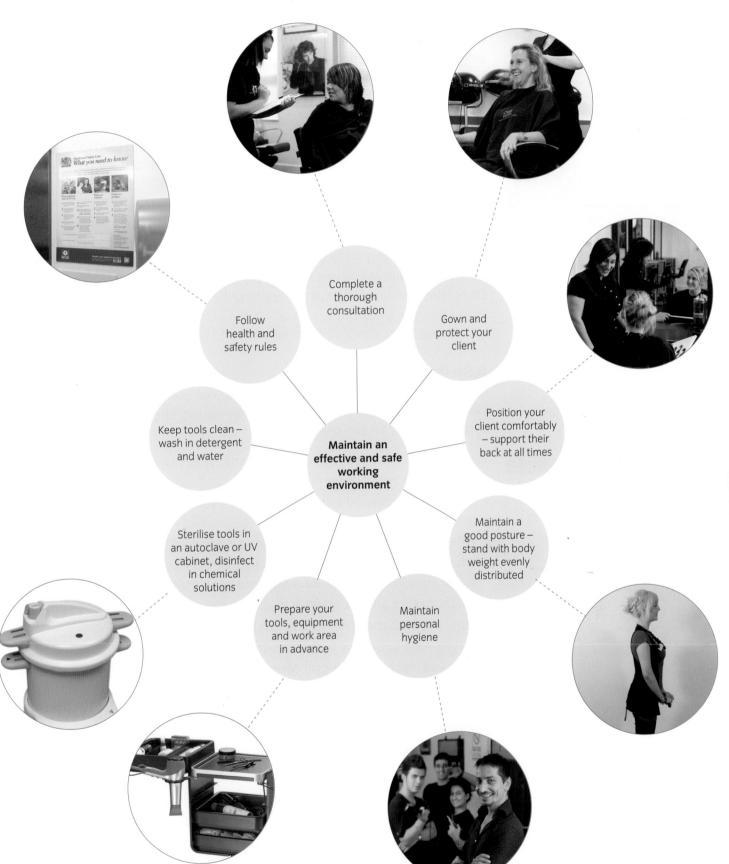

Complete a thorough consultation

Follow health and safety rules

Gown and protect your client

Keep tools clean – wash in detergent and water

Maintain an effective and safe working environment

Position your client comfortably – support their back at all times

Sterilise tools in an autoclave or UV cabinet, disinfect in chemical solutions

Maintain a good posture – stand with body weight evenly distributed

Prepare your tools, equipment and work area in advance

Maintain personal hygiene

COMMUNICATION AND BEHAVIOUR

When communicating with your client, you must remember that the impression the salon makes will start with the first person and the first words spoken! Make sure you use suitable terminology that your client will understand; speak clearly and politely and use positive body language. Listen to what your client is asking of you and look at their body language.

You must always follow relevant instructions when working with your colleagues and follow your salon rules and regulations. Before you commence the service, you should read your client's record card to check the previous history and update it with any new information.

CONSULTATION TECHNIQUES

You must always complete a thorough consultation with your client to identify their needs, decide on the most suitable tools and equipment to use, and ensure you achieve the desired result. You will need to demonstrate different styles for a variety of occasions. In the practical side of this unit, you will have the opportunity to set and dress hair for clients going to a ball/prom, a wedding, the races, nightclubbing and, of course, everyday styles, suitable for work or a day at the beach!

ASKING QUESTIONS

During the consultation you will need to ask your client questions to identify their needs, and analyse the hair by visually checking and feeling it, to identify any factors that might affect the service.

You will need to ask your client the following types of question:

- What is your vision of the finished look?
- Have you been happy with your previous style? Do you wish to change or alter anything?
- What is the occasion for which the style is required?
- What will you be wearing? Can you fit your clothes over the hairstyle? (If you are setting the hair for a night out.)
- Would you like any accessories in your hair?
- How long does the style need to last for the occasion?
- Do you want to be able to recreate the style yourself?
- Have you had any specific problems maintaining your style?
- What products do you generally use on your hair and why?
- Are there any lifestyle factors that could affect recreating the style at home?
- What styling equipment do you use at home?
- Do you have any allergies?

You must confirm the finished look that your client requires, so that you can choose the most suitable products, tools and equipment to achieve the best result.

> **HANDY HINTS**
>
> Use open and closed questions to obtain all the relevant information required. Open questions that start with 'what', 'why', 'how' and 'when' require more in-depth and specific answers, and closed questions require 'yes' or 'no' answers.

ACTIVITY

Can you think of any other questions that you could ask your client about their hair or their requirements? During this process, record any answers about allergies and the hair's condition on a record card in case you need to refer back to the information in the future, or if there are any problems and you need evidence of the client's comments.

INDUSTRY TIP

Listen to the stylists in your salon consulting with their clients.

VISUAL CHECKS ON THE HAIR

You will need to visually check the hair and scalp to identify:

- the condition of the hair and scalp
- the length, style, type, texture and density of the hair
- partings/natural fall of the hair
- any growth patterns
- the client's head and face shape/features
- any scalp problems
- how long the service will take.

HANDY HINTS

You must carry out a porosity test to identify if the cuticle scales are open, and the hair therefore porous, and an elasticity test to test the strength of the cortex.

ACTIVITY

List the types of question you would ask your client if they want their hair put up for a day at the races.

WORKING TO COMMERCIAL TIMES

It is essential you work to schedule to prevent running late for other appointments. Test all your equipment beforehand to ensure that no interruptions occur during the service. Your salon would have judged the prices charged to the clients to include salon costs and your time. Working to salon time guidelines helps the salon to maintain profit and increase their revenue. If you work on a commission basis, time is money!

BASIC SCIENCE

Hair is mostly composed of a hardened fibrous protein called keratin. Keratin is made up of amino acids and peptide bonds which originate in the hair follicle. These many amino acids and peptide bonds form the **polypeptide** chains (coils). The polypeptide chains are held together by permanent and temporary bonds inside the cortex layer of the hair.

Polypeptide

This is derived from poly (many) and peptos (broken down)

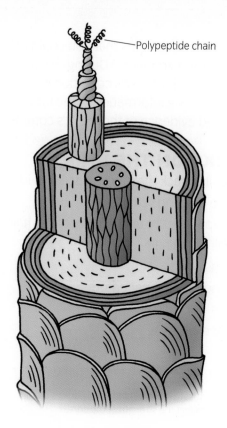

—Polypeptide chain

HANDY HINTS

Hair is composed of amino acids and peptide bonds that form the polypeptide chains. These are held together by bonds in the cortex.

THE STRUCTURE OF THE HAIR

Hair can be naturally curly, wavy or straight. Your natural hair type is determined in the cortex layer. Hair is held in its natural state by the permanent and temporary bonds. The permanent bonds are broken by chemicals, such as perm solution, and can be changed from naturally straight to chemically curly. The permanent bonds are called disulphide bonds; refer back to Unit 208. Styling the hair softens the temporary bonds and temporarily changes the natural state, such as changing from straight to curly, or wavy to straight. The temporary bonds are hydrogen and salt bonds. The flow chart below shows what makes up the hair.

The salt bonds

Hair is mostly made of protein called keratin

Keratin is made up of amino acids and peptide bonds

Many amino acids and peptide bonds form the polypeptide chains; these are held together by bonds

Permanent (disulphide) bonds are broken only by chemicals

Temporary (salt) bonds are softened by changes in the hair's pH

Temporary (hydrogen) bonds are softened by heat and water

The salt bonds are weak bonds that are temporarily softened by changes in pH, by the use of weak acids or alkalis. They are reformed by normalising the pH.

The hydrogen bonds

The main bonds that are broken when you are styling the hair are hydrogen bonds. These are broken by heat or water and hardened by drying or cooling the hair. Hydrogen bonds give the hair its strength and its flexibility to move freely; it is what makes the hair elastic. Well-conditioned hair with a strong cortex can stretch up to a further half its original length when wet; this is due to the temporary breaking of the hydrogen bonds.

Alpha and beta keratin

Hair in its natural state of curly, wavy or straight is described as being in an alpha keratin state. When hair has been wetted, stretched and dried into a new shape, it is described as being in a beta keratin state.

Heat from styling equipment, such as tongs and straightening irons, can also change the state from alpha keratin to beta keratin – when the hair has cooled into its new shape.

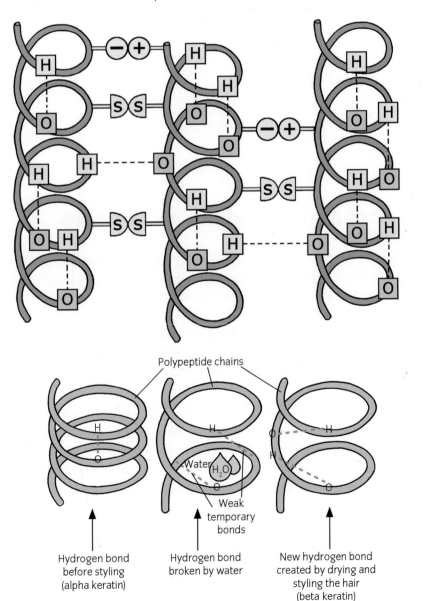

Polypeptide chains

Water H₂O

Weak temporary bonds

Hydrogen bond before styling (alpha keratin)

Hydrogen bond broken by water

New hydrogen bond created by drying and styling the hair (beta keratin)

HANDY HINTS

The weak, temporary hydrogen bonds are softened by water and heat, and hardened by drying and cooling of the hair.

HANDY HINTS

Hair in its natural state is in an alpha keratin state; when wetted, stretched and dried, its new state is beta keratin.

HUMIDITY

Hair is hygroscopic, which means it can absorb moisture from the atmosphere. The hairstyle is therefore affected by the humidity and moisture present in the air. The hair absorbs the moisture from the air and the beta keratin state changes back to alpha keratin, because the moisture softens the temporary hydrogen bonds and the hair reverts back to its original state.

The diagram below shows the alpha to beta keratin process.

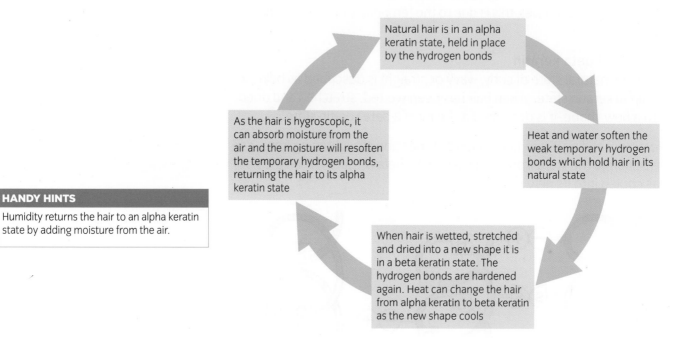

Natural hair is in an alpha keratin state, held in place by the hydrogen bonds

Heat and water soften the weak temporary hydrogen bonds which hold hair in its natural state

When hair is wetted, stretched and dried into a new shape it is in a beta keratin state. The hydrogen bonds are hardened again. Heat can change the hair from alpha keratin to beta keratin as the new shape cools

As the hair is hygroscopic, it can absorb moisture from the air and the moisture will resoften the temporary hydrogen bonds, returning the hair to its alpha keratin state

HANDY HINTS

Humidity returns the hair to an alpha keratin state by adding moisture from the air.

HANDY HINTS

Keeping the hair misted and with even moisture balance helps you to produce a smooth, even effect when blow drying the hair.

EFFECTS OF THE STYLING AND DRYING PROCESS

Each client's hair will dry out at a different rate and, as wet hair stretches allowing a new shape to form, an even moisture balance is required. If areas of the hair have started to dry during the styling process, then hair will lose its elasticity and the ability to stretch sufficiently, so the result might be uneven. You must mist the hair sections lightly with a water spray if you notice an uneven elasticity when drying the hair, to allow the bonds to be reformed evenly into their new position.

HOW TEMPERATURE AFFECTS THE HAIR

When styling the hair with heated appliances, you must always use a heat protector. These products create a protective barrier around the cuticle scales, preventing moisture in the air from penetrating. After blow drying or when you are using heated appliances, always allow the hair to cool, or use the cool setting button on the hairdryer for a minute or so at the end. This enables the cuticle scales to close and the hydrogen bonds to harden in their new shape so the result will be longer lasting.

HANDY HINTS

Always allow the hair to cool, which allows the hydrogen bonds to harden in their new shape and prolong the style.

If the temperature of your heated equipment is too hot, the scalp might get burnt and the hair will be damaged. This will cause the cuticle scales to lift and the hair to become more porous. You must adjust the temperature settings on all electrical heated appliances to suit the following:

- Texture – fine hair will need a cooler setting than coarse hair.
- Density – sparse hair will need a cooler setting than abundant hair.
- Hair type – curly hair might need a hotter setting than straight hair when straightening, and straight hair might require a hotter setting when curling.
- Hair's porosity – porous hair will not withstand high heat settings without sustaining further damage to the cuticle scales. You must ensure the airflow from a hand-held dryer flows from root to point, to ensure the cuticle scales are not lifted, causing damage to the hair.
- Hair's elasticity – weak elasticity in the hair will become weaker if the heat settings are too high.

HANDY HINTS

The overuse of heated appliances will cause damage to all hair types. You must advise your client on the amount of use that is suitable and always recommend they use a heat-protective lotion.

PROVIDE A DRESSING HAIR SERVICE

During this part of the unit you will learn:

- styling products available for use
- styling tools and equipment available for use
- factors that should be considered prior to setting and dressing hair
- step-by-step techniques for completing these services
- aftercare advice you should provide to clients.

STYLING PRODUCTS

There are hundreds of different styling and finishing products available on the market to help the stylist and client maintain great-looking hair. They are all marketed differently to attract various client groups to their designs. The instructions on the product advise you and the client how to use the product effectively and how much of the product should be used. Always read the MFIs to ensure you use the correct amount to achieve the best result and to prevent overloading the hair.

USING PRODUCTS SAFELY

When using styling and finishing products, you should ideally wear gloves during application, wash and dry your hands regularly and use hand cream afterwards to avoid contact dermatitis. Dermatitis can be recognised by inflamed skin, which might be red and sore, and the skin can weep and split.

When using styling and finishing products, you must do so safely and economically. Always ensure you follow COSHH. Using too much product is wasteful and the salon will lose profit; excessive use of products can also overload the hair, affecting the end result. Refer to Unit 202 to remind yourself of your responsibilities under COSHH.

STYLING PRODUCTS

Styling products are designed to aid the styling of wet hair. Make sure you use suitable styling products for blow drying, finger drying, wet or dry setting and dressing hair up. When using heated appliances, you must use products that protect the hair from heat and prevent damage.

The diagram below shows why you should use products effectively.

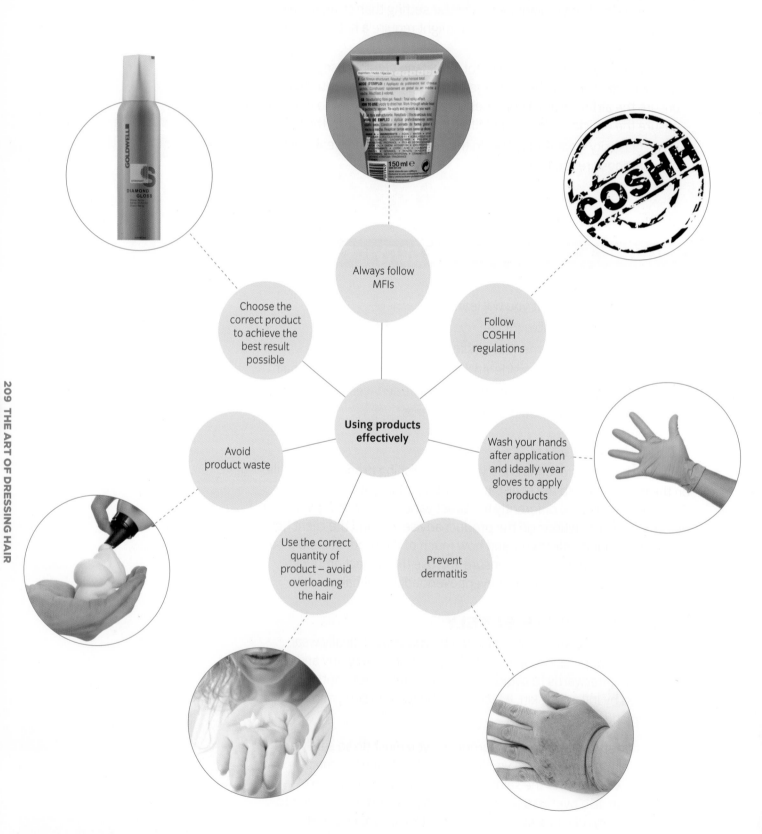

Choose the correct product to achieve the best result possible

Always follow MFIs

Follow COSHH regulations

Avoid product waste

Using products effectively

Wash your hands after application and ideally wear gloves to apply products

Use the correct quantity of product – avoid overloading the hair

Prevent dermatitis

The following table shows which styling products should be used to achieve the most effective result.

Styling product	How to use	Effect achieved and benefit to the client
Mousse	Apply a golf-ball-sized amount to towel-dried hair and comb through evenly.	Offers support and hold to hair blow dried with a radial brush. Can also be used as a curl activator.
Activators	Spray onto towel-dried wavy hair; roots to ends.	Enhances curls and offers support and hold to finger-dried hair.
Blow-dry lotion	Spray or sprinkle near the root area and work through to the ends.	Longer-lasting volume, lift and support for fine hair of any length. Can strengthen the structure when blow drying.
Anti-frizz lotion moisturiser	Distribute evenly through damp hair, dry and style with a brush and hairdryer.	Achieves a smoother, straighter appearance by taming frizz and curls. It coats the hair and forms a barrier to prevent moisture from humidity affecting the finished look. Ideal for any hair length.
Serum	After shampooing, rub 2–5 drops of serum into your palms and apply to towel-dried hair, distributing evenly.	Ultra-shine finish for all styles and hair types, enhances coloured hair and provides an anti-frizz effect by coating the hair with a smoothing liquid which forms a barrier to moisture.
Heat protector	Spray evenly through towel-dried hair.	Protects the hair from the drying effects and heat of the hairdryer, prevents frizz and gives an even finish.
Gel	Use on damp hair and distribute evenly through the hair before blow drying or finger drying.	Provides volume and texture for all hair lengths and hair types.

FINISHING PRODUCTS

Finishing products are applied to dried hair and are designed to support the finished look and give the style **longevity**.

The following table shows which finishing products are recommended to achieve longer-lasting effects.

Finishing product	How to use	Effect achieved and benefit to the client
Serum	Rub 2–5 drops of serum into your palms and apply to dry hair, distributing evenly before straightening.	To calm frizzy hair and fly-away ends, and protect from heated appliances by coating the hair and forming a protective barrier.
Oils	After drying, lightly mist the hair, avoiding the root area.	Optimal shine, texture and condition; ideal for medium to longer hair lengths.
Heat protector	Spray onto clean, dry hair prior to using heated appliances.	Provides a protective film over the outside of the cuticle scales which shields the hair from the heat of the appliance. Ideal for all hair lengths.
Gel	Massage a small amount into your palms and work evenly into the hair, shaping and moulding into shape with your fingers.	For stronger-hold looks. Gel can provide an elastic effect, causing the hair to bounce back into style.
Wax	Apply with your hands and fingertips through the hair, avoiding the root area. For funky, messy looks, apply using your palms and target the ends of the hair.	For soft, supple hold and great shine. Ideal for short hair.
Cream/dressing cream	Cream – apply using your fingertips, moving from root to point to create texture and movement. Dressing cream – apply to dressed hair to enhance individual curls, or break up the roller marks/sections on long hair.	Adds texture to shorter hair lengths and supports, lifts and adds shine and body to medium or longer hair. Adds separation to the curls, without causing a fluffy/frizzy result.
Hairspray	Shake well and spray on the hair from about 20 cm away.	Finishes the style with a shine and long-lasting shape, leaving the hair touchable and without stiffness. The spray forms a barrier to prevent absorption of moisture. Ideal for medium to longer hair lengths.

ACTIVITY

In pairs, identify your salon's product range for styling and finishing and list their benefits to the client.

ACTIVITY

Look at your fellow stylists and identify what products you would use on their current hairstyles.

INDUSTRY TIP

Always read and follow the MFIs for optimum results.

WHY DON'T YOU...

Ask a stylist in your salon what finishing products they are using when dressing and finishing the hair and why they have chosen these products.

STYLING TOOLS AND EQUIPMENT

When styling and finishing the hair, you will use a variety of tools and equipment, such as brushes and combs, hand-held hairdryers, straightening irons or curling tongs. When setting and dressing, you will use rollers, pins, grips, combs, heated rollers, straightening irons and tongs.

USING TOOLS AND EQUIPMENT EFFECTIVELY

To achieve the best results for the style and to maintain the condition of the hair, always follow the MFIs. Ensure your equipment is in good working order and fit for use. Use equipment correctly, to minimise damage to the tools and prevent any risk of injury to you and your clients. Maintain the condition of your tools and prevent a reduction in their performance by cleaning them regularly and keeping them free from product build-up and hair. Before plugging in and switching on your hairdryer, check that it is safe to use and the air vent filter is attached and clean.

When you are using your electrical equipment, be aware of potential hazards and follow the Electricity at Work Regulations. You must visually check your appliances for cracks in the main body or plug and kinks in the wires. Always label, remove and report faulty electrical equipment.

Refer to Unit 202 to recap on your responsibilities under the Electricity at Work Regulations.

Stylist checking for cracks in the main body of the hairdryer

Temperature of equipment

Before using heated appliances, always protect the hair with a heat protector to prevent damaging the hair and to prolong the style. You must take into consideration the texture and density of the hair, as fine, sparse hair will need considerably lower temperature settings to prevent damaging the cuticle scales and cortex. Always avoid contact with the skin when you are sectioning the hair and using the appliance.

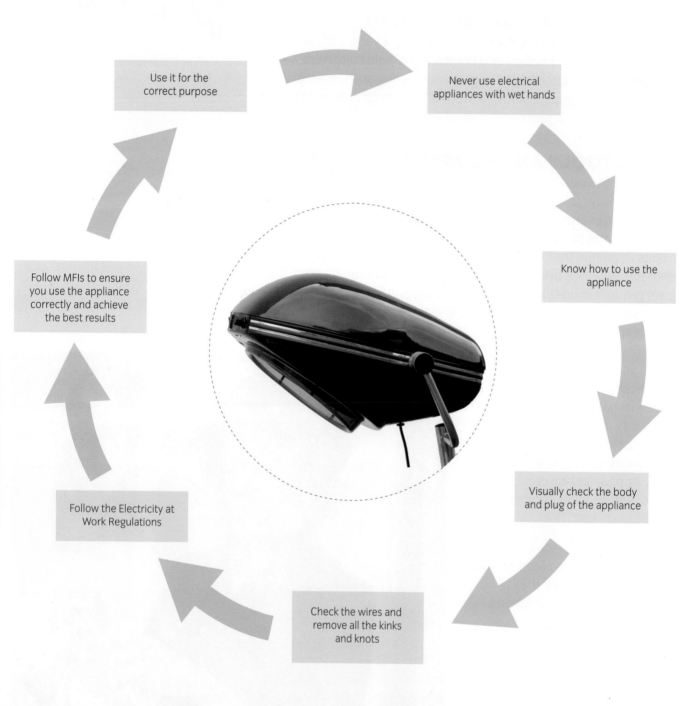

Use it for the correct purpose

Never use electrical appliances with wet hands

Know how to use the appliance

Visually check the body and plug of the appliance

Check the wires and remove all the kinks and knots

Follow the Electricity at Work Regulations

Follow MFIs to ensure you use the appliance correctly and achieve the best results

The table below shows the tools and equipment available for use and how to maintain them.

Tools and equipment available for use	How to use tools/equipment	How to maintain tools/equipment
Wide-tooth comb	To untangle the hair before styling and to section the hair cleanly. Always comb the hair from point to root, working up the hair shaft to avoid damage and client discomfort.	Clean with hot soapy water and disinfect in a Barbicide solution or sanitise in a UV cabinet.
Dressing-out comb	For back-combing, teasing and dressing out the finished result. Take a section of hair, hold it with tension and back-comb roots.	As above.
Section clips	To secure hair in place.	Clean with hot soapy water and disinfect in a Barbicide solution or sanitise in a UV cabinet.
Denman brush (flat brush)	To create a smooth, straight finish – such as a 'bob' style.	Remove any hair and product debris, clean with hot soapy water and disinfect in a Barbicide solution or sanitise in a UV cabinet.
Dressing-out brush (flat brush)	To dress and finish a blow dry, to remove roller marks from setting and to dress the hair. Can also be used for general hair brushing.	As above.
Small radial brush	To create root lift, volume and small curls in layered hair.	As above.

Tools and equipment available for use	How to use tools/equipment	How to maintain tools/equipment
Medium radial brush	To create root lift and medium-sized curls in short to medium-layered hair, and waves in longer hair.	Remove any hair and product debris, clean with hot soapy water and disinfect in a Barbicide solution or sanitise in a UV cabinet.
Large radial brush	To smooth and straighten, and create soft waves in longer hair.	As above.
Hand-held hairdryer	To dry the hair during blow drying. Direct the airflow down the hair shaft in the direction in which the cuticle lies, to smooth the overall effect.	Clean the air vent and remove hair/dust. Check the temperature settings. Wipe appliance with a disinfectant wipe.
Diffuser	To aid finger drying and encourage curls and lift in curly or wavy hair. Attach the diffuser to the end of the hairdryer and place the diffuser into the hair, to enable the flow and heat to dry the curls.	Wipe diffuser with a disinfectant wipe.
Nozzle	To direct the airflow and heat from the hairdryer down the hair shaft.	Clean with hot soapy water and use a disinfectant wipe.
Tail comb	To cleanly section the hair when setting.	Clean with hot soapy water and disinfect in a Barbicide solution or sanitise in a UV cabinet.

Tools and equipment available for use	How to use tools/equipment	How to maintain tools/equipment
Rollers with pins	To set the hair. Wind the rollers from point to root.	Remove any hair and product debris, clean with hot soapy water and disinfect in a Barbicide solution or sanitise in a UV cabinet.
Velcro rollers	Ideal for dry hair setting; hair is dampened with setting lotion and dried under a dryer. Wind the rollers from point to root.	As above.
Hood dryer	To dry wet sets. Place the client comfortably under the dryer. Set the timer for a suitable time frame considering the density and length of the hair. Check the temperature setting with your client. Ensure the metal pins are not touching the skin or scalp. Check that the hair is dry. Allow the hair to cool when dried.	Clean with disinfectant wipes.
Pin-curl clips	To hold pin-curls in place.	Clean clips and then sanitise in a UV cabinet.
Grips and pins	To secure and hold chignons, rolls and up-dos.	N/A – client will be going home with these in her hair.

Tools and equipment available for use	How to use tools/equipment	How to maintain tools/equipment
Straightening irons	To smooth and straighten dried hair. Use heat-protecting products. Comb and section the hair to be straightened. Check the temperature before use. Run straighteners down the hair section from root to point. Avoid contact of straighteners with the skin and scalp. Complete the whole head in a methodical manner. Leave hair to cool.	Clean and sterilise with disinfectant wipes.
Curling irons	To create curls and body. Use heat-protecting products. Comb and section the hair to be curled. Curl the hair section from point to root. Avoid contact of tongs/wand with the skin and scalp. Complete the whole head in a methodical manner. Leave hair to cool.	As above.
Curling wands	To create soft curls on long hair. As above. Or wind the hair from root to point to create spiral curls.	As above.
Heated rollers	To set dry hair. Use heat-protecting products. Section the hair cleanly – no bigger than the rollers' width or depth. Roll the hair section from point to root and secure with the pin. Avoid contact of heated rollers with the skin. Ensure pins are not touching the skin and scalp. Complete the full head using the chosen winding technique. Leave to cool and then remove the rollers.	Clean with hot soapy water; ensure they are dry before using them again.

Tools and equipment available for use	How to use tools/equipment	How to maintain tools/equipment
Feathers, ribbons and flowers	To add interest and accessories to a finished look. Attach securely to the hair.	N/A – client will be going home with these in her hair.

ACTIVITY

List the tools and equipment you would need to:

- blow dry long hair smooth and straight
- finger dry short, curly hair
- dry short to medium-length curly, frizzy hair smooth, but with body.

Which products would you use for these styles?

ACTIVITY

Prepare a trolley and work area with all the tools you would need for a hair-up style, on long hair, to be set using heated rollers. What products could you use to set and dress this style?

HANDY HINTS

Ineffectively maintained tools and equipment can lead to poor health and safety and hygiene, risk of cross-infection and infestation, and a negative salon image.

HANDY HINTS

Incorrect application of heat can cause damage to the hair and a loss of elasticity, damage to the cuticle scales and an increase in porosity. You could also discolour the hair or cause client discomfort.

SmartScreen 209 worksheets 1 and 4

WHY DON'T YOU...
Describe how you would protect fine hair when using straightening irons.

FACTORS THAT COULD AFFECT THE SERVICE

The following table shows the types of factors that can affect the style, causing you to have to adapt your choice of products and their quantities, and your choice of tools and equipment.

Factors	Effect on the style	Effect on product choices	Effect on tool choices	Effect on equipment
Client requirements	Identify if your client wants a blow dry, finger dry, set or hair up. Does the style need to last a few days or for a special occasion?	You will need to choose the most suitable products depending on the client's requirements.	Your tools will vary depending on the look required.	Your equipment will vary depending on the look required.
The finished look				
Lifestyle	If your client wants to recreate the style between salon visits, check for time restraints, such as their job and lifestyle. Are they able to style their own hair? Do they have any back problems that would make setting their hair more difficult?	Check if your client has suitable products at home for recreating the look.	Explain which tools would aid the styling or dressing process.	Explain and offer advice to your client on how to recreate the look at home. Could you suggest a quicker, simpler look for home styling?
Hair condition	If hair is porous it might tangle or break and take longer to dry. Weak hair has lost its elasticity and should not be over-stretched.	For porous or weak hair avoid 'sticky' products that offer strong hold as the hair will tangle easily. Suggest smoothing products, such as serums.	For porous or weak hair use heat protectors with heated appliances. Avoid using non-bristle brushes and velcro rollers, as these might cause the hair to snag and break. Use smoothing brushes and wide-tooth combs.	For porous or weak hair suggest minimal use of heated appliances, as these will cause further worsening of porosity. Nozzles attached to the dryer might be suitable, to encourage the airflow down the hair to help smooth the cuticles. Avoid too much direct heat, such as straightening irons, tongs and heated rollers.
Porous hair				
Elasticity				

Factors	Effect on the style	Effect on product choices	Effect on tool choices	Effect on equipment
Hair type	Curly hair might require smoothing prior to styling hair up; equally, straight hair might require more body.	Curly hair might require smoothing lotions or oils, or curl-enhancing products.	You might need large radial brushes or large rollers to relax tight curls, or smaller radial brushes/rollers to add body or curl to straight hair.	You might need straightening irons to aid longevity to a smoother look if the hair is naturally curly.
		Straight hair might need serums to smooth the hair, but might also need products that will hold curl or movement.		Straight hair might need an extra boost of curl from heated rollers or tongs.
Texture	Fine hair will dry quicker and will need body in the blow dry.	Fine hair will need less product. Use products which support the style and give the hair body and volume – even for smooth, straight styles.	Fine hair will need brushes/rollers to give root lift and support the style. If you use more rollers, you can make the hair look thicker. You might need to back-comb or back-brush for additional support.	Finger drying with a diffuser might work well if the hair has natural body and movement, or a brush blow dry for lift. Tonging might help give longevity to curls but take care with the heat settings on fine hair.
	Coarse hair can have a tendency to look rough and dry, and smoother styles might be difficult for the client to maintain between salon visits.	Coarse hair will need products that smooth the hair and give it shine, such as a serum.	Coarse hair will appear smoother if you use a bristle brush to smooth the hair, but you will not require much root lift.	Coarse hair will benefit from smoothing and blow drying, rather than finger drying. Straighteners can be used to smooth the coarse look of the hair.

Curly

Straight hair

Fine hair

Coarse hair

Factors	Effect on the style	Effect on product choices	Effect on tool choices	Effect on equipment
Density	**Sparse** hair should be treated in the same way as fine hair. **Sparse** Thinly scattered Sparse hair	Abundant hair will need more products and those that do not provide volume or lift but help to smooth the hair.	Thoroughly dry the root area and take smaller sections of hair; blow dry towards the ends. Avoid brushes that promote volume and root lift. Avoid back-combing the hair, as the hair will look even thicker.	Always rough dry abundant hair before sectioning and blow drying/ setting, to make effective use of your time and reduce the excess moisture. Use straightening irons to help flatten thick hair.
	Abundant hair will take longer to dry and might make the style look big, so the style needs to be considered. **Abundant** Great in amount or number Abundant hair			
Hair length	Longer hair requires more maintenance. Longer layers will need to be supported with suitable products and styling tools. Blow drying and setting will take longer, but the hair might be easier to put up. Very long hair	Many products are available for longer looks. More supporting products, such as hairsprays and root-lift products might be required. You must use heat protectors with any heated appliance. Use serum on the ends of the hair. More product will be required for longer hair.	You might need a variety of brushes/rollers to obtain root lift. Large radial brushes/ rollers will help to obtain lift and smooth the hair. Small rollers might get caught in long hair.	A professional hairdryer would be beneficial to you, to speed up the drying process time. Nozzles might help when blow drying to smooth the hair and help direct the heat where it is needed. Straightening irons, curling tongs or heated rollers might be used to enhance the longevity of the style, but wet-setting techniques will have a longer-lasting effect on the style.

Factors	Effect on the style	Effect on product choices	Effect on tool choices	Effect on equipment
Haircut Short haircut/style	When you are blow drying the hair, this is very important. As this is the how the hair has been cut for the style, you must work with it, not against it. Identify if you are blow drying or finger drying the hair to achieve the best finished result.	Suggest and use products to support the style. Identify whether you need root lift and volume, or a smooth and straight finish. Use products to suit length and condition of hair.	Use a radial brush for lift and volume, or a flat brush to smooth and avoid lift. If you are setting the hair for a special occasion, check the layer lengths are long enough for the chosen setting roller and the desired look.	Does the result require a brush and hairdryer blow dry, or can you use a diffuser and finger dry? Would a nozzle help you to smooth the hair? Would the style benefit from straightening or tonging for longevity?
Head and face shapes Oval	Oval is known as the ideal face shape. Be creative with your style, confidently knowing you are working with this face shape.	Use products to suit the style and hair type.	Use tools to enhance the style.	Use suitable equipment to achieve the desired look.
Round	Avoid width at the sides, or height with extra width which creates a round shape.			

Factors	Effect on the style	Effect on product choices	Effect on tool choices	Effect on equipment
Head and face shapes (continued)		Use products to suit the style and hair type.	Use tools to enhance the style.	Use suitable equipment to achieve the desired look.
Square	Aim for styles that soften the jaw-line and are swept on to the face slightly.			
Oblong	Avoid height but add width. Avoid hair length finishing just below the jaw. Fringes can visually help reduce the length of the face.			
Heart	Avoid width at the temple area, which exaggerates the heart shape. Add balance near the jaw-line.			

Factors	Effect on the style	Effect on product choices	Effect on tool choices	Effect on equipment
Features	If the client has pointed features, such as nose or chin, avoid a centre parting which brings unwanted attention to the areas – opt for side partings instead.	Use products to suit the style and hair type.	Use tools to enhance the style.	Use suitable equipment to achieve the desired look.
Strong jaw-line or sharp nose				
Body shape	For larger ladies, the face shape tends to be rounder. You need to consider the shape of the style to avoid adding further 'roundness'. If your client is very slim, the facial features can sometimes appear sharper. Add softness to the style if this is the case.	Use products to suit the style and hair type.	Use tools to enhance the style.	Use suitable equipment to achieve the desired look.
Large or super slim				
Hair growth patterns	A cowlick affects the fringe area; you might need to advise on a more suitable style.	When you are working with a cowlick, use a stronger styling product on the fringe area and a hairspray to hold.	Use a brush to smooth and control the cowlick, or work with it when finger drying the hair.	Use a nozzle when blow drying to aim the airflow in the direction you want the cowlick/nape whorl to go. Try using straighteners to hold the cowlick or nape whorl in place, taking care with the heat near the skin.
Cowlick				

Factors	Effect on the style	Effect on product choices	Effect on tool choices	Effect on equipment
Hair growth patterns (continued)	Nape whorls do not cause a problem to longer styles. Consider nape whorls with shorter styles and dry the hair flat at the nape area.	Use a strong finishing product on a nape whorl if it tries to defeat you; a little hairspray might help too.	Use a flat brush and dry into the neck to avoid root lift near the nape whorl.	Use a nozzle on the hairdryer to aid the direction of the airflow.
Nape whorl				
	Try to work with double crowns, as they can cause the hair to stick up. Play with the hair and see in which direction it settles the best; use this to recommend to your client the best direction for the style.	Use a strong-hold styling product around the crown area and hairspray to hold the finished look.	Use a radial brush and direct the airflow to the root, bending the hair into the desired direction. When you are setting, use an off-base technique to encourage the hair to lie flatter near the crown area.	Use a nozzle with the hairdryer to aim the airflow in the desired direction. If aiming for a funky, messy image, work with the double crown and use it in a finger dry.
Double crown				
	With a widow's peak, you should avoid fringes and aim for styles where the front section is styled backwards or slightly to one side.	Use products to hold and support the hair back or over to one side.	Use a radial brush to direct the root area back or over to one side.	Diffusers can be used to finger dry and **manipulate** the hair into the desired direction. Straighteners and irons can also be used – take care near the skin and forehead.
Widow's peak				

Manipulate
Handle skilfully

Factors	Effect on the style	Effect on product choices	Effect on tool choices	Effect on equipment
Fashion trends	Use magazines to identify what looks are trendy and most popular, then adapt these to suit all the factors considered above.	Some styles might require strong-hold products, while others that are more natural looking will require products that allow some natural movement.	Adapt your choice of tools to suit the look required.	Adapt your choice of equipment to suit the look required.

Fashion style | | | | |
| Contra-indications | If the contra-indication is contagious, such as head lice, you would not be able to carry out the service. | If the client has psoriasis or other scalp conditions, and it is sore (but not infected) you could continue with a service, but must avoid getting any products on the scalp. | Some contra-indications can cause discomfort to the client if you use certain tools. Rollers, for example, might cause discomfort if the scalp is sore and the rollers are wound too tightly. | Heated rollers, for example, might cause discomfort if the scalp is sore and the rollers are too hot, or the pins come into contact with the scalp. |
|

Psoriasis or head lice | | | | |

WHY DON'T YOU...
Practise identifying face shapes on your colleagues.

SmartScreen 209 handout 3

STEP-BY-STEP TECHNIQUES

In this section you will look at what you need to do to style, dress and finish the hair. Your clients might need their hair styled for a special occasion or at the end of a hairdressing service to complete the look. You will need to be able to create a variety of looks on differing hair types and lengths.

BLOW DRYING THE HAIR

Whether you are blow drying short or long hair you must have control, and avoid over-drying the hair and causing damage. Curly hair can be challenging to the most able stylist, but using suitable products and tools helps control the hair. A methodical working pattern with clean sections is also very important.

Sectioning the hair

When you are working on medium and long hair, you must section it cleanly and secure the hair you are not currently working on out of the way. This will prevent it from drying too quickly and disturbing the areas that you are working on.

Take manageable sections to enable you to dry each part thoroughly and obtain the required amount of root lift. Part the hair and section it from front hairline to crown, then crown to nape and finally from ear to ear. Clip and secure the front two sections out of the way and, starting from the bottom of the nape section, take a 2–3 cm thick section, securing the rest.

Airflow

Always direct the airflow away from the client's scalp to prevent burning the client and causing discomfort. Always keep the airflow moving, as keeping it in one area could cause damage to the hair and scalp.

Direct the airflow in the direction of the style to ensure root lift where required. Follow the cuticle direction, aiming downwards from root to point to follow and smooth the cuticle scales; avoid disturbing the hair you have already dried and causing the hair to tangle.

Brushes

Your brush choice and size will vary depending on the desired look, degree of curl and the movement and volume required.

Tension

Pulling the hair with tension as you dry it will make the style last longer. Curly hair being blow dried straight will need a lot more tension than straight or wavy hair. A large radial brush will help you to smooth and straighten curls, but still create volume and movement. Ensure the tension is firm but without causing discomfort to your client.

Brush at root area, smoothing hair and achieving volume

Angles

The angle in which you direct the brush and airflow through the hair will aid you in achieving root lift and volume where required. You should keep the brush on the base of the section if you require lift (on-base), and drag the hair back away from the section (off-base) if you require a flatter look.

Airflow directed away from scalp, following direction of cuticle scales root to point

Brush sitting on base at the root area for lift and volume

Client 1: Step-by-step – one length blow dry, below shoulders

STEP 1 – Section the hair cleanly.

STEP 2 – Use a medium–large brush and dry from root to point.

STEP 3 – Work from the baseline up to the crown.

STEP 4 – Complete the sides.

STEP 5 – Ensure the airflow follows the direction of the cuticles.

STEP 6 – The finished look.

Client 2: Step-by-step – one length blow dry, above shoulders

STEP 1 – Blow dry the hair, smoothing it from root to point.

STEP 2 – Use the dryer to direct the airflow over the brush.

STEP 3 – Ensure you take the hairdryer to the ends of the hair and turn the brush under.

STEP 4 – Blow dry the fringe or front section in the direction it needs to lie.

Client 3: Step-by-step – short, layered hair blow dried with small and medium brushes to add volume

STEP 1 – Apply the styling product and section the hair; blow dry from root to point.

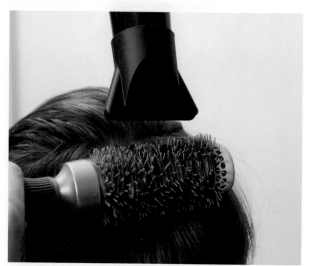

STEP 2 – Continue to blow dry, lifting the hair for root lift and support.

STEP 3 – Keep the brush on base for volume at the roots.

STEP 4 – Check the balance and ensure the client is happy with the end result.

SmartScreen 209 worksheet 3

FINGER DRYING THE HAIR

When finger drying the hair, you must ensure you achieve the required amount of volume, movement and/or curl. You should massage the root area in the direction in which the lift and volume are required. Applying products at the root area will support the style.

Short hair can be styled using a hand-held hairdryer with a nozzle, and using your hands and fingers as the tools. This works particularly well for hair with movement and texture, requiring a finished look that is modern and funky. Your choice of styling products will influence the end result, as support from the product is required.

At the end of a finger-dry service, check the balance of the finished style before applying a final finishing product. You must always check that your client is happy with the end result.

Client 4: Step-by-step – finger drying short hair

STEP 1 – Apply the product, removing any excess moisture by 'rough' drying.

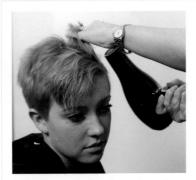

STEP 2 – Manipulate the root area to create body and movement.

STEP 3 – Ensure the airflow follows the direction of the hairstyle.

STEP 4 – Check the balance and ensure the client is happy with the end result.

Diffuser drying the hair

Hair with movement, curl or body can be scrunch-dried with a diffuser attachment. This technique works particularly well with medium to longer hair lengths. You should use curl-activating products to enhance curls and movement and to support the style, but use minimal handling of the hair.

Client 5: Step-by-step – diffuser drying curly long hair

STEP 1 – Apply the styling product and section the hair; place the hair into the diffuser.

STEP 2 – Continue the finger dry, gently manipulating the hair at the root area for lift.

STEP 3 – Avoid 'overplaying' with the curls: let the diffuser curl the hair where possible.

STEP 4 – Check the balance and ensure the client is happy with the end result.

Natural drying

Hair that is naturally curly or has been permed can be left to dry naturally with an accelerator. To do this you should:

- apply your suitably chosen products
- position the hair into the desired style, considering the natural partings rather than manipulating the hair into a direction it does not naturally want to fall into
- sit your client comfortably at a workstation with an accelerator correctly positioned above the hair
- set the timer on your accelerator to dry the hair, taking into consideration the hair length, density and texture
- check throughout the drying process that the temperature is suitable and that your client is comfortable; offer them a drink
- when the hair is dry, check the style is evenly balanced and that your client is satisfied with the finished look.

STRAIGHTENING AND TONGING THE HAIR

When using heated appliances to finish the hair, you must always use a heat protector and check that the temperature setting is suitable for the hair condition, type and density. You should use a bristle brush to smooth and untangle the hair before straightening or tonging, and cleanly section the hair into manageable sections.

Client 6: Step-by-step – straightening the hair with irons

STEP 1 – Section the hair and apply a heat protector.

STEP 2 – Heat the straightening irons to the desired temperature and slowly move them from root to point.

STEP 3 – Continue around to the side section, taking small sections at a time.

STEP 4 – Check the balance and ensure the client is happy with the end result.

Client 7: Step-by-step – using a wand to create volume, curls and movement

STEP 1 – Take small sections and wind from point to root.

STEP 2 – Continue with your sections and curl the hair from point to root.

STEP 3 – Direct the hair sections to suit the chosen style.

STEP 4 – Tease the curls if required, check the balance and ensure the client is happy with the end result.

Client 8: Step-by-step – using tongs to create curls

STEP 1 – Section the hair and apply a heat-protective lotion.

STEP 2 – Clasp the hair at the end of the tongs and wind from point to root.

SETTING AND DRESSING HAIR

When setting the hair, you will need to consider whether volume, lift and curl are required. Hair can be rolled to sit on base or off base, and the wind can be directed to suit the style, or a brick wind can be used to avoid roller and section marks. Always allow the hair to cool before you remove the rollers.

On-base or off-base angles

The more volume that is required, the more root lift is needed; this situation requires on-base winding.

When winding the hair to sit on base, you must:

- take the section of hair to be rolled and comb it upwards, straight from the head
- hold the section at 90° from the head
- wind the hair downwards from point to root around the roller, ensuring that the completed roll sits on the base of its own section, at the root area.

Ensure that you wind the hair considering the root direction required, to give maximum support to the style.

On-base winding – curls with volume and lift

On base

If the style you are creating needs less root lift and a flatter look, you should direct your wind off base. This involves dragging the root back, slightly away from the roller base and section. Use a 45° angle and complete the wind with the roller almost sitting on the root of the section below. The roots then dry or cool without creating lift.

Off base

Off-base winding – flat curls

Winding techniques

The wide choice of winding techniques helps you to create lift and curl, with varied root movement and direction. Changing your roller size enables you to achieve tighter or looser curls.

Setting the hair in the direction in which it is to be styled ensures the root movement falls in line with the desired style result. This method enables you to work with partings – style the hair to one side, creating the look of the style in the same way you would blow dry.

Directional wind

Directional wind result – end style

If the style requires a more blended look that is free from partings and section patterns, then the ideal technique is brick winding. This involves setting the hair in horizontal rows across the head, ensuring that the following row is offset, so it looks like brickwork.

Brick winding

Brick wind result – end style

Sectioning the hair

You must always section the hair cleanly using a pintail or tail comb, depending on your personal preference. When you are working on long hair, always secure the hair you are not working on out of the way.

Sectioned long hair while setting

Various size rollers

Always take manageable size sections (meches), which are no larger or wider than your roller choice. Small rollers give tighter curls, and medium to large rollers give looser curls, so choose your roller size to suit the required style, taking into consideration the hair's length and density.

Comb your section directly upwards for on-base winds (90°) and at 45° for off-base winds.

Stylist combing hair directly upwards for on-base winding

Stylist has combed/dragged hair backwards for off-base winding

Tension and controlling the hair

Pulling the hair with tension as you wind will make the set last longer and the hair stretch into its new position. Long hair can tangle easily and get caught in a roller, so take care when you are winding the hair around the roller. Control the wind, making sure you have the required sectioned hair neatly wrapped around the roller. When you are happy that the roller has been wound effectively, secure it in place with a hair pin.

Neatly winding the hair

Badly rolled hair

> **HANDY HINTS**
>
> Keeping the hair misted with water maintains a consistent moisture balance to produce a smooth, even effect.

Make sure that you keep the hair damp throughout the winding process to maintain an even elasticity and to allow the hydrogen bonds to set in their new stretched position, setting the hair in a beta keratin state.

Client 9: Step-by-step – traditional wet set, wound in a brick wind pattern

STEP 1 – Gown and prepare your client for the service.

STEP 2 – Shampoo the hair and apply styling products.

STEP 3 – Wind the rollers from point to root in a brick wind formation.

STEP 4 – Complete the whole head wind and dry the hair with a hood dryer or similar.

STEP 5 – Allow to cool and remove the rollers.

STEP 6 – Using a dressing-out brush, remove the roller marks.

STEP 7 – Dress the hair into the desired style and apply your finishing products.

STEP 8 – Check the balance and ensure the client is happy with the end result.

Client 10: Step-by-step – traditional wet set, directional wind

STEP 1 – Wind the hair into the direction in which the root lift and partings are required.

STEP 2 – Secure the roller with a pin.

> **HANDY HINTS**
>
> When dressing out a wet set, brush the hair thoroughly to ensure you break up all the roller marks, and remove all partings to blend the hair. This will also help to reduce the stiffness of the dried setting product and create a softer appearance.

STEP 3 – Complete the whole wind, dry the hair and allow to cool before removing the rollers.

STEP 4 – Brush out the roller marks and dress the style.

STEP 5 – Check the balance and ensure the client is happy with the end result.

Client 11: Step-by-step – dry set, heated rollers and directional wind

STEP 1 – Wind the hair from point to root in a directional manner.

STEP 2 – Roll the hair on base to maintain root lift and volume.

STEP 3 – Allow the rollers to cool before you remove them.

STEP 4 – Use your hands to help remove the roller marks.

STEP 5 – Dress and back-comb the hair into the desired style. Apply your chosen finishing products.

STEP 6 – Check the balance and ensure the client is happy with the end result.

Client 12: Step-by-step – dry set with velcro rollers, directional wind

STEP 1 – Apply your products to your client's dry hair and wind from point to root.

STEP 2 – Wind all the hair into your chosen wind.

STEP 3 – Dry set the hair, dress out the set, then apply finishing products.

STEP 4 – Check the balance and ensure the client is happy with the end result.

SPIRAL CURLS

You can achieve spiral curls with tongs, rollers or 'bendy rods'. The technique used is the same as with conventional setting or tonging, except the hair is wound along the length of the roller or tong. Starting from the points and working towards the roots, wind the hair along the tong or roller in a spiral wind, allowing for the direction of the root movement required. This technique gives soft or tight curls, depending on roller size, which fall in a similar way to natural curls.

Spiral curls in rollers

Spiral curls end result

PIN-CURLING

Pin-curling involves a setting technique of winding without the aid of a roller. Great skill and hand **dexterity** are required, and when you have mastered this craft it is a skill in its own right! You might not need to set without the aid of rollers often, but imagine going to a photo shoot or visiting a bride's home to style their hair, only to find you do not have enough rollers or, worse, you have forgotten them! The ability to pin-curl gives great curl results and the hair dries much faster than when it is tightly wrapped around a roller.

These curls are created by a wet-setting technique. The section patterns and winding techniques can be the same as for winding with a roller, and the hair is wound from point to root.

Pin-curls for volume

To create curls with root lift and volume, you can use 'stand-up' pin-curls, sometimes called barrel curls. Use a suitable product and comb the wet hair upwards, at about 90° to the head. Roll the hair downwards from point to root, without a roller. Secure the hair on base with a pin-curl clip. This technique produces soft curls or waves and volume.

Client 13: Step-by-step – pin-curls (barrel curls)

STEP 1 – After applying styling products, section the hair from the middle of each eyebrow and wind the pin-curl/barrel curl.

STEP 2 – Roll the hair from point to root around your fingers into the direction of the style.

STEP 3 – Secure the curl with a pin-curl clip and repeat as required.

STEP 4 – Ensure the pin-curl sits on base for maximum root lift.

STEP 5 – Dry the hair, and dress and tease the hair into the desired style.

STEP 6 – Check the balance and ensure the client is happy with the end result.

Pin-curls for flat movement

To create movement through the hair but without root lift and volume, you can use 'lie-down' pin-curls, sometimes called a flat barrel curl. After you have applied a suitable styling product, comb the wet hair downwards at about 45° and feed the hair through your fingers to create a flat, open-coiled curl. Secure the hair off base with a pin-curl clip. This technique produces flat movement and waves throughout the hair.

Client 14: Step-by-step – flat pin-curls

STEP 1 – Roll the hair from point to root around your fingers.

STEP 2 – Secure the curl with a pin-curl clip.

STEP 3 – Continue throughout the head.

STEP 4 – Dry the hair, and dress and tease the hair into the desired style.

STEP 5 – Check the balance and ensure the client is happy with the end result.

Clock-spring pin-curls for flat movement

For 'clock-spring' pin-curls follow the previous technique, but feed the hair through your fingers and create a closed-in coiled curl that is smaller in the centre and gradually gets larger towards the outside of the coil. Clock-spring pin-curls create flat movement that has tighter curls and body at the ends of the hair, where the coil was at its tightest, and gradually loosens towards the root.

Clock-spring pin-curl

FINGER WAVING

This is a styling technique that is used to produce a strong wave movement in the hair. The wave is made using the fingers of one hand and a cutting comb in the other.

Client 15: Step-by-step – finger waving

STEP 1 – Section the hair, apply styling products and comb the hair into the first wave.

STEP 2 – Secure the wave with pin-curl clips into the 'crest' of the wave.

STEP 3 – Face the pin-curl clips into each other to secure the wave, and continue down the side of the head.

STEP 4 – Pin-curl the remaining length at the sides and secure with the pin-curl clip.

STEP 5 – Create stand-up pin-curls/barrel curls throughout the rest of the hair and allow to dry.

STEP 6 – Comb out the finger waves and pin-curls to remove the dried products and create a soft wavy style.

CREATING THE LOOK – ROLLS, PLAITS, CHIGNONS AND HAIR UP

Now that you have learnt the art of setting the hair, it is time to have fun dressing it out and putting it up. By setting the hair first, you have a solid foundation to build on. Most hair-up styles require some body or curl to be added to support the up-do. Always handle and control the hair effectively; using back-combing or brushing helps you to manipulate the hair into place. Back-combing and back-brushing increases the duration of the style, improves the shape and provides security to the style. To help secure the hair in place use grips, pins and hairspray.

Client 16: Step-by-step – roll

STEP 1 – Gown and protect your client, and set the hair.

STEP 2 – Apply styling products to dry hair and back-comb the roots.

STEP 3 – Grip the hair down the centre, criss-crossing the grips.

STEP 4 – Fold the hair, and gently twist it over the grips, securing the hair with pins.

STEP 5 – Tuck the ends under the roll, smooth over the top section and apply finishing products.

STEP 6 – Check the balance and ensure the client is happy with the end result.

Client 17: Step-by-step – bouffant style using a 'beehive' attachment for extra root lift

STEP 1 – Gown and prepare your client, and set the hair with heated rollers.

STEP 2 – Apply hairspray and attach and secure the hair padding.

STEP 3 – Back-comb each section of hair.

STEP 4 – Dress the hair over the hair padding into a bouffant and secure with grips and pins.

STEP 5 – Tease the hair into place and apply finishing products.

STEP 6 – Smooth any stray hairs with a comb or dressing-out brush and add more spray.

STEP 7 – Check the balance and ensure the client is happy with the end result.

STEP 1 – Set the hair prior to putting up.

STEP 2 – Take sections of hair from the back and sides and grip into place.

STEP 3 – Manipulate the curls to add softness to the style.

STEP 4 – Check the balance of the style.

STEP 5 – Add flowers or feathers.

STEP 6 – Ensure the client is happy with the end result.

INDUSTRY TIP

Adding flowers, feathers or ribbons to any 'up-do' can help turn a daytime look into a special occasion look.

Scalp plait

To complete a French plait, start with a 'V' section at the front hairline, pointing towards the crown. Divide this 'V' section into three and cross the right stem over the middle stem and then the left stem over the new middle stem.

Add a new section of hair to the right stem, take this new, enlarged right stem over the current middle stem, and add hair to the left stem, taking that enlarged left stem over the current middle stem. Continue this pattern for the whole head of hair.

Client 19: Step-by-step – French plait

STEP 1 – Section the hair at the middle of the front hairline into three stems ready to start the French plait.

STEP 2 – Apply hairspray to aid control of the hair.

STEP 3 – Have your trolley and equipment to hand.

STEP 4 – As you section the hair, ensure your client's head is upright, otherwise the plait may be too loose.

STEP 5 – Cross the right stem over the middle stem and add to the left stem.

STEP 6 – Continue this process, adding hair to the right stem and crossing it over the middle.

STEP 7 – Secure the completed plait with a professional band.

STEP 8 – Apply hairspray to the completed French plait to aid longevity.

Styling products

Finishing products

AFTERCARE ADVICE

During and after the service you should recommend aftercare and give your client advice on maintaining the style and condition of the hair. During your consultation you would have identified what the client does on a day-to-day basis, and how much time they have to spend on styling and finishing the hair.

Providing your client with advice for maintaining an everyday style will be a little more straightforward than the aftercare required for hair-up styles and dressed looks. You should offer some tips for recreating the style themselves, but it is fair to say that the look they will achieve is unlikely to be of a professional standard. After all, the client came to you, the expert, to obtain the required look.

You should provide advice on which products, tools and equipment would be most suitable, how to use them and how to recreate the style between salon visits.

PRODUCTS AND THEIR USE

You should advise your clients on the products you used to create their initial style, asking them about the products they already have, and suggesting which new products they would benefit from purchasing and using. Always advise your client on how to use the products and how to remove them from the hair to prevent build-up. If you are recommending back-combing or back-brushing techniques, they would also benefit from occasional conditioning treatments.

Your advice should include which products are best suited for styling the hair and supporting the finished look. Recommend products for styling the hair while it is wet and those that will aid longevity on dry hair.

You should consider the following.

- Condition of the hair – recommend shampoo and conditioning products to maintain condition and improve porosity and elasticity. You should advise the client on how to remove the products from the hair, to prevent build-up.
- Density and texture – recommend products that will protect, support and give root lift if required for fine/sparse hair; and smooth and give shine to coarse/abundant hair. Advise on how much product is required and how to apply it.
- Required result – suggest products that provide strong or light control to the hair, movement, root lift or curl enhancers where required.

EQUIPMENT AND ITS USE

If you are recommending the use of hairdryers, straightening irons or tongs, offer advice on using them safely. Explain that using heated appliances repeatedly, too close to the scalp, and concentrating on one area for too long can cause damage to the hair and scalp, increase porosity, decrease elasticity and cause colour to fade. Recommend the use of heat-protecting products.

For setting and dressing, the correct tools are essential, eg you must not use the wrong brush type for back-brushing as you could damage the hair. Advise your client on the best use of the tools they have and recommend any new purchases to achieve the look at home.

CREATING AND MAINTAINING THE STYLE

If your client has sufficient time to spend on their hair, then offer advice on how to set the hair with heated rollers and how to dress it up. For quicker looks, recommend tonging the hair to create body and curls. A hair-up style for a wedding or special occasion can often be simplified for a more natural look that suits day-to-day wear, and makes it easier for the client to create the look themselves. Offer these alternative suggestions to enable them to have fun with their hair.

Together with advising on the best products and equipment for maintaining the style at home, you should give advice on which tools to use. Recommend brushes that will help the client to recreate the look, explain how to use them and show them how to follow the direction of the cuticle. You should explain how to section the hair and demonstrate how to clip hair out of the way, to help them control their hair and methodically style it, enhancing the end result.

Advising the client – demonstrating how to create the look

Turn to page 485 for the answers

1 Which **one** of the following identifies the **best** reason why the stylist should remove their own jewellery before styling hair?

  a It minimises the risk of contact dermatitis and hair snagging.

  b It creates a professional image to the client.

  c Clients' hair may become tangled around necklaces and earrings.

  d Bacteria under rings and bracelets could cause harm to the client.

2 Which **one** of the following identifies the **best** reason for carrying out a thorough consultation before dressing hair?

  a To ensure that the client feels comfortable and at ease during the process.

  b To identify client needs and the most suitable products and tools to use.

  c To ensure that the stylist follows the client's instructions.

  d To identify the suitability of products and to be polite.

3 Statement 1:
It is important to work to commercial timings to ensure that the salon runs smoothly and makes a profit.

Statement 2:
Working to commercial timings will prevent the stylist from running late for other appointments.

Which **one** of the following is correct for the above statements?

	Statement 1	Statement 2
a	True	True
b	True	False
c	False	True
d	False	False

4 Statement 1:
For porous or weak hair it is best to avoid 'sticky' products that offer strong hold as the hair will tangle easily.

Statement 2:
Curly hair may require smoothing prior to styling hair up and straight hair may require more body.

Which **one** of the following is correct for the above statements?

	Statement 1	Statement 2
a	True	True
b	True	False
c	False	True
d	False	False

5 A client with a pointed nose and chin should avoid:

  a A centre parting.

  b Very curly looks.

  c A fringe.

  d Width.

6 When using straighteners on fine hair it is important to:

  a Apply plenty of serum to give shine.

  b Apply mousse to give volume and bounce.

  c Use a conditioner designed for chemically damaged hair.

  d Use a heat protective spray and turn the temperature down.

7 **Statement 1:**
Use a Denman brush to create a smooth, straight finish – such as a 'bob' style.

Statement 2:
A large radial brush is used to create root lift, volume and small curls in short, layered hair.

Which **one** of the following is correct for the above statements?

	Statement 1	Statement 2
a	True	True
b	True	False
c	False	True
d	False	False

8 Hair in its natural state of curly, wavy or straight is described as being in:

a An alpha keratin state with hydrogen bonds in their original position.

b A beta keratin state with hydrogen bonds in their original position.

c An alpha keratin state with hydrogen bonds in a new position.

d A beta keratin state with hydrogen bonds in a new position.

CASE STUDY: PATRICK CAMERON

As one of the most sought-after international hairdressers and a global ambassador for the hairdressing industry, Patrick Cameron has influenced the way stylists all over the world dress long hair. There are very few within the industry who have not been inspired by the work created by the long hair maestro from New Zealand.

Quite simply, Patrick has turned the world of long hairdressing on its head, producing fabulous breathtaking collections, showcasing his talent for all that is glamorous. During his demonstrations he creates stunning long hair looks so simplistic that even a novice hairdresser can feel confident enough to try it for themselves. Renowned for his energetic and effervescent personality, you cannot fail to be inspired by him. Patrick views the art of dressing hair as the most fun and creative part of our craft.

Here are Patrick's top tips.

1 As a hairdresser you should never put yourself in the position where you have to say 'I can't do that' – a feeling that will be with you for the rest of your hairdressing life if you do not sort it out now. Long hairdressing really *is* easy to learn when you tackle it in stages, just like cutting hair, step-by-step. Remember, we are called hairdressers, so we should be able to dress hair.

2 Start with a good foundation. You need to perfect your roller setting, pin-curling, back-combing and, yes, your finger waving, to make your up-dos stand out from the rest. I cannot stress enough that every successful skill needs practice. With a good foundation, half the battle is won.

3 Always have a starting point. What does the client want, or if they are unsure, what does the client not want? During your consultation show the client some finished looks from magazines or books that she may like. Maybe she has seen a style she likes on a celebrity – this will help you arrive at a style choice.

4 Prepare the hair before you start, either with a hot roller set or a blow dry.

5 When you are prepared, start with your base. A good foundation is sometimes a ponytail, because that means the base is secure.

6 Remember putting hair up is like building a house; you just have to follow some simple steps. First, the foundation, a ponytail or a pinned base; second, place and pin the hair wide out from the base (perhaps curls or barrel curls) – this section will ground the style; third is the middle layer, the shape and contour of the style, building on top of the base; and fourth is the top layer, the final decoration of the style, which I always think is the most enjoyable part.

7 Always remember – less is more. Often the simplest styles are the ones that get the most compliments. Consider this rule for flowers: the bride does not need to be wearing a garden on her head. A few small flowers like rosebuds, or similar, can look very effective. Small pearls or diamante clips are a favourable alternative.

8 Remember, classic sleek up-dos never go out of fashion and are real head-turners.

CUT MEN'S HAIR

Men can spend as much time and effort on their hair as women, and the techniques you will learn in this unit will enable you to create a variety of looks from one haircut. Learning the basic techniques will give you the knowledge, skills and confidence to generate a clientele that you can build on. Enhancing your skills will give you the opportunity to produce a variety of different styles.

There are two learning outcomes in this unit. The learner will be able to:

- prepare for a cutting service
- provide a cutting service.

During this part of the unit you will learn:

- safety considerations for cutting hair
- communication and behaviour requirements
- consultation techniques that should be used
- factors that should be considered when cutting hair.

SAFETY CONSIDERATIONS

When cutting men's hair, you can use scissors, clippers and/or razors, so it is important that you use them correctly, know how to clean and maintain them and store them safely.

Tool	Correct use	Maintenance	Correct storage
Scissors (and thinning scissors)	Always carry them with the blades closed. Do not drop them as you might damage the blades.	Clean the hairs from the blades with warm soapy water. Sterilise scissors in an autoclave, sanitise in a UV light cabinet or disinfect in a Barbicide solution. Oil the blades after cleaning and sterilising.	Keep them away from young children and store them in a barber's cutting pouch or scissor case.
Clippers – mains electricity	Keep the blades well oiled throughout use. Ensure the blades are properly aligned and adjust the blades to achieve the correct cutting length. Use on dry hair.	Remove the cut hairs from between the blades after every haircut (using a small clipper brush). Spray the blades with a chemical disinfectant and wipe the body of the clippers with chemical disinfectant wipes. Oil the blades after cleaning.	Unplug from the mains and look for any knots in the wires. Hang on a designated hook or place somewhere safe, where they cannot fall to the floor and get damaged.
Clippers/mini clippers – rechargable	As above.	As above.	Place the clippers back on the battery-charger base, to ensure they are charged and ready for the next client.

Tool	Correct use	Maintenance	Correct storage
Razors	Always hold the razor carefully to ensure you and your client are not accidently cut with the razor blade. If you accidently drop the razor – let it go – do NOT try to catch it!	Remove the razor blade carefully and dispose of in the sharps bin. Clean the body of the razor with warm soapy water and chemical disinfectant wipes. **Sharps bin**	Ideally, store your razors without the blade attached. Attach a new blade as you need it. Store the razor in a suitable scissor pouch/case.
Combs and attachments (grades)	Cutting combs are used to section the hair. Clipper grades are attached over the clipper blades and designed to create a variation of longer cutting lengths when clipper cutting.	Remove all loose hairs from the comb and grades, wash them in warm soapy water and sanitise them in the UV light cabinet.	Keep all grades together and store them according to your salon policy.

HANDY HINTS

Always clean your non-electrical tools prior to disinfecting or sterilising, using detergent with warm water. Toothbrushes or nail brushes work particularly well for removing hair cuttings and scalp debris from between the teeth of combs and clipper blades.

HANDY HINTS

When you are using electrical clippers follow the Electricity at Work Act. If the salon clippers are faulty, remember to label them, remove them from use on the salon floor and report it to your salon manager.

 SmartScreen 210 handout 2 and worksheet 2

HANDY HINTS

If you accidently cut your client, apologise to him, and wearing gloves, remove any hairs from the wound and cover it with a plaster – checking first that he is not allergic to plasters! Dispose of the contaminated waste in a suitable bin with a lid and complete the accident book. Ask your client if he is happy for you to continue with the rest of the haircut.

PREPARING FOR WORK

Ensure that you are fit and prepared for work, make sure you have:

- showered
- brushed your teeth and have fresh breath
- used deodorant
- prepared clean, presentable clothes – wearing your salon's uniform dress or following their dress code
- cleaned and moisturised your face
- either shaved or have well-groomed facial hair
- no contagious ailments.

PREPARING FOR YOUR CLIENT'S ARRIVAL

When preparing for your client's arrival, you must ensure that all work surfaces are cleaned and sterilised with chemical disinfectant spray/wipes. Check that your workstation is ready for your client's service, with clean sterile tools and equipment. Make sure the floors are hazard free – no hair cuttings/wet floors that your client could slip on and no trip hazards from trailing wires, etc.

Always ensure that the salon has a plentiful supply of clean, washed gowns and towels and check if any need to be washed or dried. You should change your Barbicide solution regularly, so that it can be used between every client for disinfecting your cutting tools.

HANDY HINTS

Keeping your work area clean and tidy prevents accidents, injuries and risks of cross-contamination.

POSITIONING OF YOU AND YOUR CLIENT

The positioning of you and your client are most important when cutting the hair, as the result and balance of the finished look can be affected.

Your body position

You must stand with your body weight evenly distributed throughout the entire cutting process. This will not only prevent fatigue and back problems, but ensure the haircut is balanced. Sit on a cutting stool while cutting hair short or for working on the back of your client's head, and adjust the height of the barber's chair to ensure you work comfortably. This will prevent you from bending and over-stretching and help to maintain your comfort, which is essential during the cutting service.

Your client's positioning

When gowned and protected, you must ensure that your client sits comfortably with his back supported by the chair, in an upright position with his legs uncrossed and evenly balanced.

DURING THE SERVICE

While you are cutting the hair you should regularly remove the hair cuttings from the neck area; this will help maintain the comfort of your client and show a professional way of working. Also, you should make sure you have removed any jewellery or accessories that might catch in his hair. If your client regularly has his hair cut very close to the skin (with clippers without a grade or with a razor) you must be mindful of the risk of in-growing hairs occuring. At the end of the service, remove all the loose hair cuttings from the neck area, show your client the back of the haircut and check he is happy with the end result. When your client has left your work area, ensure it is cleaned and swept, in readiness for your next client.

HANDY HINTS

Revisit Unit 203 for more in-depth information on consulting with your client.

SmartScreen 210 handout 1

HANDY HINTS

If your client's posture is unbalanced or he is sitting with his legs crossed, your resulting haircut could be unbalanced, as your client might have a tendency to lean to one side. Always ensure your client is sitting upright with his legs uncrossed.

COMMUNICATION AND BEHAVIOUR

As we have mentioned in previous units it is very important that you are polite to your clients and speak to them in a friendly manner. Engaging in neutral conversation such as recent football results and which teams they support might help to relax your client. You should be clearly spoken and show positive body language at all times. When speaking with clients or your colleagues, ensure you are respectful to them and respond to their needs.

Use client-friendly terminology and speak in a reassuring and confident manner. Make sure you really listen to what your client is asking of you and respond by nodding and maintaining eye contact to prove you are listening. Before your client arrives, it is good practice to read your client's record card and during/after the visit record any changes or update it with today's service.

ACTIVITY

List three positive body language points which show you are listening to the client.

CONSULTATION TECHNIQUES

You must always carry out a thorough consultation with your client, to identify the service objective, your client's needs and whether you are able to carry out his request. During the consultation you should tell him how long the service should take, and how he can maintain the look between salon visits. The consultation process should continue throughout the cutting service, as you should update him on the progress of the haircut and check you are cutting to the agreed lengths.

THE CONSULTATION PROCESS

It is advisable to begin the initial consultation before you gown your client, to see his style of dress and overall image. You should ask him about his day-to-day lifestyle, work patterns and available time to commit to styling his hair. Always listen to what your client is asking of you, and be honest yet tactful with the advice you give him. You should use open questions to obtain as much information as possible and finish with closed questions to confirm what has been agreed.

During the consultation you should ask questions about how much hair he would like taken off the length and the layers. You must be specific with your questions to achieve an accurate account of his needs. Show him in the mirror how much hair you are going to remove to confirm what you assume to be the agreed lengths and amounts. Use visual aids, such as hairdressing images/magazines, to agree on styles and shapes. Always give your client the option to try something different from his current style, and give him the opportunity to express his thoughts about the finished look.

When you have decided on a style together, ask him which products he currently uses to style his hair, to identify whether you need to recommend any alternative products for his new image.

WHY DON'T YOU...
Ask a male colleague to pretend to be your client. Ask him to visualise a style and then ask the relevant questions to identify the image and look he requires. Use at least three open and two closed questions to obtain as much information as possible about his requirements.

HANDY HINTS

Reasons why clients leave their barber/hairstylist:
- The barber did not recommend anything new or interesting.
- The barber did not listen to the client's request.
- The barber created a style which was not suitable for the client.
- The barber cut the hair too short/left it too long, even after consultation and agreeing the lengths.
- The service took too long.

HANDY HINTS

Always give clear instructions and repeat back what your client has asked of you; this will help you to gain the client's confidence in the service.

HANDY HINTS

Ask your client where he wears his parting, but always check visually for the natural fall of the hair.

FACTORS THAT SHOULD BE CONSIDERED WHEN CUTTING HAIR

You need to consider factors that might affect the outcome of the service required.

As some men have a more manual job, they can be prone to bumps on the head; as they tend to wear their hair shorter than women the head is not as well protected. Always check the hair and scalp for any lumps and bumps that could cause discomfort to your client when you are combing through the hair.

Some scalp disorders might require consideration in the style recommended, as your client might want them covered up. Always ask about scalp disorders during your consultation and check for infections and infestations which would prevent the service from being carried out. Check the eyebrows and ears for piercings that could cause an injury if you accidentally caught them with the comb.

SmartScreen 210 interactive worksheet 1

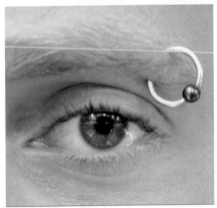

Eyebrow piercing – take care with your scissors

INDUSTRY TIP

If during the consultation you identify an infectious condition, you must not continue with the service. Instead give your client some advice about how to deal with the problem or suggest he visits his GP. Try to keep these conversations discreet so the client is put at ease, and explain that you will welcome him back when the infectious condition has cleared.

FACTORS THAT MIGHT AFFECT THE SERVICE

There are many factors that could affect how you cut the hair, the tools that you use and the styles that you recommend. You must consider these factors prior to and during the service. The first factor that you must take into consideration is what your client wants! His requirements are what your whole consultation is all about, and now you must determine whether there are any factors that might affect you achieving the desired result.

You should discuss your client's lifestyle to ensure that he does not have any barriers that could prevent him achieving the desired result. Is the chosen style easy to maintain and does it fit around work requirements?

Now let's look at factors outside of your client's control! The table below shows how various factors affect the service and the end result.

Factors	How they can affect the service
Elasticity 	Elasticity can affect the cutting technique. For medium to longer hair with poor elasticity you should avoid pulling with too much tension during the cutting process. Ensure the hair has an even moisture balance when you cut it – either all wet, or all dry, to ensure the effects of poor elasticity are not worsened.
Hair type  	Hair type can affect the choice of style and cutting technique. Curly hair will spring up after the hair has been cut when it is dried. Consider the amount of tension you place on the hair during the cutting service and use a wide-tooth comb. Straight hair might not achieve the desired result, and regular use of products might be required. You will need to consider whether you should cut the hair wet or dry, when considering the hair type.
Density  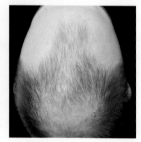	Density can affect the choice of style and cutting technique. Abundant hair might need to be thinned out to create the desired look. Consider whether abundant hair will enhance the look; if not, suggest alternatives. Sparse hair will need to be blunt cut/club cut to maintain as much thickness as possible. Avoid cutting the hair too short.

Factors	How they can affect the service
Texture  	Texture can affect the choice of style and cutting technique. Coarse-textured hair might not suit the desired look; you will need to recommend styling products to help achieve a smoother result. Fine hair might not suit clipper cuts or very short cuts; you might also need to use supporting hair products.
Head and face shape    	The head and face shape can affect the choice of style. For round face shapes, avoid styles that add more roundness, such as too much width or height. For oblong face shapes, avoid height but add width if you can, and suggest a fringe to shorten the illusion of a long face shape. The shorter the haircut the more prominent the oblong shape will appear. For square face shapes, avoid square styles, such as 'flat-tops', unless your client wishes to make his face look squarer. The head shape should be considered within the overall shape of the style. The head should be rounded from the crown to the **occipital** bone and then dip in slightly towards the nape. Some crowns are flatter than others and very short styles could make the back of the head look too flat. Others have very pronounced crown areas and need the cut to make the shape look flatter. **Occipital** The bone between the crown and the nape area that normally sticks out a little bit
Prominent features   	Facial features can affect the choice of style. For clients with **protruding** ears, you can suggest styles that cover the entire ear, or are not cut too short around the ear. For strong nose features or jaw-lines, avoid centre partings that encourage the eye to follow down from the parting to the nose and chin. For high foreheads, suggest the haircut has a fringe or some hair styled forward over part of the forehead. **Prominent or protruding** Sticking out

Factors	How they can affect the service
Neck shapes	When considering the length of the haircut at the neck area, you should look at the shape of the neck. Thicker necks might suit a slightly longer cut.
Hair growth patterns	Hair growth patterns can affect the choice of style and cutting technique. For cowlicks avoid fringes; instead suggest a side half fringe that works with the cowlick. For widow's peaks avoid fringes completely and suggest styles that are constructed with the top area going over to one side or straight back. For double crowns suggest maintaining a little length around the crown area and ideally work the natural fall into the style, Alternatively, very short haircuts around the crown area will prevent the hair from sticking up. For nape whorls suggest maintaining the length at the nape area, or at least a little weight, and avoid cutting into the hairline unless you are using the clippers or cutting the nape area very short. This growth pattern can affect many men's hairstyles, as they generally like to wear their hair shorter than women.
Male pattern baldness	If your client wants to cover the hair-loss area, then suggest leaving the overall style slightly longer, particularly on the top. Some clients prefer to have the hair cut short around the thinning area, to make the rest of the hair look a little thicker.
Hairlines	If the hair is being cut short at the nape area, you need to consider the natural hairline shape. Along with a nape whorl, you can have hairlines that grow in different directions each side, or grow into the middle from both sides. This might affect the length you want to cut to, or the shape of the end result.

Factors	How they can affect the service
Facial hair	When you are cutting the hair, you will need to consider where the head hair stops and any facial hair starts. Head and facial hair should blend together and not appear as two separate features.
Age	When cutting men's hair, you need to consider the age of your client and whether the style will be suitable. Try to tactfully suggest alternatives if you feel your client's suggestion is not suitable, but equally avoid causing offence to your client.

HANDY HINTS

When checking dry hair before the service, you are looking at a styled head of hair which might have products on, or have been styled to change the natural fall and make the hair feel thicker. Always recheck the hair type, natural movement and fall of the hair when it has been shampooed.

 SmartScreen 210 handouts 3 and 4 and worksheet 3

ACTIVITY

Look into a mirror and using a dry wipe pen, draw around your face shape. This will help you to understand face shapes. Ask a colleague to do the same and compare the shapes.

ACTIVITY

Draw the different face shapes and add sketches of hairstyles that will enhance the facial shape.

HANDY HINTS

Male pattern baldness is known as the 'Hamilton pattern' due to the progressive patterns it follows that were identified by Dr J. B. Hamilton.

During this part of the unit you will learn:

- correct use and maintenance of tools and equipment
- techniques used to cut men's hair
- step-by-step guides to creating the looks
- aftercare advice that should be given to clients.

CUTTING TOOLS AND EQUIPMENT

Your scissors are likely to be the most expensive item in your tool collection. Dropping them with the blades open or pointing downwards can be very costly and affect the position of the blades. Care of scissors should include:

HANDY HINTS

Control your tools and use them safely to minimise damage to your client's hair and scalp, to avoid accidents and maintain client comfort.

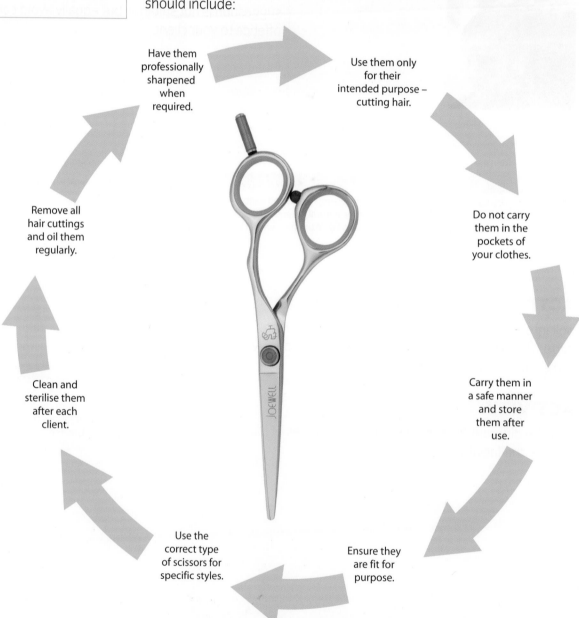

Have them professionally sharpened when required.

Use them only for their intended purpose – cutting hair.

Do not carry them in the pockets of your clothes.

Carry them in a safe manner and store them after use.

Ensure they are fit for purpose.

Use the correct type of scissors for specific styles.

Clean and sterilise them after each client.

Remove all hair cuttings and oil them regularly.

ACTIVITY

Discuss with a colleague how you think a client would feel if you used combs, scissors or clippers with the previous client's hair still on them!

CHOOSING SUITABLE CUTTING TOOLS

For most basic cutting techniques, you will use scissors with an average blade length of 12.5–15 cm (or 5–6 inches), depending on the size of your hands. However, barbers' scissors tend to be longer than those used by stylists. Choosing the right scissors for you to work with comfortably is important. As you become more experienced you are likely to want a selection of scissors for a variety of techniques, and you will probably buy more expensive scissors as your skill level increases.

Scissors

Although at a glance, all scissors look the same, they are indeed very different. They can vary in size and weight due to the metals they are made from, and the type of cutting blade might also differ. At varying costs, you can purchase scissors that have a movable thumb area, which can make it more comfortable for you to cut baselines and achieve exaggerated angles. Scissors are available with serrated or straight blades.

Serrated scissors are most suitable when you first start cutting hair, as they aid control and grip the hair as you cut. However, if you wish to use texturising techniques and slide or slice cut the hair, these will not be suitable as they pull the hair, affecting the cut, and might cause discomfort to your client.

Straight scissors, or non-serrated blades, are the sharpest for cutting, slicing and chipping. You can use these for most techniques and can buy them from around £30 up to a few hundred pounds.

Thinning scissors are used to remove bulk at the end of the haircut and have 'teeth' or 'notches' all the way up one or both blades. Thinning scissors with notches on both blades remove less bulk than those with only one notched blade.

Texturising scissors can be used to add texture to a finished haircut. These have wider notches along the blades and remove weight from the hair section as you cut.

Straight edge blades

Thinning scissors – one blade with notches

Texturising scissors

Store your scissors in a cutting pouch

Thinning scissors – two blades with notches

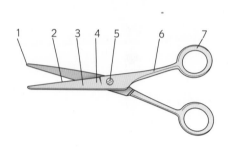

Using clippers correctly

ACTIVITY

Use the Internet to research the types of scissors available. Decide which ones would be most suitable for you and consider the following:

- How much can I afford to spend?
- What size do I need?
- What size is most suitable?
- What type of blade would I like?
- What cutting techniques do I need my scissors for?
- How am I going to store them when they are not in use?

You could look at colours or styles that are available too!

1 The points of the scissors – used for point-cutting or chipping techniques and freehand.
2 The cutting blade edges – used for all club-cutting and scissor-over-comb techniques and some freehand angles.
3 The blades – outside of blade edges.
4 The heel – the strength of the scissors.
5 The pivot – an adjustable screw to loosen or tighten the movement of the blades.
6 The shanks – the length between the pivot up to the thumb and finger holes.
7 The handle – thumb and finger holes.

ACTIVITY

To help you to decide on how tight or loose your blades should be, try this simple exercise – do not have your thumb in the hole during this exercise. Place your ring finger in the finger hole and support your scissors with your other fingers. Lift and open the thumb blade and let the thumb blade drop towards the finger blade. Ideally, the thumb blade, when dropped, should stop just short of the finger blade. If the blades touch, they might be too loose; if there is a large gap between the blades, they are too tight. This can be adjusted by loosening or tightening the pivot screw.

Clippers and trimmers

Clippers can be used to blend in hair on the back of the neck, create outlines and definition, or for clipper cuts with a grade attachment or over a comb. Clipper grade attachments are made in a range of sizes; they are used to graduate hair which is too short to hold between your fingers.

Trimmers can be used to blend or remove neck hair and create lines in the hair. They can be mains electrical or rechargeable battery-operated clippers.

Razors

Razors can be used when you are confident with your cutting techniques. They are used with or without a safety guard. A safety razor is used to add texture or definition to your style; a shaper tapers and removes bulk from the hair; and an open razor cleanly removes the hair from the neckline.

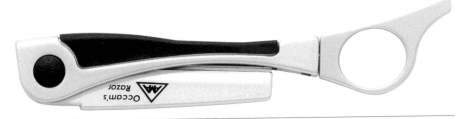

Razor

Razor being used on wet hair

Clippers – rechargeable

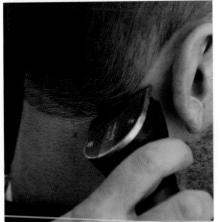

Trimmers

TECHNIQUES USED TO ACHIEVE THE LOOKS

In this part of the unit you will look at how to cut men's hair using a variety of techniques, while following a guideline to achieve a range of different looks.

The looks that you will create might involve a number of techniques, including club-cutting, freehand, thinning, fading, clippers and clipper grade, or scissor-over-comb cutting techniques. You will learn how to use these techniques to achieve uniform layers and graduated looks, how to fade into the neckline and how to cut the hair around the ear area.

CLUB CUTTING

Club cutting is also known as blunt cutting, and is the most popular cutting technique. It involves cutting the hair straight across, while holding the hair with tension between your fingers. This technique will reduce the length of the hair and layers but will retain the thickness of the hair.

Holding the hair for club cutting

FREEHAND TECHNIQUE

When using the freehand technique, you must not hold the hair with any tension but instead comb the hair into position and cut. This technique can be used when you do not need any tension, such as when cutting fringes, or allowing for the natural fall of the hair and cutting around the ears.

Use freehand for cutting around the ears

THINNING THE HAIR

You can use thinning scissors to remove unwanted bulk from the hair but maintain the length. Hair should be dry while this technique is carried out, otherwise you might remove too much 'bulk'. When using thinning scissors, you must cut into the section of hair towards the mid-lengths and ends – avoiding the root area. Thinning out the root area can cause hair to stick up and show signs that it has been thinned out!

Thinning out the hair

FADING

Fading is used to blend short haircuts into the nape of the neck. If hair has been clipper cut or if scissor over comb has been used, blend the hair from the occipital bone down to blend in with the nape area and fade out to the hairline. This technique can enable the hairline shape to appear more natural looking.

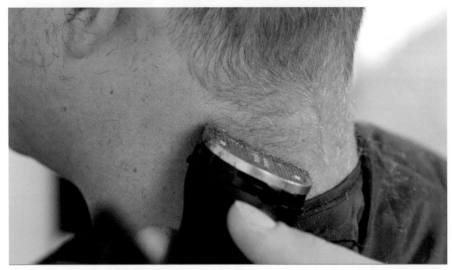
Shaping the neckline after fading

USING CLIPPERS

Clippers can be used with or without a clipper grade attached. If using clippers with a grade, you will need to decide the size of the grade required and this will depend on your client's requirements. Clipper grades vary in size from grade 1 to grade 8, gradually getting about 3 mm bigger with each grade (as a guide):

- grade 8 – 24 mm (approximately 1 inch)
- grade 7 – 21 mm
- grade 6 – 18 mm (approximately ¾ inch)
- grade 5 – 15 mm
- grade 4 – 12 mm (approximately ½ inch)
- grade 3 – 9 mm
- grade 2 – 6 mm (approximately ¼ inch)
- grade 1 – 3 mm

Various clippers grades

A common grade for the 'short back and sides' is a grade 2; grade 1 can be used for the back and sides but it is often used to blend a grade 2 down into the hairline, keeping the hairline very short and maximising the longevity of the cut. Grades 3 and 4 can also be used around the back and sides of a cut, but are also used to blend in the grade 2 up into the occipital area of a scissor cut.

Grades 5 through to 8 are mostly used on the top and crown areas for short, layered effects. Some men have a clipper cut all over the head, and any grade can be used for this depending on the overall length required, or a variation of grades can be used so the hair gradually gets shorter towards the back and sides and hairline.

If using the clippers all over the head, start with the largest grade and blend down to the smallest grade. If you are using just one grade size all over the head, make sure the clippers are moved across the head in different directions – front to back, side to side, etc. This is because the hair will grow in many different directions and if you followed one direction only, the hair might be cut at varying lengths.

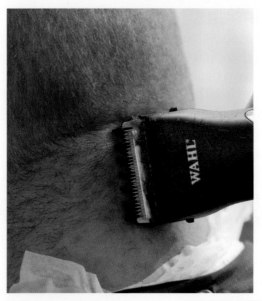

If you are using clippers with a grade at the back and sides and a scissor cut on the top and crown, you can start with the clipper grade cut first and then blend with your layer cut. It is very likely you will need to use a clipper-over-comb or scissor-over-comb technique to fully blend these two techniques.

SmartScreen 210 handout 5

CLIPPER OVER COMB

Clipper over comb can be used to blend in scissor or clipper cuts. This technique helps to remove any bulk or definition lines from the varying clipper grades, or where the scissor cut meets a clipper cut. It is a popular technique to blend and fade into the hairline.

To use this technique, follow the comb with the clippers through the back and sides, angling the comb at +45° or −45° to create longer or shorter effects.

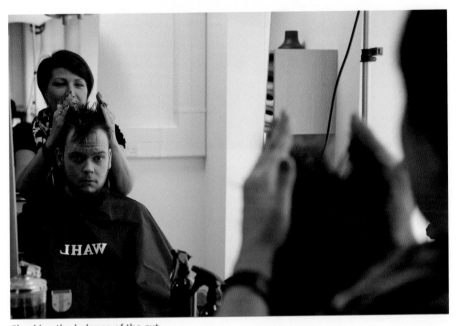

Checking the balance of the cut

Shaping the neckline

SCISSOR OVER COMB

When you are using the scissor-over-comb technique, run the comb up the hair and use it to lift and support the hair to be cut. The hair is cut with the scissors over the comb. This technique gives a graduated effect to the cut and blends short hair into the neck.

Scissor-over-comb technique

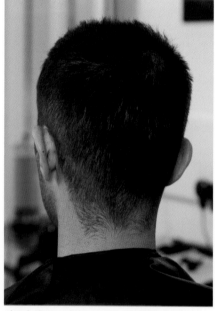

Check the neckline suits your client's requirements

GUIDELINES

The guideline is the most important part of the haircut. If you are cutting the hair and you lose your guideline – STOP! The guideline determines the finished length of the cut and the overall shape and balance. Without a guideline you cannot work methodically through the haircut or maintain accuracy. Even the most experienced barbers will follow a guideline and use accurate sectioning.

Guidelines are the first cuts of the hairstyle. For some styles you might cut in a baseline length (when the length has been agreed with your client). This baseline length becomes your guideline for the overall length of the haircut. Alternatively, if a baseline is not required, your first internal layer that you cut into the hair becomes your guideline for the rest of the haircut.

When the baseline length has been agreed and cut, you are ready to begin the guideline for the internal layers of the hair. This internal guideline will help you achieve the shape of the style. Again, agree the desired length of the layers with your client and then cut in your internal guideline to suit the angle at which the hair will be cut. You can either cut in your internal guideline from front to back and ear to ear, or work in stages, cutting the back first from crown to nape, and then working towards the front and sides.

Barber following the guideline when cutting

Internal guideline crown to back

When you have cut your guideline, every section you cut afterwards will follow this guideline to the same length, so you must hold the hair at the same angle on both sides of the head. Always ensure that your cutting sections are clean and that you take manageable sized sections. Make sure you maintain your balance otherwise the haircut might be uneven.

CUTTING HAIR AT DIFFERENT ANGLES

The cutting angles that the hair is held at will vary for every haircut and style. The diagram below shows the most common angles that you use for cutting the hair for creating one-length, uniform layers and graduated looks.

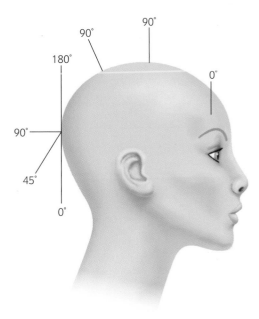

Look	Cutting angle	Cutting angle diagram	Cutting techniques
One length	The hair is pulled directly down at a 0° angle.		Club cutting Freehand
Uniform layers	Use 0° for the baseline, and for the layers the hair is pulled out at a 90° angle throughout the entire haircut.		Club cutting Freehand
Graduation	The inner layers of the hair lengths are longer than the outline shape and generally pulled out at 45°.		Club cutting Freehand Texturising Tapering Scissor over comb

Look	Cutting angle	Cutting angle diagram	Cutting techniques
Fringes	Often cut freehand to allow for the natural movement and fall of the hair growth patterns, but fringes can be cut under tension and pulled down to 0°.		Freehand Club cutting

SmartScreen 210 worksheet 5

CUTTING HAIR WITH TENSION

When you are cutting hair with tension, you must remember that wet hair stretches more than dry hair, so make sure that the end result is not shorter than you expected. You must always keep the same tension to ensure an even result. This includes keeping an even moisture balance during the cutting service, so that the hair is not of mixed porosity or elasticity. This could cause tangles, damage to the hair or uneven cutting results.

CUTTING HAIR WET OR DRY

Whether you cut the hair wet or dry, it will affect the technique you use and the end result. Hair should be checked while it is dry to identify the fall of the hair, and rechecked after shampooing.

Dry cutting

You must check the hair while it is dry to see how your client is currently wearing his hairstyle, to identify any natural movement or hair growth patterns and to feel the density and texture of the hair. Always carry out a porosity test on dry hair prior to the service.

Freehand and scissor-over-comb cutting techniques are best carried out on dry hair. Thinning scissors and clippers must only be used on dry hair.

Wet cutting

When the hair has been shampooed and prepared for the service, check through the hair to identify the natural parting. On wet hair you will be able to see the hair type in its natural state, such as curly or straight, and recheck the movement of the hair.

The elasticity in the hair allows wet hair to be stretched up to 50% of its original length, and you must consider this when you are cutting the hair wet, as the dried result could be much shorter than you or your client anticipated. Always carry out an elasticity test on wet hair. Razor-cutting techniques should only be used on wet hair.

WHY DON'T YOU...
Practise sectioning and pulling the hair out at the angles described in the diagrams.

HANDY HINTS
Curly hair will spring up when dry – use less tension when cutting curly hair. This can be achieved by using the wider tooth end of your comb.

HANDY HINTS
As hair only grows about 1.25 cm (½ inch) each month, it is important that you do not cut the hair too short.

Poor sitting position could result in an uneven haircut

THE IMPORTANCE OF CROSS-CHECKING THE CUT

It is important that your client's body position is balanced and upright throughout the haircut. If your client has his legs or ankles crossed, then the balance of the baseline cut could be uneven. Equally you must ensure that you have an even distribution of body weight.

Cross-checking the haircut during the service and at the end ensures an accurate finish. You can cross-check the haircut at any point during the service to check for balance and even cutting lengths. Using the mirror will help you to check for balance.

For layered haircuts you can cross-check the whole cut by sectioning the hair in the opposite direction to which you cut the layers. If you cut the layers in vertical sections, then you should cross-check horizontally and vice versa.

If you have cut the sideburns, you will need to check if they are even on both sides. You can visually check on both sides or use the mirror. If you turn your client to one side, so one sideburn is in the mirror and the other sideburn is facing you, you can check both sideburns at the same time for balance.

The final and most commonly used method of cross-checking is used as you progress through the haircut. Pull out sections of cut hair on both sides to feel if the lengths are the same.

Cross-checking horizontally

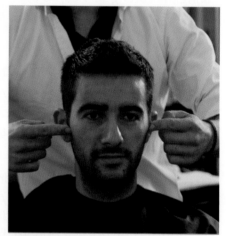
Cross-checking sideburns in the mirror

Cross-checking in the mirror

Ensure your client is sitting straight

STEP-BY-STEP GUIDES TO CREATING THE LOOKS

In this part of the unit we will look at how to cut hair to create uniform layers and graduation, cutting around the ear and fading into the hairline.

CREATING A UNIFORM-LAYER LOOK

When cutting the hair to create a uniform-layer look, you will need to make a guideline section for the length of the hair and one for the internal layers of the hair. The hair is cut at 90° all over.

Uniform layers

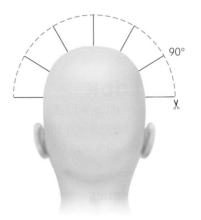
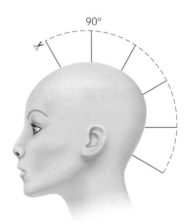

Step-by-step – cutting uniform layers

STEP 1 – Cut in a guideline from crown to nape.

STEP 2 – When the back has been cut, section off the side areas.

STEP 3 – Continue to cut the sides, pulling the sections out at 90°.

STEP 4 – Blend the top sections into the sides and back (still at 90°).

STEP 5 – Shape the hair and personalise around the front hairline.

STEP 6 – Add products and complete the style.

CREATING A GRADUATED-LAYER LOOK

When you create a short graduated haircut, the hair must gradually get shorter towards the nape and neck area. The top can be cut in a similar way to the uniform layers and held out at 90°, but the sides and back of this style must be cut at 45°.

Graduation with clippers and blunt cutting techniques

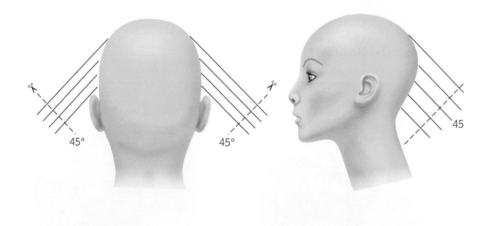

Step-by-step – cutting graduations

STEP 1 – Section the hair above the crown out of the way.

STEP 2 – Using clippers with a grade 2 attachment, clipper the back and sides.

STEP 3 – Angle the clippers outwards to create graduation.

STEP 4 – Blend the back clippered hair with scissor over comb.

STEP 5 – Repeat with the side sections.

STEP 6 – Pull the layers out at 90° for the crown.

STEP 7 – Follow the 90° angle through the top and sides.

STEP 8 – Fade out the clipper cut into the sideburns/facial hair.

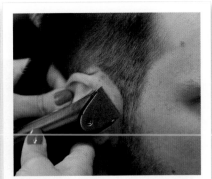

STEP 9 – Tidy the hairline around the ears and neckline.

Cutting around the ear

When you are cutting a style above the ear, you need to cut the hair cleanly around the ear area. If the hair is left too long around the ear, then it might appear as if it needs cutting again just a week or two later. To help achieve a clean cut around the ears, hold/gently fold your client's ear forward towards the face (or ask your client to hold their ear if you prefer). While the ear is held gently forward you can freehand cut around the shape of the ear. Sometimes the clippers are used without a grade, to carefully follow the hairline around the ear area and create a neat finish.

Step-by-step – cutting around the ear

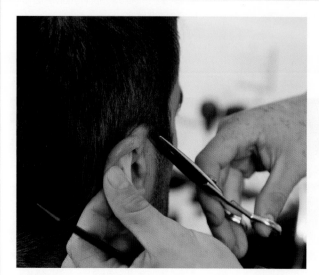

STEP 1 – Gently pull the ear back to cut the shape in front of the ear.

STEP 2 – Gently 'fold' the ear down and cut a clear shape around the ear.

Step-by-step – clippering around the ear

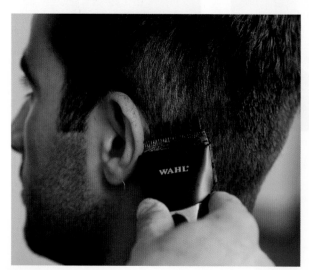

STEP 1 – Follow the hairline around the ears with the clippers.

STEP 2 – In front of the ear, angle the clippers upwards but pull outwards to create graduation.

Graduation with clippering techniques

STEP 1 – Clipper the back and sides to just above the occipital bone.

STEP 2 – Use the clipper-over-comb technique to blend clippered hair.

STEP 3 – Continue this through the side into layers.

STEP 4 – Club cut the top.

STEP 5 – Continue layering the top section.

STEP 6 – Use thinning scissor to remove bulk.

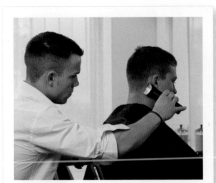

STEP 7 – Discuss the neckline shape with your client.

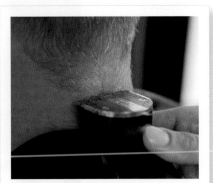

STEP 8 – Shape the neckline to suit your client's requirement.

STEP 9 – Check your client is happy with the end result.

Cutting the neckline

When you have clipper cut or cut the hair into the neck with a scissor-over-comb technique, you will need to decide with your client how to fade into the neckline.

Tapered neckline

One of the more popular necklines is to blend the main haircut into the natural hairline. To create this effect, the hair is gradually cut shorter and blended into the natural shape of the hairline. You will need to consider the natural movement of the hairline, checking for any nape whorls or inward/outward nape growth patterns.

STEP 1 – Tapering and blending into the natural hairline.

Faded neckline

A faded neckline is where the hair is clipper cut and faded out using clippers without a grade attached. To create this effect, the hair is clipper cut with a grade and gradually blended into a clipper cut without a grade, into the hairline.

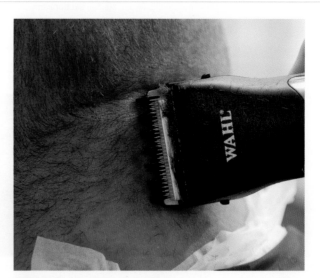

STEP 1 – Fading the clipper cut into the hairline with a grade 1 attachment.

Square neckline

To create a square neckline, the end result will be a blunt, clean finish. Use scissors or clippers to literally square off the edges of the hairline around the neck.

STEP 1 – Create a squared neckline with clippers.

STEP 2 – Cut the baseline straight across with scissors.

STEP 3 – Square off the edges.

Rounded neckline

To create a rounded neckline, use the scissors or clippers as above but, rather than leaving square corners, round off the edges. Although this result is not as harsh as a square neckline, it is still a blunt finish to the cut.

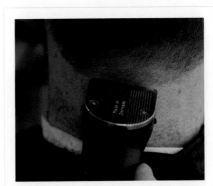

STEP 1 – Create the rounded shape at the back.

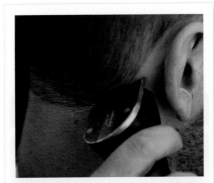

STEP 2 – Round the shape off towards the sides.

> **WHY DON'T YOU...**
> Create a mood board of varying graduated-layer looks and write up how to achieve one of the images.

 SmartScreen 210 worksheet 4

AFTERCARE ADVICE

It is essential that you provide suitable aftercare advice to your client on maintaining the look you have created. You should advise on products and how to use them, what equipment would best enable him to recreate the look and even suggest colouring services that might enhance the style.

RECOMMENDING RETAIL PRODUCTS

If your client has had a full cut-and-blow-dry service, you should have talked about the products that you used during the styling service and explained why and how you used them. If the service was a wet cut, discuss how your client should finish the look himself.

Advise your client on which styling and finishing products would enhance and support his finished look. Explain how particular styling products will aid the drying and styling process, help control the hair and provide longevity to the finished result. You should advise him on how much product to use and how to apply it. If the product could cause a build-up on the hair, advise him on how to remove the product effectively.

Styling and finishing products

You could suggest the following products to help your client style his hair in between salon visits.

Wax – use on dry hair to finish; adds pliable hold

Grooming cream – use on wet or dry hair; gives a firm hold with a matt finish

Clay – use on wet or dry hair to support the shape and offer a medium shine

Pomade – use on dry hair; this is a wax-free wax offering a flexible hold and creating a wet look

Fiber – use on dry hair for a firm hold that leaves hair pliable

Gel – use on wet or dry hair to create a textured 'gloss' look

RECOMMENDING TOOLS AND EQUIPMENT

Throughout the styling service you should advise your client on which tools to use at home to recreate his look, and during the blow-dry service demonstrate what you are doing and why. This gives your client a thorough understanding of what he will need to do when he is styling his hair at home. Talk to him about how to create body or movement if required, or how to prevent it. Remember to discuss the health and safety side of styling and the use of electrically heated styling equipment, such as straightening irons and how this could cause damage to the hair.

Show your client how to add texture to the style

Ask your client if he would like to buy any products or equipment

RECOMMENDING FURTHER SERVICES

During the cutting and styling service is a good time to recommend colouring services to your clients; this will enhance the image created. Adding colour and highlights to a haircut helps to add texture and definition to the shape. Without doubt, colour enhances and complements every style you create.

RECOMMENDING WHEN TO RETURN

You should advise your client on when to book his next cutting service. To help guide him, explain that it depends on how quickly his hair grows. You should suggest that he returns to the salon when the style grows out of shape and when he has trouble maintaining the style, as this might indicate it is ready for a cut.

You could recommend enhancing a haircut with subtle colours to add depth, tone and shine

Turn to page 485 for the answers.

1 Scissors can be sanitised in:

   a An autoclave or Barbicide.

   b An ultraviolet cabinet or Barbicide.

   c With chemical wipes or an autoclave.

   d With warm soapy water or an autoclave.

2 Which **one** of the following identifies the **best** reason why the client should be positioned correctly when having their hair cut?

   a The client could be injured.

   b The cut could be unbalanced.

   c The stylist could be injured.

   d The client could be uncomfortable.

3 **Statement 1:**
   Hair density, head and face shape, alopecia and facial hair are all factors that need to be taken into account when cutting men's hair.

   Statement 2:
   It is important to consider the natural hairline shape before cutting the hair as it might affect the length of hair to be left in the nape.

   Which **one** of the following is correct for the above statements?

	Statement 1	Statement 2
a	True	True
b	True	False
c	False	True
d	False	False

4 Serrated scissors are best used when learning to cut hair because:

   a They help when using slicing techniques.

   b They are the sharpest for cutting.

   c They easily remove weight from the hair.

   d They aid control and grip the hair.

5 **Statement 1:**
   Scissors are held with the thumb and the middle finger as this gives the most control.

   Statement 2:
   Razors are used to create texture and definition by slicing and removing bulk.

   Which **one** of the following is correct for the above statements?

	Statement 1	Statement 2
a	True	True
b	True	False
c	False	True
d	False	False

6 Using the fading technique will:

   a Blend in longer layers from the crown to the occipital bone.

   b Blend in shorter hair from the occipital bone to the hairline.

   c Remove unwanted bulk from the fringe.

   d Reduce the natural texture of the hair.

7 A common clipper grade for a 'short back and sides' style is a 2, which leaves the hair length at approximately:

   a 3 mm in length.

   b 6 mm in length.

   c 9 mm in length.

   d 12 mm in length.

8 Cross-checking a layered cut will ensure that it is even and can be done by:

   a Sectioning the hair in the opposite direction to which it was cut.

   b Sectioning the hair at 45° to the way it was cut.

   c Allowing the hair to sit in its natural fall.

   d Confirming the look with the client.

CASE STUDY: JAMIE STEVENS

Thirty-year-old Jamie Stevens opened his own salon at the age of 18, before moving to London and working for Beverly C, Daniel Hersheson and now Errol Douglas (where he is Art Director). He has done shoots and cuts for Kylie Minogue, Stella McCartney, Elle Macpherson, Eva Herzigova, Myleene Klass, Hugh Grant, Christian Slater and Gok Wan to name a few. In 2009 he added the title of British Hairdressing's Men's Hairdresser of the Year to his accolades, and he is the hairdresser-in-residence for TV shows *This Morning*, *Gok's Fashion Fix*, *How To Look Good Naked* and *The X Factor*. Here are Jamie's top tips on men's cutting.

1 The men's fringe is a great area to reflect current trends. You can keep the shorter back and sides but the fringe comes in a variety of lengths, so you are going to be able to play with the look to suit your face shape, like a lot of guys in the '80s (Spandau Ballet, for example.) A great way of truly making it your own cut is to play with the length of the fringe itself, and also play with different textures like crimping and quiffs, it is not just for the ladies!

2 The tool side of men's hairdressing is great to work with; learn all the techniques from scissor over comb to clippers to razors, so you can mix old and new techniques. You should be able to scissor over comb perfectly but also be able to use a pair of clippers and your guards. If a gent who wants a short back and sides walks in and says he does not like clippers you need to be able to scissor over comb perfectly.

3 What helped me in my men's career is that I did an old school barbering course, so I can use a cut-throat razor and learnt about how to shave against the growth of hair. I always offer to do facial hair as well. You are grooming with a man, so if a man's got hair growing out of his ears and nose just sort it out! It is your job to make them look as good as possible and they might be embarrassed to ask, so just have the confidence to do it.

4 Do not be afraid to experiment with colour, if someone's going grey or a colour would complement your cut then suggest it. Colour can disguise thinning hair as well.

CUT FACIAL HAIR

For years, beards and facial hair were considered signs of sandal-wearing hippies or men who were too lazy to groom themselves properly! During the 'noughties' facial hair and 'celebrity designer' beards have become increasingly popular; barbershops have noticed an increase in clients visiting the salon to have either facial hair trimmed and styled or that 'clean-shaven' look. Whatever your client's choice, facial hair grooming is now a very popular service at the barbers, and these are skills that you must master.

There are two learning outcomes in this unit. The learner will be able to:

- prepare for a cutting facial hair service
- provide a cutting facial hair service.

During this part of the unit you will learn:

- safety considerations for cutting hair
- communication and behaviour requirements
- consultation techniques that should be used
- factors that should be considered when cutting facial hair.

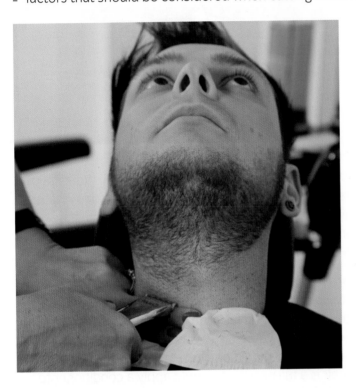

SAFETY CONSIDERATIONS FOR CUTTING FACIAL HAIR

When you cut facial hair, you will be using sharp tools and cutting very close, if not onto, your client's skin; this increases the risks to you and your clients. Along with the previously mentioned safety considerations (refer to Unit 202 – Follow health and safety practice in the salon and Unit 210 – Cutting men's hair) you will need to consider the following:

- preparation of yourself, your work area and your client
- body positioning of you and your client
- health and safety – care with your tools and equipment
- risks of cross-contamination
- risks from the hair clippings.

PREPARATION

You must always ensure that you are prepared for the working day ahead! Arrive at work clean and showered, wearing deodorant, with fresh breath, dressed in clean clothes and with your own hair and/or facial hair well-groomed/presented. You should avoid wearing any accessories that might get caught in your client's hair or put you at risk of contact dermatitis.

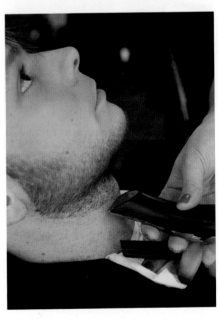

SmartScreen 211 handout 1

Ensure that your work area is ready for your client's arrival. Workstations and barber's chairs must be hair free, cleaned with warm soapy water, and wiped or sprayed with disinfectant. Your cutting tools must be sterilised before and after use; this is particularly important if you are using razor blades or cutting very close to the skin.

When your client arrives, you should gown and protect him with a clean cutting gown and towels, placed at the front and back of the shoulders. If you are cutting the head hair and facial hair, then you should shampoo the hair prior to the service. If you are carrying out a beard and moustache cut, then the face should be washed with a facial soap and water. If the facial hair is a full beard, you could apply a conditioner to the hair to soften it slightly. However, due to the coarseness of the hair, the conditioner will not work as well as it does on head hair. If you are trimming a moustache only, then a facial wipe would suffice to cleanse the facial hair. Comb all beards and moustaches through with a wide-tooth comb to untangle the hair and to allow all of the hair to be cut.

BODY POSITIONING

The comfort of you and your client is paramount during this service, as both of you need to stay still during the service. Any sudden movements could cause your client to get a cut from the scissors.

You should always stand with your body weight evenly distributed; this will ensure that you are evenly balanced and that you are not putting undue stress on your back. You should place your work area and trolley to your preferred side of working and never over-stretch to reach for your tools.

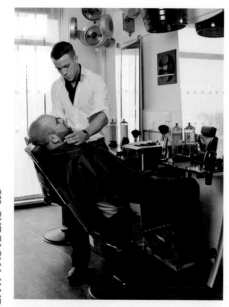

HANDY HINTS

For a stylist, poor posture can lead to fatigue and back injuries.

HANDY HINTS

COSHH must be followed when using any substance – including when washing facial hair.

INDUSTRY TIP

If you are cutting facial hair, tuck tissue or cotton wool in the top edge of the towel to prevent the coarse hair from falling down the client's clothes. Use cotton pads on his eyes to protect him from stray hair cuttings.

When your client is seated comfortably in the barber's chair, you must check that his legs are not crossed and that both feet are either on the floor or supported by the foot rest. You need to ensure that your client is positioned comfortably and just as importantly – sitting squarely and not off balance. When your client's body position is suitable, recline the chair and adjust it to a suitable position/height for you to work. During the facial cutting, you will need to ask your client to move his head in various directions, so that you can cut around the neck area and follow the contours of the face and neck.

HEALTH AND SAFETY

Although many of the tools that you will use will be similar to those used for cutting head hair, you are cutting very near to the skin and lip, so you need to take extra care.

Always carry your scissors in a pouch or case and **palm** them when not in use. If you are using razor blades, you must use a fresh blade for every client, unless of course the razor blades are not disposable. These types of razors must be sterilised in an autoclave, sanitised in a UV cabinet or disinfected with a chemical solution or wipe.

HANDY HINTS

Barber's chairs are much heavier and more bulky than salon chairs. If you need to move them, do so carefully so you do not hurt your back or cause injuries.

Palm
Hold your scissors with the blades closed in the palm of your hand

ACTIVITY

How would you sterilise your scissors, clippers and combs?

Before and after using electrical or rechargeable clippers, you must remove all the hair clippings from in between the blades, spray the blades with a clipper disinfectant solution and oil them before storing them away/using them again.

211 CUT FACIAL HAIR

Clipper disinfectant

Clipper oil

SmartScreen 211 worksheet 1

Sharps bin

When using electrical appliances, you must follow the Electricity at Work Regulations and always be mindful of trailing wires, as these can cause trip hazards.

ACTIVITY

What action would you take if you dropped the electrical clippers and the blades were now making a terrible noise when switched on?

RISKS OF CONTAMINATION

Before any facial hair cutting commences, you must check beneath it for open wounds, hidden cold sores that might not be visible due to hair growth and for signs of infection or infestation. Some clients might have facial hair to hide scar tissue, acne, facial moles or other potential skin disorders. These might pose a risk to you, or cause discomfort to your client if they are caught with a comb.

If you were to accidentally cut your client's skin or the lip, you must administer some minor first aid. Firstly put on some gloves to prevent cross-contamination, stem the blood flow with clean, dry cotton wool, remove ALL lose clippings from the surrounding area and, if necessary, apply a suitable plaster, checking first that your client does not have an allergy to plasters. Remember to record the incident in the accident book.

Disposal of waste

Dispose of any soiled cotton wool (and plasters) in the designated salon waste bin with a lid, to prevent any cross-contamination.

Dispose of used razor blades in the sharps bin. Collection of these bins can be arranged by your local council and sometimes with your local pharmacy.

ACTIVITY

What would the risks and potential consequences be if a razor blade was disposed of in the salon waste bin?

HAIR CLIPPINGS

Hair clippings on the floor make for a slippery surface, so sweep the floor after every client and, if necessary, during the service.

Facial hair is often very coarse and can travel great distances in the air as it is being cut! You should ensure that your own clothes are protected and try to avoid the tiny hair cuttings entering your eyes.

Make sure that your client is well-protected and that you remove loose hair clippings from him on a regular basis throughout the service. These can penetrate into the skin and cause infections, such as boils. Both you and your client are at risk of infection from loose hair clippings.

HANDY HINTS
Make sure any wounds are free from hair clippings to prevent infections.

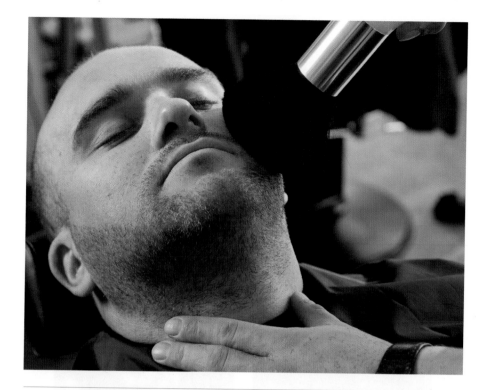

COMMUNICATION AND BEHAVIOUR

As we have mentioned in previous units, it is very important that you are polite to your clients and speak to them in a friendly manner. Engaging in neutral conversation such as recent football results and which teams they support might help to relax your clients. You should be clearly spoken and show positive body language at all times. When speaking with clients or your colleagues, ensure you are respectful to them and respond to their needs.

You should use client-friendly terminology and speak in a reassuring and confident manner. Make sure you really listen to what your client is asking of you and respond by nodding and maintaining eye contact to prove you are listening. Before your client arrives, it is good practice to read your client's record card and during/after the visit record any changes or update it with today's service.

CONSULTATION TECHNIQUES

The consultation with your client for a facial haircut is no different to any other consultation; you still need to identify the service objectives. There are over 40 different styles of beards and moustaches; you will need to confirm which one of these your client desires and assess the potential of his hair to achieve the look required.

A series of open questions, starting with 'what', 'how', 'when' and 'why', will help you to obtain specific answers from your client about his requirements. Finish the conversation with closed questions to confirm both of your understandings.

To help your client choose a style for his facial hair, you can use magazines or print off photos of celebrities with facial hair from the Internet. Always listen carefully and hear what your client is asking you to achieve for him. Repeat any instructions back to clarify what has been agreed and discussed.

ACTIVITY

Use the Internet to search for sites about beards and moustaches. How many websites on beards and facial hair can you find?

When speaking to your client and colleagues, you should demonstrate mutual respect. Speak to them confidently and politely, expressing yourself clearly and portraying positive body language.

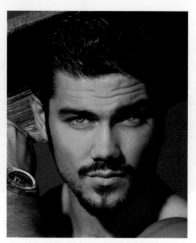

FACTORS THAT SHOULD BE CONSIDERED WHEN CUTTING FACIAL HAIR

Beards and facial hair have become an important fashion accessory for men, with more and more celebrities supporting these looks. R&B and Hip Hop music artists, movie stars, models and sportsmen have brought beards and designer-stubble looks back into the forefront of fashion and the media.

The following factors will need to be considered, as these can influence your client's decision on the chosen design and style.

LIFESTYLE

Although the factors that you need to consider for cutting facial hair are very similar to those for cutting head hair, the reasons why they are considered are very different. Facial hair is generally cut much shorter in length than head hair, and therefore can grow out of style much more quickly. You will need to ensure that your client's requirements will suit his lifestyle, so that the shape and style of the beard or moustache will last and can be maintained, as and when required.

It is becoming increasingly acceptable to wear facial hair in the workplace and it does not look out of place with a suit, or with jeans and casual wear. The 'unshaven look' however is not easy to achieve and requires a lot of care and attention. Some of the designer-stubble styles need maintaining every couple of days, and the initial days/weeks of growing facial hair might make your client look scruffy, so planning when to grow a beard also needs to be discussed. Before the chosen style is decided, check that your client has the time to maintain the desired look.

Some jobs can affect whether men can have beards! Firemen for example will need to ensure that any breathing apparatus fits snugly around their mouth and airways and a thick beard could prevent this. When consulting with your client about his facial hair requirements, you must discuss whether this might impact on his job and make judgements as to which style would be most suitable.

Religion and belief has always played a big part with facial hair and beards, but did you know that your client's choice of sport can have an impact on his facial hair decisions? Boxers, for example, are not allowed facial hair, so discuss with your client their choice of leisure activity.

TEXTURE AND DENSITY

Clients who request a full beard but have sparse or no hair around the mouth should be advised to have a disconnected beard and moustache, so that the look balances well.

It might not be possible to achieve a thin or fine moustache if the facial hair growth is naturally very dense or abundant. You might need to cut the facial hair with clippers, as cutting dense hair could take too long using a scissor-over-comb technique.

LENGTH AND TYPE

This partially comes down to client requirements – how long your client wants his beard, but you also need to consider the length and type of hair your client has. If your client wants a different beard style, you need to identify whether the beard needs further growth, or needs to be cut shorter to achieve the desired shape. If the beard hair is curly, this might also affect the achievement of the desired style, particularly for longer beards.

INDUSTRY TIP

When discussing the facial hair design, you should always consider your client's age and the suitability of the chosen style.

HAIR GROWTH, DISTRIBUTION AND QUALITY

As with the head, the facial hair can have varied growth directions and this can cause the results to affect the finished shape, look uneven or grow out unevenly and untidily. A whorl growth direction needs to be cut or clippered in several directions, to ensure all the hairs are cut to the same length. You will need to consider the distribution of hair, as one side of the face might have more hair than the other. Also the quality of the facial hair might not suit certain styles, so check both sides of the face when you are consulting and discussing the style requirements.

HEAD AND FACE SHAPES

It is important that the facial hair/beard complements the current hair style. A 'bald' head and a big beard could look out of place, so always ensure the two are balanced.

If your client has a round face, suggest a squarer cut and finish for the beard or moustache. For square faces and jaw-lines suggest a rounded beard or curved moustache.

FACIAL FEATURES

Cutting the facial hair of clients with dimples can sometimes cause you difficulties in achieving a balanced result. To ensure the end result is even, ask your client to poke their tongue in the dimple area to push the cheek area outwards when you cut/clipper the hair.

Clients with heavy-set chins generally prefer a fuller beard and moustache to balance the chin feature.

Clients with small mouths tend to suit smaller/thinner moustaches, and those with large noses suit a thick or wider moustache which will minimise the look of the larger feature.

If your client has any facial scarring, this can be disguised more easily with a beard or moustache.

> **INDUSTRY TIP**
>
> Always check the face for any facial piercings; you must be extremely careful not to catch these with the comb or your cutting tools.

ADVERSE SKIN DISORDERS

Some adverse skin disorders or contra-indications could affect the service. If the skin condition is infectious or contagious you must not proceed with the service.

Along with any adverse skin and scalp conditions mentioned in Unit 203, you will also need to be mindful of the following adverse skin disorders when cutting facial hair. Always check in the beard growth for any signs of infection.

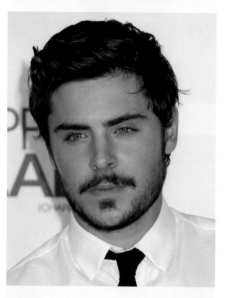

THE CITY & GUILDS TEXTBOOK

Condition	Description	Cause	Infectious?	Treatment
Barber's itch (sycosis barbea)	Folliculitis – inflammation and infection of the hair follicles on the hairy parts of the face	Bacterial infection	Yes, can be spread by infected shaving tools	Refer to GP if it does not clear up after improved hygiene.
Boils/abscesses	Raised, inflamed puss-filled spots	Infection in the hair follicle	Yes	Do not carry out facial hair-cutting treatments – refer to GP.
In-growing hairs (razor bumps)	In-growing hairs are just like they sound – hairs that grow inwards and cause a mild infection or discomfort	After repeated close shaving, the hair gets trapped under a layer of skin but continues to grow.	No – as long as the blocked follicle has not become infected	Service can continue if it is not infected. Recommend exfoliating treatments and products.
Cold sores (herpes simplex)	A cold sore – on the facial area or lip	Virus infection	Yes	Do not carry out facial hair-cutting treatments – refer to pharmacy for treatment.
Impetigo	Yellow crusts on the skin, often around the mouth area	Bacterial infection, often a secondary infection caused by scratching the skin	Yes	Do not carry out facial hair-cutting treatments – refer to GP.

Condition	Description	Cause	Infectious?	Treatment
Psoriasis	Silvery yellow scales and thickening of the skin	Unknown	No	Services can be carried out, but avoid using open-blade razors on psoriasis – refer to a dermatologist or GP.
Cysts	The most common cyst on the face and neck area is a sebaceous cyst – a small pea-sized, non-cancerous lump/bump that is filled with pus or fluid	Blocked sebaceous gland	No – unless the cyst has been infected	Services can be carried out, as these cysts are often painless, but will become so if they are knocked or combed, and could get infected if they are accidently cut with clippers or scissors. Sometimes cysts disappear by themselves, or they can be drained by a GP.
Moles and skin tags	Skin lesions – either under or on the skin	Some are caused by a pigment growth in the skin – **melanocytes** – causing a dark colour. Others occur from a **subdermal** growth – under the skin.	No	Continue with the service; be careful not to catch the skin tag or moles with your tools. If the mole looks like it is infected or has grown in size – refer to GP.
Scars	Skin is a seamless organ and any tears in it get repaired but leave behind scars from the healing process	Accident or injury to the skin	No	Proceed with the service, but the area might be tender, so do so with care. Medical referral is not required.

Melanocytes

Melanin-producing cells

Subdermal

Under the skin

SmartScreen 211 handout 3

THE CITY & GUILDS TEXTBOOK

PROVIDE A CUTTING FACIAL HAIR SERVICE

During this part of the unit you will learn:

- cutting tools and equipment
- techniques used to cut facial hair
- step-by-step guides to creating the looks
- aftercare advice that should be given to clients.

CUTTING TOOLS AND EQUIPMENT

The tools and equipment you are likely to use during these services are:

- combs
- scissors
- clippers
- clippers with grade attachments
- T-liners.

Tools and equipment	How to use	Maintenance
Combs 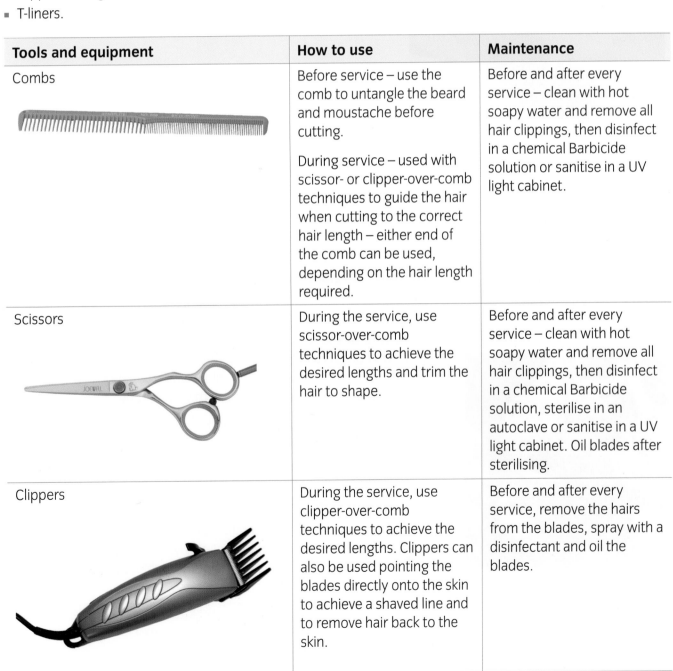	Before service – use the comb to untangle the beard and moustache before cutting. During service – used with scissor- or clipper-over-comb techniques to guide the hair when cutting to the correct hair length – either end of the comb can be used, depending on the hair length required.	Before and after every service – clean with hot soapy water and remove all hair clippings, then disinfect in a chemical Barbicide solution or sanitise in a UV light cabinet.
Scissors	During the service, use scissor-over-comb techniques to achieve the desired lengths and trim the hair to shape.	Before and after every service – clean with hot soapy water and remove all hair clippings, then disinfect in a chemical Barbicide solution, sterilise in an autoclave or sanitise in a UV light cabinet. Oil blades after sterilising.
Clippers	During the service, use clipper-over-comb techniques to achieve the desired lengths. Clippers can also be used pointing the blades directly onto the skin to achieve a shaved line and to remove hair back to the skin.	Before and after every service, remove the hairs from the blades, spray with a disinfectant and oil the blades.

Tools and equipment	How to use	Maintenance
Clipper grade attachments 	During the service, use clippers with various grades attached to achieve different lengths.	Before and after every service – clean grade attachments with hot soapy water and remove all hair clippings, then disinfect in a chemical Barbicide solution or sanitise in a UV light cabinet.
T-liners	During the service T-liners are used to create small precise lines in the beard line or moustache.	Before and after every service – remove the hairs from the blades, spray with a disinfectant and oil the blades.

SmartScreen 211 handout 2 and worksheet 2

TECHNIQUES USED TO CUT FACIAL HAIR

During this part of the unit we will look at the techniques used, such as:

- scissor over comb
- clipper over comb
- clippering with grade attachments
- freehand.

SCISSOR OVER COMB

Scissor over comb is a popular technique that is used for beard and moustache trimming and shaping. It allows for graduation in the shape but you will need to be very accurate with your cutting.

When you are using scissor-over-comb techniques, ensure that the beard has been washed and towel-dried thoroughly, place your comb on the skin and work upwards from the neck area towards the lower lip. You can use either side of your comb, or angle the comb at 45° to achieve shorter or longer lengths, depending on your client's requirements.

Some barbers prefer to use this technique to demonstrate their skills and personalise the look, but this is not always possible on thick or dense hair, so clipper-over-comb techniques might be used instead.

HANDY HINTS

For both scissor- and clipper-over-comb techniques, remember to work with the various directions of the hair growth.

CLIPPER OVER COMB

Clipper over comb is used in a similar way to scissor over comb, but produces quicker results. Using the clipper-over-comb technique still requires accuracy with your hand and comb balance, otherwise the result will be uneven.

CLIPPERING WITH GRADE ATTACHMENTS

In the same way that you might clipper the back and sides of a haircut with clipper grades attached to clippers, you can do so for beard trimming. When the desired length has been agreed, attach the appropriate clipper grades and work through the facial hair from the neck upwards. When you have cut the beard or moustache to length, remove any unwanted hair outside the outline of the shape by removing the clipper grades and cutting the hair against the skin.

Clipper grades range from grade 1 – the shortest, up to grade 8 – the largest. Each grade leaves the hair longer by about 3 mm, starting from 3 mm up to 24–25 mm – refer to Unit 210 for a reminder.

SmartScreen 211 handout 5

FREEHAND

Use freehand to finalise the detail of the shape; to create a blunt line above the lip, shape and blend into the sideburn area or enhance the outline shape of the beard or moustache. Take extra care when you are cutting near the ears and especially around the lip area, as the skin might not be as easy to see through the hair growth and you might cut your client.

STEP-BY-STEP GUIDES TO CREATING THE LOOKS

When you are cutting a full beard, it is advisable to remove all excess bulk from the beard first, so that you can see the natural hairline of the facial hair. When this is done, you can cut in your outline shape, with either clippers or mini-clippers.

When cutting the beard or moustache, you must work in a methodical manner – establish a cutting guideline and ensure you follow it throughout. It is important to always use your mirrors to make sure the cut is even and balanced, and regularly cross-check your cut.

OUTLINE SHAPES

With so many beard and moustache designs and styles to choose from, make sure you do not forget to discuss with your client the finer details, such as the hairline and outline finish.

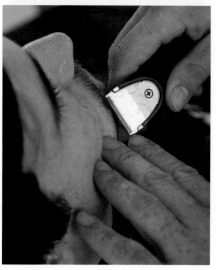

Beards generally mean chin and cheek hair, therefore the hair on the neck is often cut back to the skin or much shorter than the beard length itself. You will need to check the following with your client: does he want a full beard? Where does he want the cheek and the neck hair to stop and be blended out to?

HANDY HINTS

When you cross-check the cut, check the weight distribution, balance, shape and your client's satisfaction.

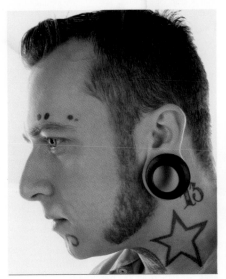

Sideburns

If he has sideburns – does he want them blended into the beard or left longer?

Would he like a beard without sideburns – a beard that is cut to either side of the jaw-line but does not go up the cheeks or meet with the sideburns?

Does he want a chin curtain – beard hair that travels from ear to ear along the chin but does not meet up with the lower lip or have an accompanying moustache?

Beard without sideburns (an anchor beard shape)

Chin curtains

Does he want a goatee – a beard that covers the chin only and is not attached to a moustache, or a chin puff – a narrower version of the goatee?

Chin puff

Goatee

Does he want a pencil moustache (also known as a mouth brow), a thicker moustache, a curved edge or a straight edge?

With so many beard and moustache options to choose from, ensure you discuss with your client the cheek hair, neck hairline, sideburns and moustache shapes and hairlines. When you have agreed where you are cutting to along the natural hairline, make sure you remove all the hair outside of this outline shape.

ACHIEVING THE LOOKS

Before you run off and try to create Brad Pitt's next facial hair design, you will need to master some of the basic skills and facial haircuts first! Let's look at how some of these are achieved.

Cutting a full beard

You can achieve this by using uniform layers on longer beards, or scissor- or clipper-over-comb techniques on shorter, full beards.

Step-by-step: cutting a full beard using clippers with grades and clipper-over-comb techniques

STEP 1 – Remove the excess length from the beard.

STEP 2 – Lift the head and cut, blend or remove the length under the chin.

STEP 3 – Trim the moustache to the agreed length.

STEP 4 – Blend and personalise the facial hair with clipper-over-comb techniques.

STEP 5 – Personalise the moustache outline.

STEP 6 – Ensure the client is happy with the finished look.

ACTIVITY

Practise cutting a full beard on a training block head.

INDUSTRY TIP

Ask your client to move their head for you so you can follow all the contours of the neck and face shapes.

INDUSTRY TIP

At the end of every facial haircut, ask your client if he would like his eyebrows trimmed! Some clients are surprised by this question, but reassure them that eyebrows are also facial hair, and trimming them enhances the whole image of the beard and moustache.

 SmartScreen 211 handout 4 and worksheet 3

Cutting a goatee
Step-by-step: cutting a goatee-tapered beard line using the scissor-over-comb technique

STEP 1 – Remove the excess length with the clipper-over-comb technique.

STEP 2 – Shape the goatee beard and cut to the desired length with the scissor-over-comb technique.

STEP 3 – Trim the moustache length with clippers and grades.

STEP 4 – Trim the goatee using clippers and grades.

STEP 5 – Use mini-clippers to create the lipline shape.

STEP 6 – Check you client is happy with the finished result.

ACTIVITY

Practise cutting a goatee beard on a practice block head.

Cutting a traditional moustache
Step-by-step: cutting a moustache using freehand techniques

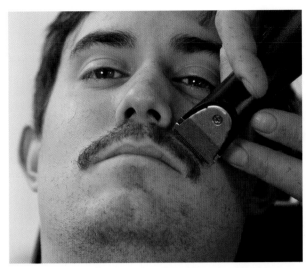

STEP 1 – After removing excess length with scissor-over-comb techniques, create the top lipline shape with mini-clippers.

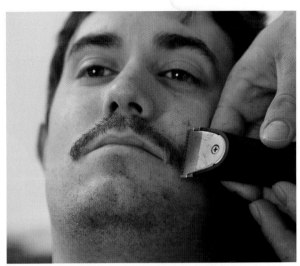

STEP 2 – Agree the width of the moustache and use clippers, blade down onto the face.

STEP 3 – Check the balance on both sides.

STEP 4 – Create the bottom lipline and shape to personalise the moustache.

STEP 1 – Cover the eyes with cotton pads and lift the chin upwards for ease of working.

STEP 2 – Remove the excess length of the beard with clipper-over-comb techniques.

STEP 3 – Remove the beard length under the lipline.

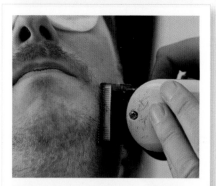

STEP 4 – Adjust the clipper grade length and remove the unwanted facial hair.

STEP 5 – Tilt the clippers to the side and create the lipline moustache length required.

STEP 6 – Using the mini-clippers, define the lipline shape.

STEP 7 – Using the clipper-over-comb technique, remove the moustache length.

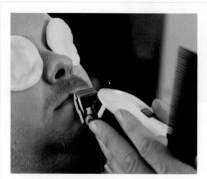

STEP 8 – Check the moustache length is defined before you show the client the end result.

Cutting a straight line top-lip moustache
Step-by-step: cutting a moustache straight across the top lip, using club cutting

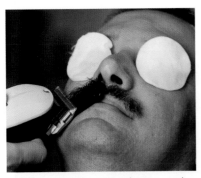

STEP 1 – Cover the eyes with cotton pads to prevent stray hairs from entering the eyes and cut the length with the clipper-over-comb technique.

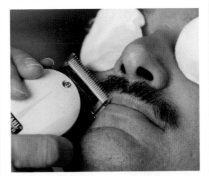

STEP 2 – Remove the hair length from the bottom of the lipline.

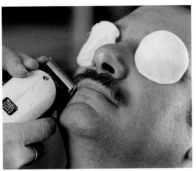

STEP 3 – Define the length and check both sides for balance.

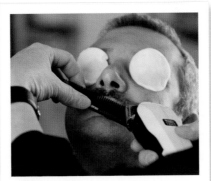

STEP 4 – With the new shape in place check the internal lengths are cut to the agreed length.

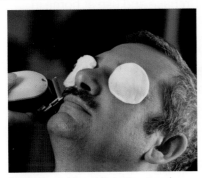

STEP 5 – Cut the width to the agreed length.

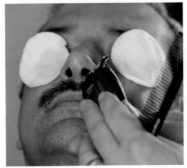

STEP 6 – Check the width balance is even on both sides and then show the moustache shape to your client.

Practise cutting various moustache styles on a practice block head.

Eyebrow grooming
Step-by-step: cutting the eyebrows to shape

STEP 1 – Using either clipper- or scissor-over-comb techniques, remove excess length.

STEP 2 – Using freehand, remove any stray long eyebrows.

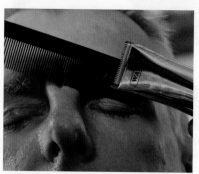

STEP 3 – Comb up and down the eyebrow to cut any stray long eyebrows.

AFTERCARE ADVICE THAT SHOULD BE PROVIDED TO YOUR CLIENT

As with every service that you provide, you must offer aftercare advice to your client. This should include which products to use at home, recommendations for any equipment for home maintenance, how to maintain the current look, which additional services are available for him and when he should return for his next appointment.

PRODUCTS

You should recommend to your client that he regularly exfoliates the skin outside the facial hair shape to prevent any in-growing hairs or the increased risk of 'barber's itch'. Show your client how to carry out this exfoliating treatment, suggesting how often and demonstrating the products that are available for him to purchase and use at home in between salon visits.

If your client suffers with dry skin and very coarse beard hair, you can recommend shampoos and conditioners to be used on the beard; this will work for full beards only. Equally, for clients with less facial hair or those that close-shave more regularly, you can suggest a gent's skin-care range to help moisturise the face.

EQUIPMENT AND MAINTENANCE

If the style requires minimal trimming on a regular basis, it is likely that your client will want to maintain this himself in between visits. Suggest which clippers he should use, or razors, if he is removing most of his facial hair. Demonstrate the areas of the cheek or neck that he should clipper cut, explaining how to do it and advising how often he should do it.

HANDY HINTS

Advise your clients not to use a razor or clippers with blunt blades; these are common causes of minor skin infections and may induce inward growing hairs.

The hairiness of men varies from male to male. Men with very hairy chests might need guidance on where to stop shaving the neck hair before it becomes removal of chest hair. A clean-shaven neckline can help to lessen the overall look of a hairy chest.

ADDITIONAL SERVICES

Shaving for men is as individual as faces, and some clients like to personalise their beards. This might be in the form of colouring or bleaching their facial hair. If your salon offers this service, discuss with him any ideas you have for making his beard individual to him.

Recommending when to re-book

The recommendations you make will very much depend on the style you have created. Maintaining a more rugged look requires more regular up-keep, otherwise the rugged look quickly becomes a scruffy look. These styles might need grooming every 3 days or so. A full-beard style might last from 3 to 5 weeks depending on the length of the beard and the rate of hair growth; you will need to personalise this part of the service to suit every individual look and every individual client. As with head hair, facial hair growth is about 1.25 cm per month.

Advise your client to oil their clipper blades

211 SmartScreen handout 6 and interactive worksheet 1

Turn to page 485 for the answers.

1 Which **one** of the following is the **best** reason for taking extra care when cutting facial hair?

   a The eyes and lips are very close and could be easily cut.

   b Infections and infestations can be more easily passed on.

   c Beard hair is more easily damaged.

   d It is easy to get an unbalanced look.

2 **Statement 1:**

Risk of contamination is high when cutting facial hair because cold sores or bacterial skin infections can be disguised by facial hair.

Statement 2:

Care should be taken if the client has acne or moles, as it can cause discomfort if they are caught in the comb.

Which **one** of the following is correct for the above statements?

	Statement 1	Statement 2
a	True	True
b	True	False
c	False	True
d	False	False

3 Cross-contamination can be minimised by:

   a Wearing a mask when emptying the contents of the sharps bin.

   b Washing razor blades in warm soapy water before using.

   c Ensuring the client has washed his face before cutting the beard.

   d Disposing of sharps and soiled cotton wool in the correct containers.

4 Which **one** of the following is the **best** way of cutting a beard that has whorls?

   a Leave the hair longer on the whorl.

   b Clipper the hair in several directions.

   c Take the hair shorter on the whorl.

   d Shave the face to reduce the growth pattern.

5 Which **one** of the following describes the **best** action to take if sycosis barbea is suspected?

   a Advise the client to avoid using open razors.

   b Take extra care when combing around the area.

   c Do not carry out the service and refer to a GP.

   d Complete the service and refer to a GP.

6 Which **one** of the following describes the reason why T-liners are used?

   a To create small precise shapes.

   b To blend in longer layers.

   c To thin the hair.

   d To texturise.

7 **Statement 1:**

Goatees and chin puffs are types of beards that cover the chin only.

Statement 2:

Eyebrows should never be trimmed as this can make them thicker and encourage further growth.

Which **one** of the following is correct for the above statements?

	Statement 1	Statement 2
a	True	True
b	True	False
c	False	True
d	False	False

8 Which **one** of the following is the **best** aftercare advice to give a client following a facial hair shape?

   a To exfoliate and keep the skin healthy.

   b To use firm-hold products to maintain the outline.

   c To demonstrate how to use clippers.

   d To demonstrate how to shave using an open razor.

CREATE AN IMAGE BASED ON A THEME WITHIN THE HAIR AND BEAUTY SECTOR

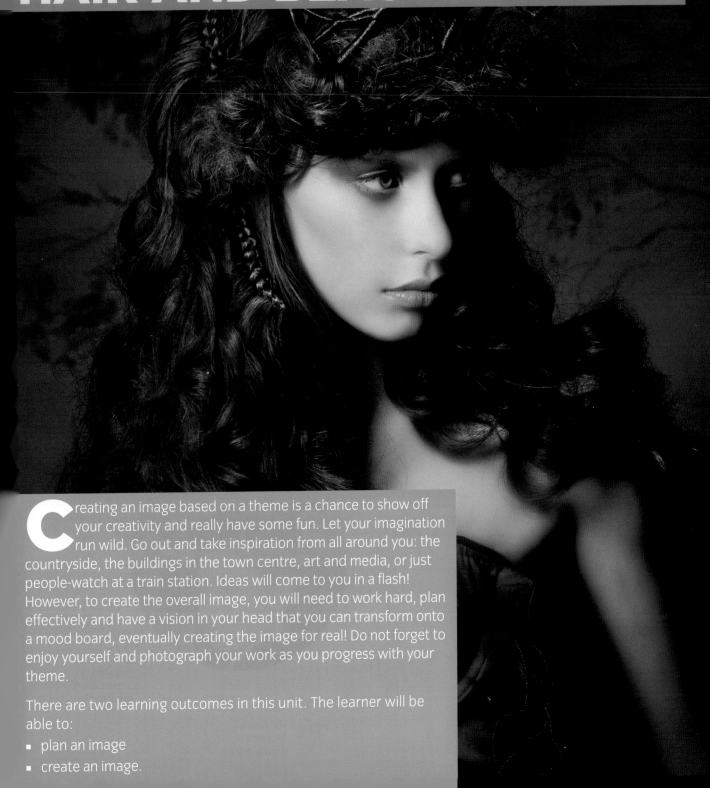

Creating an image based on a theme is a chance to show off your creativity and really have some fun. Let your imagination run wild. Go out and take inspiration from all around you: the countryside, the buildings in the town centre, art and media, or just people-watch at a train station. Ideas will come to you in a flash! However, to create the overall image, you will need to work hard, plan effectively and have a vision in your head that you can transform onto a mood board, eventually creating the image for real! Do not forget to enjoy yourself and photograph your work as you progress with your theme.

There are two learning outcomes in this unit. The learner will be able to:

- plan an image
- create an image.

Historical
Event in the past

Fantasy
Unrestricted imagination

PLAN AN IMAGE

During this part of the unit you will learn:

- how to identify media images to create a theme
- the purpose of a mood board
- how to present a mood board
- the concepts of advertising to a target audience
- the salon requirements for preparing yourself, your work area and your client.

IDENTIFYING MEDIA IMAGES

For your assessment you will need to create a mood board based on one of the following themes:

- a competition
- a themed event
- a special occasion.

From the above themes, you will need to create a look from the following options:

- a **historical** look
- a **fantasy** look
- a special occasion.

MEDIA

Whichever look you choose to create from the above themes, you will need to consider the following:

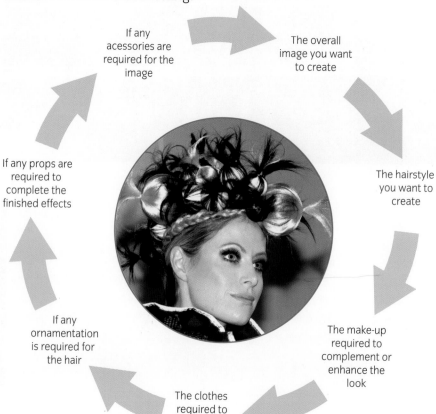

- If any acessories are required for the image
- The overall image you want to create
- The hairstyle you want to create
- The make-up required to complement or enhance the look
- The clothes required to create and capture the image
- If any ornamentation is required for the hair
- If any props are required to complete the finished effects

 SmartScreen 212 handout 3 and worksheets 1 and 3

PURPOSE OF A MOOD BOARD

A mood board can come in many formats. It does not have to be a 'board', although this is usually the simplest way to present your work to others. It could be a poster design or a scrapbook that shows images, text and samples of materials that helped you to create your work of art!

The main purpose for creating a mood board is to present the linking ideas from the research you have undertaken, showing the journey you took in obtaining your inspiration for creating your image. A mood board:

- shows a collection of ideas
- reflects the thought processes behind the image to be created
- demonstrates the inspiration behind the image to be created
- displays a collection of key colours, images, materials and sketches.

To help create your mood board, you could use:

- media images – newspaper or magazine articles, music videos, Internet sites or TV programmes relating to the industry or the theme of your event
- photographs of where your inspiration came from
- sketches of ideas you have had along the way
- materials – textures, fabrics or materials that have given you a brainwave or a motivating idea.

HOW TO PRESENT A MOOD BOARD

Your mood board needs to be large enough to show your first ideas through to your end results. Make it colourful and exciting but ensure it tells your story.

Your mood board should outline how your thought processes and ideas were developed to create your image. It shows links from the inspiring ideas to your creative thoughts and the end result – your model. You should describe what technical skills you expect to be using to create your 'vision' and how you would advertise/present your idea to others.

Attach your photos, sketches, magazine/newspaper clippings, showing the hair, clothes, make-up, nails, etc and add brief text descriptions about your ideas and how the images link to your theme.

Add combinations of images, such as the fabrics and materials used that enthused you. These can be anything, from drinks cans – as used to set hair in Lady Gaga's music video – to candy floss or chopsticks. Add the make-up, nail colours/art, hair products, equipment and technical skills that you will be using in the mood board – in fact add anything and everything you used that inspired you.

You might need to present your mood board to an audience, explaining what motivated you and where you obtained this inspiration from, so be prepared to talk about your creational journey too.

SmartScreen 212 worksheet 4

ACTIVITY

Search for the following on the Internet:
- avant-garde hairstyles – you will be amazed at what materials stylists use in the hair to create their images
- media make-up and creative facial art to create an image
- creative nail designs that will help to inspire you.

ADVERTISING TO YOUR TARGET AUDIENCE

If you are planning an event, you will need to consider the **concept** of the event and who your targeted audience is.

If you are putting on a show, you might need to advertise the event to ensure that you have an audience on the day. If the show has a fantasy theme and is a loud, high-colour, funky event, then your target audience is more likely to be younger. If the show is about 'hair through the ages' then it will appeal to a wider audience.

If your salon is demonstrating the skills of the staff, then you will want to capture new trade and custom, so you need to ensure that the invite list or advertisements are distributed further afield and not just to the regular client base.

A target audience can be anybody:
- your family and friends – to show them what you are learning at college

Concept
Idea

HANDY HINTS
Your attention to detail and planning of who to invite is as crucial as planning your image.

- a school – promoting your college
- in-house – showing other learners what you can do.

On a larger scale, the audience could be 'brides-to-be' visiting a wedding fare, or potential clients for a clothes designer. It does not matter how large or small your audience is, as long as you promote it to the target audience.

SALON REQUIREMENTS

You will need to prepare yourself, your work area and then your client.

PREPARING YOURSELF

On the day you create your masterpiece make sure you follow these steps:

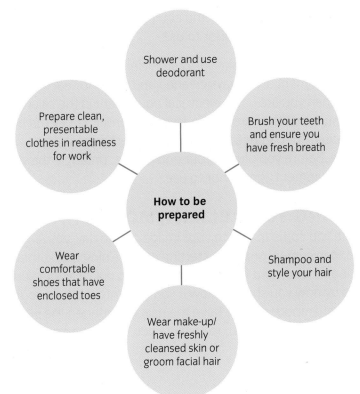

ACTIVITY

If you were hosting a show tomorrow, how would you present yourself and what would you wear? Think about comfort and working in a busy environment where you might get hot and bothered.

PREPARING YOUR WORK AREA

When preparing the salon for your client/model's arrival, you need to follow the usual standards of safety and hygiene. Ensure that your work area is clean, hair free and sterilised prior to starting. Wipe the chairs and work surfaces down with hot soapy water and spray with disinfectant. Prepare your tools and equipment, making sure they have been cleaned and sterilised prior to use.

If you are working off-site, take spray sterilisers with you; ensure your tools and equipment are always cleaned and ready for each model/situation. When you are using electrical equipment in the salon or off-site, ensure that they are in good working order; check the body, wires and plugs for damage, and follow the Electricity at Work Regulations. Before you plug in your equipment, untangle the wires and check the equipment again prior to use.

PREPARING YOUR CLIENT/MODEL

By the time you come to create your image on the day, you should have practised many times, probably starting on a training block, then creating it on friends and family, before trying it out on your client/model. So by now you should know if you prefer to work on your model's hair freshly shampooed, or to have the hair shampooed the night before. Whichever you prefer, make sure you agree the arrangements with your model (or client).

 SmartScreen 212 worksheet 2

You will probably want to start creating your vision using a blank canvas. Ensure the hair is free of products (unless you have requested otherwise) and the face is clean and make-up free. Depending on the style of clothing you have chosen for the image, you might even need to discuss what type of underwear your model should wear – your image will not look so good if you have visual bra straps or strap marks.

PLANNING THE IMAGE

Preparation and planning are essential. Make sure you are organised and work in a methodical manner; good planning is the key to your success! Planning and creating your mood board will be calm and leisurely compared to creating your finished image on the actual day. To help your presentation run smoothly, plan in advance, think about what could go wrong and plan for that too!

WHY DON'T YOU...
If you are working off-site, you could visit the work area in advance of the day, in case you need to take extra items such as extension leads for your electrical equipment, etc.

INDUSTRY TIP

Make sure your model can step into and out of any clothes she is wearing, so as not to disturb the hairstyle/make-up when it is finished, and damaging your creation.

Research

You will need to decide individually or as a group what your theme is going to be. When this has been decided, you will need to research ideas for your image. You can use the following resources to find ideas for creating your total look:

HANDY HINTS

Do not forget to gown and protect your client/model; you will need to protect their clothing.

HANDY HINTS

Do not forget about your PPE – you should wear an apron to protect your clothes and gloves to protect your hands.

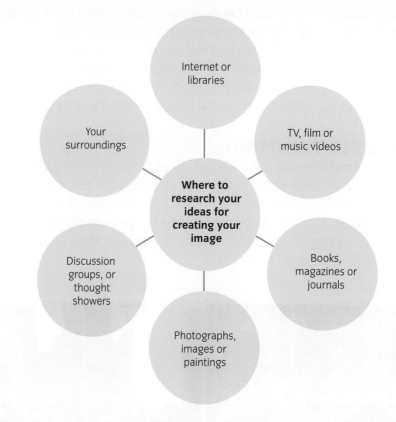

Internet or libraries

Your surroundings

TV, film or music videos

Where to research your ideas for creating your image

Discussion groups, or thought showers

Books, magazines or journals

Photographs, images or paintings

ACTIVITY

Discuss with your colleagues ideas for other resources or places you could visit as research for ideas.

Planning for a competition

If your event is a competition, this could be a salon or college in-house competition or a regional event. These could have a set theme or have a variety of options, such as cut and colour, hair up, gents' cut and style or a fantasy look. Whichever event you have decided to enter into, plan, practise and prepare.

Planning for a themed event – fashion show

Again, this could be a college or salon fashion show, showing off the talents of the salon staff, or an in-house college fashion show for students in hair and beauty. If the theme is decided by a group vote, it might not be your first choice. If this is the case, try to get into the spirit of what the show is all about and take this opportunity to experiment and 'think outside the box'. Let your imagination and creativity go wild.

SmartScreen 212 handout 1

Semi-professional fashion show

Your themed event might be for a clothes designer, who has asked your salon/college to style the hair for the show. If this is the case, it is likely that the clothes designer will want some input into the ideas behind the hairstyles and make-up look. Listen to their ideas and, of course, make some suggestions of your own. You will need to know about the clothes that the models will be wearing, to ensure the hair and make-up matches the style of clothing. If the clothes designed are wacky and way out, the hair and make-up must be too. If the clothes are more traditional daytime wear, this should also be reflected in the hairstyles and make-up.

Planning for a special occasion

If the image you are creating is to reflect a special occasion, this might be a wedding day or a prom-night theme. You would need to consider the required look ensuring the hair, make-up, nails and dress complement one another.

PREPARATION OF MATERIALS AND CLOTHING

When planning your image, you might want to write checklists or you will need to have a good memory to make sure you do not forget anything on the day. Sometimes, creating an image can involve the stylist starting early in the morning, and when you start it is go, go, go!

By the time you are ready to create your image, you will have a completed mood board to help remind you of what you need, but it is always best to also have a written list to hand.

Depending on your chosen theme, you might need accessories that could range from a bridal gown for a special occasion, or tree branches to add to your competition entry, or a pair of Disney Mickey Mouse ears to create your fantasy image. These are not the sort of things you can pick up from the local hair wholesalers if you forget them on the day!

To help you decide on where to get your clothing and accessories from, consider the following ideas:

SmartScreen 212 handout 2

ACTIVITY

Discuss with your colleagues other places you could visit to obtain your clothes and accessories.

As you prepare to create your image make sure you have the following:

- your chosen accessories
- the model's clothing
- the required make-up
- artificial nails or polish (and spare nails – just in case)
- false eyelashes
- pins, grips, styling products
- plenty of hairspray – your finishing product saviour.

Tick these off your checklist as you prepare your working area.

ACTIVITY

If you were planning a bridal themed event, what resources could help you save the day? List all the tools, materials, clothes, accessories, products and tools/equipment you would need for this event.

THEMES AND IMAGES

You will need to choose a theme for your mood board and an image to create.

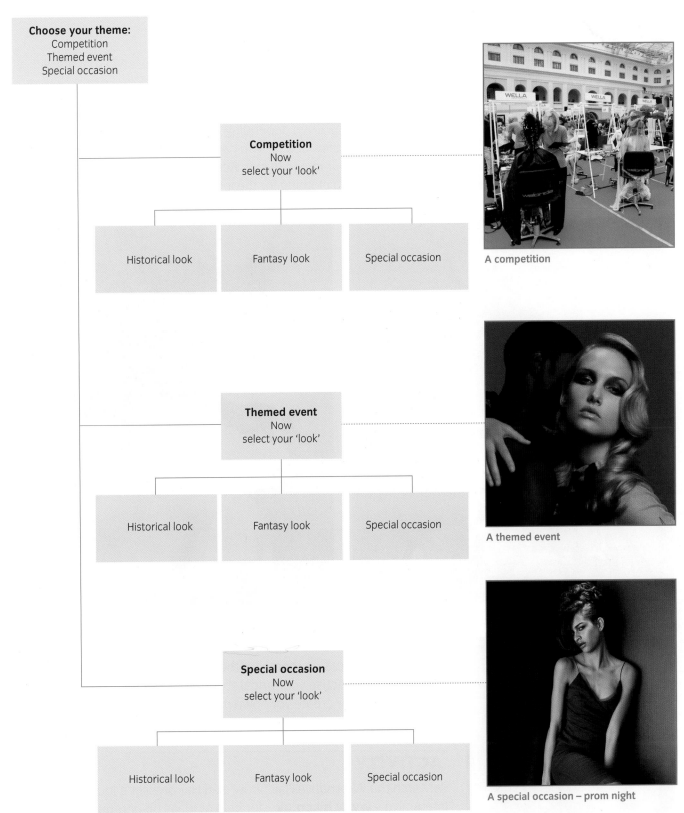

Choose your theme:
Competition
Themed event
Special occasion

Competition
Now
select your 'look'

Historical look

Fantasy look

Special occasion

A competition

Themed event
Now
select your 'look'

Historical look

Fantasy look

Special occasion

A themed event

Special occasion
Now
select your 'look'

Historical look

Fantasy look

Special occasion

A special occasion – prom night

Competition

Depending on whether this theme is to be held in-house at your salon/ college, or at a regional event, the theme might be decided for you. If your college is holding a competition for your assessment, then a theme needs to be decided.

Historical look

If the look is historical, you will need to choose one style that fits with a historical image and takes into account the hair, make-up and clothes.

Fantasy look

If it is a fantasy look, then depending on whether it is open for you to decide on the fantasy look, or you have been given a title theme, you will need to create your image to suit. Remember to consider the hair, make-up, nails and clothing for the look you want to create.

Special occasion

If it is a special occasion theme for the competition, you might get the opportunity to practise your bridal styles. Whether you go for a traditional bride or create your own masterpiece – this is for you to decide. You choose the hair-style, make-up and the dress.

ACTIVITY

Research the 'Alternative Hair Show' and Hairdresser's Journal Interactive – **www.hji.co.uk** – for help or ideas on entering competitions and creating your own avant-garde image. You should also search for ideas on how you want the nails, make-up and clothing to look.

Themed event

This has lots of room for flexibility and creativity. If your themed event includes a historical look, a fantasy look or a special occasion then you can pretty much create any look you want.

Historical look

Creating a themed event based on a historical look, could include:

Rock/Goth

Hair and beauty in Ancient Britain

Hair and beauty in Ancient Greece

The history of hair and beauty in Ancient Britain

Hair and beauty trends from the past – such as Punk, Rock, Goth, etc

The history of hair and beauty in Ancient Egypt, Rome, Greece, etc

Historical look

Hair, fashion and make-up from a chosen decade

Hair, fashion and make-up through the ages – '20s, '40s, '60s, '80s, etc

Hair and make-up from the '60s

Hair and make-up from the '20s

Step-by-step: creating a historical look

STEP 1 – Cover and secure the hair with a headband. Cleanse, tone and moisturise the skin in preparation for the make-up.

STEP 2 – After completing the base which includes applying a foundation concealer and powder, create your look on the eyes.

STEP 3 – Define the eyebrows for a more dramatic look.

STEP 4 – Add blusher to the cheek area. Highlight and shade areas as needed.

STEP 5 – Define the lips with your chosen lip colour.

STEP 6 – Check the finished result of the make-up.

STEP 7 – Dry set the hair with heated rollers and comb out the curls into soft waves.

STEP 8 – Dress the curls into your chosen style and secure with grips.

STEP 9 – Ensure your client is happy with the end result.

ACTIVITY

Research on the Internet 'The History of Hair' for ideas on hair through the ages. **www.ukhairdressers.com** provides information on the history of hair. Wikipedia provides information on 'The History of Cosmetics'.

Fantasy look

Open your mind and go wild, you have the chance to create a fantasy image, so basically anything goes!

This could include:

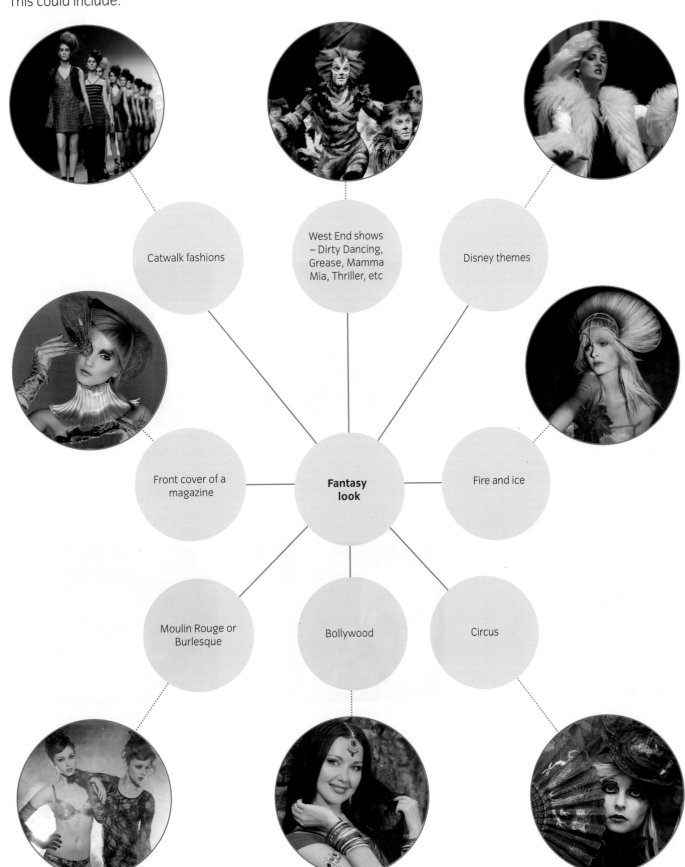

Catwalk fashions

West End shows – Dirty Dancing, Grease, Mamma Mia, Thriller, etc

Disney themes

Front cover of a magazine

Fantasy look

Fire and ice

Moulin Rouge or Burlesque

Bollywood

Circus

Step-by-step: fantasy themed image 1

STEP 1 – Cover and secure the hair with a headband. Cleanse, tone and moisturise the skin in preparation for the make-up.

STEP 2 – Using white face paint, apply evenly all over the face. You need to use quite a lot of the face paint to avoid a streaky look.

STEP 3 – Use vibrant colours on the eyes to create your fantasy image.

STEP 4 – Personalise your look to create a more dramatic effect.

STEP 5 – Add a contrasting bright colour to the cheeks either side of the nose to create definition.

STEP 6 – Present your finished fantasy image.

Step-by-step: fantasy themed image 2

STEP 1 – Prepare the hair and face for the service.

STEP 2 – Starting at the bottom and at the back, tong the hair to create curls.

STEP 3 – Continue tonging the hair towards the crown area, taking small sections.

STEP 4 – Ensure you curl the hair all the way to the root, for an even result throughout.

STEP 5 – Pin the front sections up securely to create some height.

STEP 6 – Finish creating your image by adding some dramatic make-up and ornamentation.

ACTIVITY

Search on the Internet for themed venues – they might give you inspirational ideas for a theme, or even props that you could use to create your image.

Special occasion

If you choose a special occasion as the theme for your image, then you might create a prom-night style or a traditional bridal look.

Fantasy look

People are becoming more creative with their weddings these days, so a themed wedding might be your choice. A winter wonderland wedding, or a Las Vegas style, or even a Charlie and the Chocolate Factory themed wedding (as featured on *Don't Tell the Bride*) are not unheard of for wedding themes.

Historical look

Going back in history is also quite popular at weddings. The 1940s are making a comeback, so you might choose a historical look for your special occasion.

Step-by-step: special occasion 1

STEP 1 – Prepare the hair for the service.

STEP 2 – Section the hair from the top and apply hairspray, then set the hair into a barrel curl. Secure with pin-curl clips.

STEP 3 – Check the curls are balanced and in proportion as you work through the head.

STEP 4 – Ensure the curls sit on the base, to create maximum lift where required.

STEP 5 – Continue to secure the hair in place carefully with the pin-curl clips.

STEP 6 – Continue to roll all of the hair into barrel curls.

STEP 7 – Check that all curls are secured and apply more hair spray and allow the hair to set into place.

STEP 8 – Dress out the curls, and add a row of overlapping grips just above the occipital bone.

STEP 9 – Back-comb or back-brush the hair to prepare a secure base.

STEP 10 – Smooth the top layer of back-brushing and roll the hair into a horizontal roll.

STEP 11 – Secure the roll in place and smooth stray hairs with a comb and hair spray.

STEP 12 – Dress the front into a wave and present your finished image.

Step-by-step: special occasion 2

STEP 1 – Prepare the hair for the service.

STEP 2 – Style the hair off of the face and secure a doughnut ring into position.

STEP 3 – Make sure the doughnut ring is secure by using grips and pins.

STEP 4 – Roll the hair around the doughnut ring and secure in place.

STEP 5 – Smooth the hair, apply finishing products and secure any ornamentation in place.

STEP 6 – Dress the front sections and present your finished image.

> **HANDY HINTS**
>
> Practise a variety of ideas on your training block to see if they are **feasible**, before trying them out on your model or presenting your final image on your training block. Your training block will not get bored of you practising – a model might!

Feasible

Possible

CREATE AN IMAGE

During this part of the unit you will learn:

- the correct way to communicate and behave
- technical skills used to create an image
- how to evaluate the effectiveness of the theme-based image
- how to follow safe and hygienic working practices.

COMMUNICATING AND BEHAVING APPROPRIATELY

If you are planning a group presentation, show or competition, it will require a whole-team approach to ensure that it runs smoothly and the day itself goes to plan. The lead up might require team meetings to identify everyone's responsibilities. Draw up a schedule of who is doing what, where and when and discuss issues arising from the meetings tactfully with others. Always treat your colleagues with respect and address any issues politely, clearly and calmly. Make sure that you follow any instructions that you have been given and be a team player, assisting others where you can.

On the day you present your image you are likely to be running on adrenaline, but you might also get a little stressed and nervous. This is quite normal – even celebrity hairdressers get nervous! Just think of how James Pryce and Richard Ward – from Richard Ward's salon – must have felt, styling Kate Middleton's hair on her wedding day. A royal wedding – the biggest wedding of the century, with millions of people all over the world looking at her hairstyle – now that's pressure!

To help you deal with the pressure on the day, make sure you:

- plan the event
- follow the plan!

> **HANDY HINTS**
>
> There is no 'I' in TEAM! Work harmoniously together and create a great team effort that your salon/college can be proud of.

On the day you present your image, demonstrate positive body language and be confident. Believe in yourself, you already know you can do it, you have practised and you have prepared – you are ready!

If you are working in a group situation and are running ahead of schedule, you can help others by responding to their needs. If you are working on a live model (rather than a training block), make sure you check she is comfortable and offer some refreshments. If your model is nervous, speak to her in a reassuring manner to put her at ease.

TECHNICAL SKILLS USED TO CREATE AN IMAGE

You will need the following technical skills to create your image:

- Hairdressing skills – the most important technical skills you will use to create a theme will be your styling and dressing skills.
- Some basic beauty skills such as make-up, and possibly nails.

HAIRDRESSING SKILLS

You are likely to use waving, curling, crimping or straightening techniques and add hair or accessories. You might need to add colour to the hair, cut it to shape and length, and possibly even relax the curls already present in the hair.

MAKE-UP

The make-up look might be subtle daytime or bridal, or media make-up, showing dramatic effects for fantasy themes.

 SmartScreen 212 handout 5

Assist others and work as a team

If the application of make-up is not within your skill area, you could arrange to have a make-up artist or beauty therapist complete this for you; make sure you plan this in advance of the day.

If you want to apply your own model's make-up, first design the effect on paper, choosing the colour scheme and look, and then practise on your model's face.

NAIL ART

The great thing about artificial nails is that you can buy many varieties of glue-on nails from shops and wholesalers. This means that you can often do this yourself, for a reasonable cost. You should always experiment with the required look in advance and carry spare nails on the day. If a professional is not applying the nails they might not last as well, so be prepared.

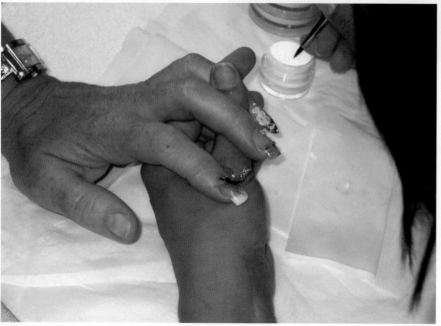

Of course, the hard work and technical skills do not stop there. This is a total look you are creating – you also need to consider the clothing and co-ordination of the dress. You will need to blend in the hairstyle with the make-up and the clothing. Think about the detail of your image, so it all comes together to create the overall look you are trying to achieve – a keen eye for detail is essential. Make sure you check the balance of the style regularly. Stand back from your model and look at the image you have created. Use fresh eyes and try to imagine what other people are seeing.

AVOIDING DISASTERS AND DRAMAS

After all your careful preparation and planning, what could possibly go wrong on the day? Well, hopefully nothing, but always plan for the worst-case scenario, then you will know that you have covered all options.

ACTIVITY

In pairs or groups, consider what could go wrong on the day and discuss how you could plan to avoid the problems.

EVALUATING THE EFFECTIVENESS OF THE THEME-BASED IMAGE

During your preparation you will need to evaluate how effectively your theme-based image is progressing. After the event you will need to evaluate the service you have provided and whether it met with expectations.

HANDY HINTS

Write on a record card or in a journal the comments that you received that were valuable and those you learnt from.

HANDY HINTS

If you identify any requirements for your model's/client's future treatments, write these on the client record card. This will enable you to have a record in readiness for her next appointment, or if you have the opportunity to use her as a model again.

HANDY HINTS

Ask your model for feedback; what does she think of the image you created?

HANDY HINTS

Keep photographs of your work each time you practise your image, so you can see your progress and evaluate it too.

SmartScreen 212 handout 4

SmartScreen 212 revision guidance, revision cards and sample questions

You might receive feedback from team meetings along the way, and have the opportunity to offer and receive constructive verbal feedback. This will be particularly useful when you are planning the event, and you should always listen to this feedback as it might help you to develop and improve your plan.

During and after you have created your image, you might receive feedback from your salon managers or college tutors, and occasionally from your peers or model. When you have worked hard on a task and someone criticises you, constructively or otherwise, it can hurt! Try not to get upset by the feedback. Instead, consider how you can benefit from it. Constructive feedback is important – you will learn from any errors you made and you can act on the advice to improve and develop your weaker areas for next time. If the overall result gets improved because of the comments/feedback you receive, then you have learnt something and progressed with your skills; this can only be a positive outcome.

SELF-EVALUATION

Throughout the planning, construction, development and creation of your mood board and image, you should be evaluating yourself. You will be using a combination of technical skills, some of which you might not have mixed together before. You will be learning new skills along the way and you should evaluate your progress.

Often in life, we are our worst critics, so keep a diary/journal of how you have felt on your journey to creating your image based on a theme.

- Do you feel it went well?
- Could it have gone any better?
- How would you have changed it?
- What would/could you do differently next time?

You should also evaluate your mood board. Did it work well and present your final image effectively?

SAFETY CONSIDERATIONS

As with all previous chapters, the health and safety of you, your model (or client in some instances) and those around you are vital! Preparing your image can put you under pressure and there might be deadlines and timescales that need to be met. However, you must always follow health and safety legislation.

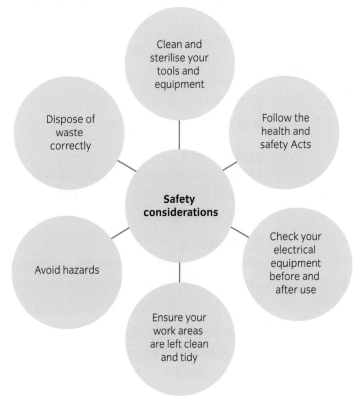

DISPOSAL OF WASTE

At the end of the event, when you have completed your finished look and you pack away your tools, ensure you dispose of any waste materials properly. Recycle where you can, dispose of empty hairspray cans following the manufacturers' instructions, so as not to harm the environment. Any contaminated waste needs to be disposed of in a lidded bin.

Turn to page 485 for the answers.

1 **Statement 1**
The main purpose of a mood board is to present ideas and inspiration.

Statement 2
Mood boards could also be in the form of a scrap book or poster.

Which one of the following is correct for the above statements?

	Statement 1	Statement 2
a	True	True
b	True	False
c	False	True
d	False	False

2 Which one of the following would **not** usually be shown on a mood board?

a Photographs and sketches.

b Textured materials and decorations.

c Financial costs and budget.

d Newspaper clippings and adverts.

3 Which one of the following is the **most** important consideration to take into account before planning an event?

a The materials to create the mood board.

b The model's hair length and style.

c The concept and target audience.

d The cost of advertising the show.

4 When working off-site on an event, it is good practice to

a Take a training block in case the model is late.

b Take spare equipment and sanitising wipes.

c Ensure that hair is previously shampooed.

d Ensure that client records are kept.

5 When creating a theme for a fashion show, it is important to

a Stick to your own original ideas to minimise confusion.

b Only use the fashion designer's ideas as she will know the best look.

c Agree and stick to the designer's ideas in advance to save time.

d Be flexible and creative as ideas progress.

6 **Statement 1**
When sourcing clothing and accessories, remember that the model might have a good range that can be used.

Statement 2
Making your own accessories with off-cuts from market stalls is a good way to keep costs down.

Which one of the following is correct for the above statements?

	Statement 1	Statement 2
a	True	True
b	True	False
c	False	True
d	False	False

7 Which one of the following would be described as a fantasy look?

a Burlesque.

b War time.

c Egyptian.

d The '60s.

8 **Statement 1**
Using questionnaires to obtain feedback is one method that could be used to help evaluate an event's success.

Statement 2
Record any comments that are received after the event as they might help to focus ideas for the future.

Which **one** of the following is correct for the above statements?

	Statement 1	Statement 2
a	True	True
b	True	False
c	False	True
d	False	False

CASE STUDY: FIONA CHANDLER DAY

I am a creative director at Richard Ward, who looked after Pippa Middleton, chief bridesmaid at the wedding of the Duke and Duchess of Cambridge.

I left sixth form college to go to Brighton Technical College to do a City & Guilds course. I passed this with flying colours and went on to win several competitions for Freestyle Exotic Hair.

I came up to London as a qualified hairstylist but took a job as a junior with Hugh Green, who is now the personal hairdresser to the Duchess of Cornwall. Working with Hugh taught me the skills of how to dress hair and create the most stunning chignons, which today for many is a dying art.

After working as a stylist with him for four years, I left to work at Neville Daniel on Sloane Street, where my reputation and loyal following began to grow. Over the years I worked at a couple of other Chelsea salons, finally returning to Neville Daniel and what was to become Richard Ward Hair & Metrospa. I have been part of the team with Richard and Hellen for 19 years, since the beginning.

Within the hairdressing world it felt like a huge accolade to be involved with the royal wedding. From the very positive public response to all our work I feel a new energy and I am really enjoying still being part of the hairdressing industry.

213
DISPLAY STOCK TO PROMOTE SALES IN A SALON

Salon competition is tough, there is no doubt about it, so your salon must compete to encourage new trade. Over the last decade, the purchasing of salon-branded products has increased while most people's 'spare money' has decreased. But beautiful, eye-catching, exciting and enticing display showcases are the main reason for the increase in salon retail sales. It is vital that your salon's display of stock is attractive to the client and artistically exhibited.

There are two learning outcomes in this unit. The learner will be able to:

- prepare the display area
- maintain and dismantle the display area.

During this part of the unit you will learn the:

- safety considerations for displaying stock
- purpose of a display
- information required to display stock effectively.

SAFETY CONSIDERATIONS FOR DISPLAYING STOCK

Before you begin unpacking your stock boxes and start stacking shelves, let's look at a few safety considerations that you will need to be aware of, or reminded about.

SAFE WORKING AND HYGIENIC PRACTICES

When displaying the salon's stock, you will need to follow all the relevant health and safety regulations and keep all areas clean and tidy. When you start a display area or change a current one, you should choose a suitable time during your working day in which to do so. Make sure that you do not disrupt the daily running of the salon and block any exits or walkways with boxes as you unpack them and load the shelves.

It might be a good idea to organise the display area first thing in the morning or last thing at night, before the salon closes for the day. Also, choose a quieter working day rather than a busy Saturday, when you might be needed elsewhere in the salon and the waiting areas and reception areas are at their busiest.

If you are stocking a salon reception or waiting area, ensure that all surfaces are wiped clean and sterilised with a disinfectant spray. If you are updating or maintaining a display area, always make sure the stock displayed is clean and dust free.

Retail stand and tidy reception area

THE MANUAL HANDLING OPERATIONS REGULATIONS 1992

When stocking the shelves with products and equipment, you will need to move boxes of products around the salon. This is called manual handling. Remember to lift these boxes correctly so you do not injure yourself. Follow the Manual Handling Operations Regulations 1992.

Your employer's responsibility under these regulations is to carry out **risk assessments** on all employees for manual lifting, to make certain they are able to lift boxes without causing injury.

Your responsibility under these regulations is to always ask yourself, 'Can I lift this?' If the answer is no, then don't! Ask for someone to move the boxes for you, to the area in which you are working, or unpack the box **systematically** by removing the contents one at a time.

Risk assessments
Evaluations of potential risk

Systematically
In a methodical manner

If you are able to lift it, remember these tips:

Step-by-step guide to lifting correctly

STEP 1 – Bend your knees.

STEP 2 – Keep your back straight.

STEP 3 – Lift the weight with your legs.

STEP 4 – Check the area in front is clear and hazard free.

When stocking shelves, you must stand on a stepladder or similar to reach higher shelves. Never stand on tables that might tip up or break, or salon chairs that might swivel as you stand – you will be putting yourself at risk of injury. Be sensible and safe at all times to avoid injuries.

THE CONTROL OF SUBSTANCES HAZARDOUS TO HEALTH REGULATIONS (COSHH) 2002

Hazardous substances must be:

- **S**tored correctly – in a cold, dry place
- **H**andled correctly – using PPE
- **U**sed correctly – following MFIs
- **D**isposed of correctly – following local by-laws, salon policy and MFIs.

Your responsibilities under these regulations are to follow **SHUD**, read and follow the MFIs, and follow local by-laws and your salon policy.

Your employer's responsibilities under these regulations would be to supply you with PPE and make sure waste disposal is suitable for the environment and follows the local by-laws.

The MFIs will instruct you on how to store, handle, use and dispose of the substances; the local by-laws will tell you how to dispose of the substances and their packaging to suit the environment. They follow the local authority's guidelines on waste and refuse. Your salon policy will explain where to store them and where to dispose of them in the workplace.

PERSONAL PROTECTIVE EQUIPMENT

When preparing stock for the display area, you will be storing substances. Although you might not come into direct contact with these products, you should be cleaning the items ready for the display, so it would be good practice to protect your clothes with an apron and wear gloves to protect your hands when you clean and restock.

THE CITY & GUILDS TEXTBOOK

HANDLING EQUIPMENT

Displayed equipment will look much more appealing outside of its packaging than displayed in its box. You can creatively display it across the box, so the packaging is visible, or display it on its own. If it is electrical equipment and you are going to plug it in for demonstration purposes, check that all wires are tangle free and complete your normal checks for electrical appliances. Ensure you follow the Electricity at Work Regulations if you are using electrical items.

HANDY HINTS

Ideally, you would demonstrate the electrical equipment to a client using the salon's stock, rather than switching on a retail item from the cabinet.

DISPLAY POSITIONS

Where possible, try to keep your display and stock items away from direct sunlight. This will prevent fading and sun damage to the packaging. The manufacturers' instructions might also say to avoid high temperatures, and any displays in a sunny window position will get very hot behind the glass window. This could cause the product condition to deteriorate and in rare but severe cases, there could be a risk of fire/explosion. Alternatively, you could use empty boxes/bottles in sunny positions.

You will need to give serious consideration to suitable locations of your displays; they need to be at the forefront of your clients' focus point. If the displays are fixed, permanent stands, then this will be out of your control. If you have been tasked to present a temporary display, then you will need to consider where the most suitable position will be.

SmartScreen 213 worksheet 4

THE PURPOSE OF A DISPLAY

Ask yourself why your salon displays stock. When you enter retail premises, whether this is a clothing store, a department store or a perfume counter, a lot of thought would have gone into the eye-catching display of the goods.

It is paramount that your display attracts your clients' eye. If clients do not look at the display, then the likelihood of a sale is dramatically reduced. Equally, if the display area is untidy, too busy or unattractive, then the purpose of the display is lost.

Purpose of a salon display area

- To attract clients
- To increase sales
- To increase client awareness

ATTRACTING CLIENTS

To a client, a well-promoted display looks attractive and demonstrates a professional environment, which is both reassuring and encouraging to clients.

An effective display can attract new clients into the salon and encourage regular clients to keep returning. We all like to indulge ourselves once in a while and hair-care products are very popular treats. If clients are spending a lot of money having their hair coloured and styled, then they often want to invest in the maintenance of the look. Although purchasing retail is an additional cost for hair-care, it is often justified by your client as a necessity; this is good news for salons.

INCREASING SALES

Promoting retail and equipment to your clients is not only good for your clients, but it is financially beneficial to the salon and staff members, for reaching commission targets.

Selling should never be forced and unnatural. You are not 'flogging' an unwanted Christmas gift, but promoting the longevity of the style, and supplying your services and expertise. YOU are the expert and your client wants and needs your guidance.

Selling should not be something to dread, it should be embraced. When you have created a beautiful style for your client, you want them to get the best they can from it, and so does your client. If they leave the salon without purchasing suitable products and use their own home-care products, your client might struggle to maintain the new look and it will not look at its best. Your client is an advert for your salon, so it is important that they have the correct products and equipment.

INCREASING CLIENT AWARENESS

We are naturally 'nosey' people; we cannot resist looking at an attractive display area. It is like window shopping, which everyone does. Of course, window shopping can lead to a purchase, so it is very important to get the window right.

When clients are gazing at your attractive presentations, they might come across a product that is new to them, they are attracted to, they have read about or they are interested in. Giving your client a chance to look at the displays helps to increase their awareness of what is on the market and trigger an interest. This gives you a perfect opening in which you can make recommendations and close a sale.

THE INFORMATION REQUIRED TO DISPLAY STOCK EFFECTIVELY

Firstly, you need to know where your display is going to be located. Is it a fixed position display area, or a temporary promotional display?

LOCATION

The most suitable locations in the salon for displays are:

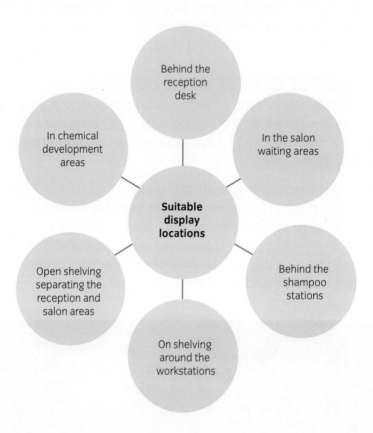

FIXED POSITION DISPLAY

Fixed position displays are likely to be either:

- new showcases or displays in the salon
- the updating of a previous showcase/display.

TEMPORARY DISPLAY

Temporary displays might advertise special offers, new products or re-launches. They are likely to be displayed in the reception area or in heavy-duty cardboard display cases provided by the manufacturer of the new product.

NEW DISPLAY AREAS

When setting up a new display area, you will need to consider the following:

- What stock and equipment do you require?
- Do you need materials to enhance the display?
- What are the principles behind the display?
- What is your theme (if you have one)?
- What colours are you working with?
- What advertising materials do you have or need?
- Do you have any salon images and photographs that can be displayed alongside the products?

If you have been supplied with some advertising materials from the manufacturer, you need to decide where to position these to maximise the number of potential sales and allow as many people as possible to look at the display area.

If you are labelling the products, make sure they are high quality, accurate, clearly marked and you have followed the legal requirements.

If the salon staff have had professional photographs taken of their work, you could exhibit these alongside the displays. These work particularly well if you advertise the products, equipment and even colours that have been used to create the image.

SmartScreen 213 handout 1

MAINTAIN AND DISMANTLE THE DISPLAY AREA

During this part of the unit you will learn:

- how to display stock effectively
- how to maintain a display
- the legal requirements.

EFFECTIVE DISPLAYS

When you have decided on the location, you will need to categorise the items. If you are selling more than one manufacturer's brand, decide whether you will sell all brands of shampoos and conditioners together, followed by a styling and finishing product section, or whether you want to keep each manufacturer's products together.

You will also need to decide if you want to promote your equipment in a section on its own or alongside the styling and finishing products.

Whatever theme you choose, ensure the display is not too fussy or overcrowded. Clients could be put off picking up a product if they think it might cause a 'domino' effect on the surrounding products and topple them over.

To make certain the display is effective and successful regarding sales, you should sell and advertise what the salon uses – the stock must match the services offered in the salon. You could sell trial sizes or give away free sample sachets.

TYPES OF DISPLAYS

Depending on what your salon already has in place, you could display your stock in a cabinet or showcase. Ideally this would have solid lockable doors at the bottom, with a glass or wooden front area for display. Alternatively you could display your stock in glass or acrylic cubes that can be built up, stacked in various ways or suspended from the ceiling.

213 DISPLAY STOCK TO PROMOTE SALES IN A SALON

INDUSTRY TIP

Some manufacturers supply their own retail stands, and in some cases insist their products are displayed this way.

ACTIVITY

Search on the Internet for companies that design displays for large companies; this will give you some inspiring ideas.

MAKING THE DISPLAY ATTRACTIVE

It is vital that the display is attractive and eye-catching, as this will increase your sales.

If your salon offers beauty treatments and barbering services, you must ensure that you promote all areas and cover suitable ranges for all relevant services.

You need to consider your target audience. If you are creating a display for your college, you must consider the cost of the product range. Some clients visit a college to give young people the chance to learn hairdressing; others choose this option because the price is generally substantially reduced. Along with considering the financial status of your clients, you will need to consider their age and gender! Some manufacturers promote funky, bright-coloured, modern products aimed at young people, while others promote ranges suited to the older market.

When you 'think' you have finished creating your display, always ask other people for their opinion and take any constructive criticism on board. At the end of the day you want the display to be effective, so if one person does not like it, your clients might not either!

HANDY HINTS

When you have finished your display, walk out of the salon and come back in to check it with fresh eyes; always check the display from different angles and viewpoints in the salon.

At the close of business, make sure the retail and stock displays are lit up so they can be seen by passing trade. Remember to protect the environment where possible and use energy-saving bulbs.

Advertising

Generally speaking, the manufacturers will provide salons with promotional advertising materials for their stock. This ensures that the advertising is accurate, set to a standard and uniform across all salons.

Advertising materials can be in the form of wall or suspended window posters, banner stands, pop-up stands and/or leaflets. These should be displayed in prominent areas of the salon, as well as near to the display.

Alongside the manufacturers' advertising materials, you could promote the stock with additional images or photos, or use DVDs of the products' features and benefits, shown on a PC or flat screen TV in the salon waiting areas.

RECEPTION AND WAITING AREAS

The main area of your display should be showcased with plenty of eye-catching stock that is well-positioned. Your prime location will be in full view of any client that walks in and, where possible, available to people walking past the salon too.

You might decide to feature small quantities of the full-sized products, covering the full range, near the point of sale area. These can be handled and demonstrated to your client for smell and texture, and they can see the size and price of the product.

AT THE SHAMPOO AREA

Around the salon shampoo area, you should display the range of shampoos, conditioners and treatments that are available to your client for home maintenance. This is a prime location, allowing the assistant to discuss with your client, during the shampoo process, what they are using on the client's hair and why. For the benefit of the client, the assistant can demonstrate what they are using, explain why they are using it and let the client feel and smell the product, enabling them to see and try the product before they purchase it.

SmartScreen 213 handout 2 and worksheets 1, 2 and 3

AT WORKSTATIONS

It is often an effective way to promote styling and finishing products by displaying them around the stylists' workstations. When stylists are using similar products during the service on the client's hair, they can show the client the new product from off the shelf.

AT CHEMICAL DEVELOPMENT AREAS

When clients are having a colour or perm service, they are often seated in a designated salon area and supplied with refreshments and magazines while their products develop. Clients are likely, during this time, to have a look around their surroundings, so a display of colour-enhancing/conditioning products can be effectively displayed here.

ACTIVITY

Look around your salon or college and note where you could set up temporary or permanent displays. Design a layout of your planned display area.

HOW TO MAINTAIN A DISPLAY

When you are setting up a display or maintaining it, you need to do so without causing any disturbance to the running of the salon, or inconvenience to clients/staff.

The display should be cleaned and dusted daily and you should change the design regularly, circulating the stock and/or changing the location (where possible) along with any temporary displays.

MONITORING THE STOCK

Some salons have PCs with suitable software that can monitor the sales and stock balances of products and equipment, as well as tracking appointment bookings.

This software can help you to keep a stock inventory and check on the sales and demand for products. If you use this type of software, you should be able to assess which products are popular and selling well, to guarantee you have enough stock, and also identify poor sales of products. From these reports, your salon can either decide to actively promote poor-selling items, or choose not to stock these items in the future.

Stock inventory

It is ultimately the manager's responsibility to check the security and levels of the stock, but he/she might delegate this task to you or another member of the team.

When stock arrives direct from the manufacturers or wholesalers, it should arrive with an invoice or a delivery note. You should check the stock received against the delivery note (or invoice). This will confirm that the correct amounts have been delivered. When you know you have received the correct amount of stock, you can check against your salon stock levels to ensure you have enough stock for your displays.

Security of stock

When you have completed your stock inventory, any reductions in stock levels should be from sales only. Small items are often irresistible to thieves and items small enough to fit into pockets or handbags might be too tempting for some. This costs the salon a great deal of money in loss of revenue and the cost of replacement items.

To ensure you are not losing any stock through theft, follow these simple suggestions:

- Check the stock levels on the displays daily against the sales recorded.
- Keep handbags (staff and clients') away from any display areas.
- Store any additional stock supplies away from the staffroom areas, in a designated lockable cupboard.
- Keep displays behind the reception areas and away from exits and entrances.

HANDY HINTS

Locked cabinets are not always very accessible but might be the only option, especially if theft has occurred before.

HANDY HINTS

Rotate the stock weekly. Remember FIFO – first in, first out; and LILO – last in, last out.

 SmartScreen 213 worksheet 5

Although the following are not ideal solutions, and they might create a barrier to purchasing, in some cases the only other options available to prevent theft could be:

- placing empty containers on display
- keeping stock displays in lockable cabinets in busy areas.

ACTIVITY

Design a stock inventory list for your salon or college. Estimate how many of each item you think you should have in stock and then check against the current stock levels. Compare this list with your manager or tutor, to identify how close your estimate was.

Some salons base commission targets on the stock inventory being accurate, as well as items sold in the salon. Any loss of stock could therefore affect the staff achieving their commission targets, as well as the costs incurred by the salon for replacement items.

You should rotate the display stock weekly; placing any new stock at the back and older stock towards the front. When you rotate the stock, complete a stock inventory to check you are ordering sufficient quantities.

THE LEGAL REQUIREMENTS

You and the salon are also bound by legislation and must adhere to the rules of the following Acts. This will ensure the clients' rights are protected when you are selling retail products, equipment and services.

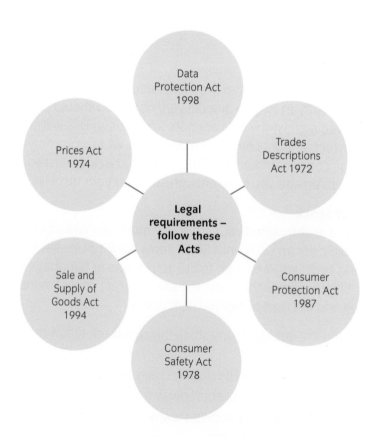

Data Protection Act 1998 – protecting the client's personal details by ensuring that:

- only authorised staff have access to client details
- you record the details accurately and keep them up to date
- you only use them for official use
- you destroy any out-of-date details securely
- the salon is registered with the Data Protection Registry if the details are held on a computer system.

Trade Descriptions Act 1972 – ensuring the items are described accurately:

- The quality must be as stated.
- It must be sold at the stated price.
- It must be fit for purpose.
- It must be clearly labelled as to where it was made.
- Verbal or written advertisements must be true and accurately describe the product.

Consumer Protection Act 1987 – ensuring safety standards of consumer goods and goods used in the workplace. Under this Act anyone who suffers personal injury, damage to personal property or death can take legal action against:

- producers
- importers
- own-branders.

Consumer Safety Act 1978 – reducing the risk to the consumer from any products that might potentially be dangerous.

Sale and Supply of Goods Act 1994 – when you go shopping, anything you buy is covered by an Act called the Sale of Goods Act 1979 which forms part of this Act. This means that when you buy a product it should be:

- as described
- fit for purpose
- of satisfactory quality.

As described – This means that the item you buy should be the same as any description of it. A description could be what the seller has said to you about the item or something written in a brochure.

Fit for purpose – What you buy should be able to do the job that it was made for. Goods should also be fit for any specific purpose that you agreed with the seller at the time of sale. For example, if you are looking to buy a shampoo and ask the seller how many washes it will give you, then the advice you are given has to be correct.

Of satisfactory quality – Goods that are of satisfactory quality are free from minor defects (problems), of a good appearance and finish, strong and safe to use.

Prices Act 1974 – ensuring that the prices are accurate and displayed, so the consumer is not mislead as to the value or price of the item.

Turn to page 485 for the answers.

1 Which one of the following is the best time to organise a retail display area?

a At the start of a busy day.

b When the salon is busy.

c During a lunch hour.

d On a quiet day.

2 The Manual Handling Operations Regulations puts a responsibility on the employer to

a Ensure that employees are able to lift heavy boxes.

b Ensure that employees have been trained to use electrical appliances.

c Train employees to use safe lifting techniques.

d Train employees to use protective equipment such as gloves and aprons.

3 **Statement 1**
A good way of displaying products is by taking them out of their packaging and stacking them creatively.

Statement 2
It might be better to use empty packages if the display is behind a sunny window as sunlight can adversely affect products.

Which one of the following is correct for the above statements?

	Statement 1	Statement 2
a	True	True
b	True	False
c	False	True
d	False	False

4 Which one of the following best identifies the purpose of a salon display area?

a To present a professional image of the salon.

b To attract clients and increase sales.

c To increase staff commission.

d To maintain client loyalty.

5 **Statement 1**
Colours and themes need to be considered before setting up a new display.

Statement 2
Fixed position displays are generally made of cardboard and have handwritten price tags.

Which one of the following is correct for the above statements?

	Statement 1	Statement 2
a	True	True
b	True	False
c	False	True
d	False	False

6 An effective technique for selling retail items is to

a Display stock that the salon uses and give away trial samples.

b Give away trial size samples and demonstrate to all visitors.

c Have all valuable items in a locked cabinet.

d Ensure that plenty of stock is on show.

7 Which one of the following displays would have a young, female student as a target audience?

a Expensive, professional-looking products.

b Brightly coloured, affordable products.

c Vividly packaged, male grooming range.

d Luxurious, high-end female range.

8 Which one of the following is the best way to maintain the security of stock on retail displays?

a Have all stock in lockable containers and do not allow clients to touch displays.

b Display a written notice to explain the legal consequences of theft.

c Only use empty containers and regularly check clients' bags.

d Regularly check stock levels and keep displays away from exits.

CASE STUDY: GUY REYNOLDS

Guy Reynolds is the Work Based Learning Manager for Francesco Group in Stafford. Guy manages the provision which looks after the apprenticeship training for over 120 trainees and for over 45 salons. Guy believes that good training ensures that high standards are achieved and maintained. Guy worked as a Wella Master Colour Expert in the Rugeley Francesco Group salon for a number of years and specialised in all aspects of hair colouring. Retail products, or home care as Guy prefers to refer to it, are closely linked to all aspects of hairdressing and should NEVER be ignored!

Here are Guy's top tips for displaying stock to promote sales.

1 Display shelves must always be clean and well-lit.
2 Stock must be clean and displayed neatly on the shelves.
3 Special offers must be at eye level for the clients to see and take advantage of.
4 Price lists must be included or the items must be individually priced.
5 New stock must be placed behind old stock when you are replenishing the retail area.
6 Home care must be discussed during the consultation and referred to throughout the service.
7 Prescription cards are handy and clients refer to them in the future.

PROVIDE SCALP MASSAGE SERVICES

The human body is amazing; it has the ability to fight infections, pump blood and oxygen around the body and keep us mobile, all at the same time. The largest of the body's organs is the skin, which allows us to feel sensations, protects us and keeps us warm. When massaging the scalp, we do so to suit the individual client's needs, whether that means massage for relaxation or for treatment purposes. Either way it can be invigorating and stimulating, relaxing or therapeutic, depending on the type of massage and the equipment used.

There are two learning outcomes in this unit. The learner will be able to:

- prepare to provide scalp massage services
- carry out scalp massage services.

PREPARE TO PROVIDE SCALP MASSAGE SERVICES

During this part of the unit you will learn:

- safety considerations for massage services
- the correct way to consult and communicate with your clients
- massaging products
- massaging equipment
- factors and contra-indications that can affect the service.

SAFETY CONSIDERATIONS

As with all services you must be prepared! This includes preparing yourself, the salon and your client for the service.

YOUR PREPARATION

You must ensure that your standards of personal hygiene meet with your salon's and clients' requirements. Before coming to work you must:

- shower
- use a deodorant
- brush your teeth.

You should also pay attention to the following:

- Clothes – make sure they are clean, ironed and follow your salon's dress code/uniform requirements.
- Hair and make-up, or hair and facial hair – ensure you represent the salon in a professional, well-groomed manner.
- Shoes – make sure they are enclosed and comfortable – you will spend most of the time on your feet!
- Jewellery – ensure that you have removed any accessories prior to the massage service, this is particularly important if you are using **high-frequency massage machines**.
- Posture – look keen and ready for work and remember your body language can give a negative as well as a positive impression.

High-frequency massage machine
A machine that provides electrical current to stimulate the nerve endings, and tiny vibrations to increase blood circulation

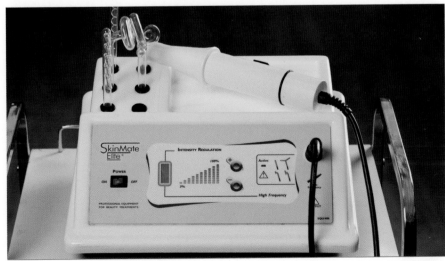

A high-frequency massage machine

As well as looking professional, you need to ensure you are protected, so wear your PPE where necessary and position yourself so you are comfortable while working.

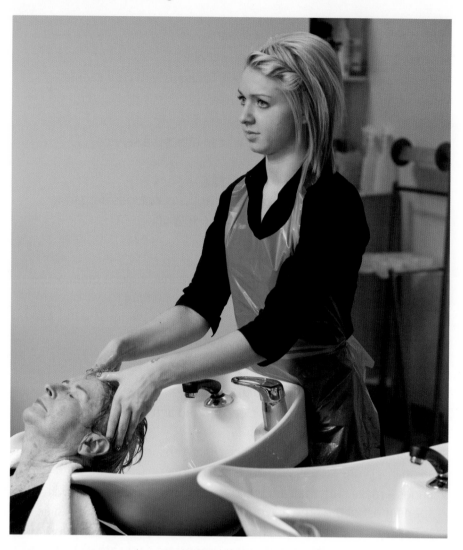

SALON PREPARATION

During the scalp massage service, you might use electrical equipment, such as high-frequency massage or **vibro-massage** machines. This type of equipment might not be used regularly in the salon, so it is vital that you check it is in good working order prior to the service. Always follow the Electricity at Work Regulations and check cables, plugs and the main body of the appliance before you use it.

Vibro-massage

Pulsating massage to increase blood circulation

A vibro-massage machine

You must clean both the high-frequency massager and the vibro-massage machine externally before and after use with warm soapy water, taking care not to immerse the appliance in water, and wipe with disinfectant.

You will also be working with **massage media**, some of which you might not use on a daily basis. Some of these products contain alcohol and are spirit based, others are made with **pre-blended oils**. As with all substances, you must follow the rules and regulations of COSHH. Make sure you protect your hands and wear gloves where possible.

 SmartScreen 215 worksheet 1

Massage media

Range of massage products

Pre-blended oils

Products already mixed together with scented oils, eg lavender with almond

ACTIVITY

Find out what COSHH stands for.

Salon hygiene

You must ensure that the salon has a plentiful supply of clean gowns and towels for your clients and that the whole salon is clean and tidy. You should clean and tidy the salon before your client arrives, set up your working area and work trolley and have the correct massage products and equipment available for the service.

HANDY HINTS

Always follow the manufacturers' instructions, and dispose of all waste in accordance with your salon policy and in line with environmental requirements and local by-laws.

SmartScreen 215 handout 1

CLIENT PREPARATION

When your client arrives, you will need to complete a thorough consultation and prepare him/her for the service ahead. Some scalp massage treatments take place on dry hair and therefore you might not need to shampoo the hair prior to the massage. If the hair is oily, has product build-up or needs conditioning, then you should shampoo the hair prior to the service. This might mean you will need to rough-dry the hair, and then shampoo it again after the service.

You should always gown and protect your client and, when they are prepared for the service, ensure you maintain their comfort throughout. You can apply some scalp massage services at the shampoo area while others will be performed at your workstation.

Before you start the actual service, check the scalp for any cuts or abrasions, and make sure you identify any factors or contra-indications that might affect the service.

CONSULTATION AND COMMUNICATION

The main purpose of your consultation is to identify your client's requirements and the service objective; during this process you will need to find out if these service requirements can be met.

You should agree the service procedures you plan to carry out, and discuss with your client what the benefits and the effects of the massage will be.

When you are communicating with your client, avoid using confusing language and hairdressing terminology – make it client friendly! You will need to identify whether there are any restrictions to the service and what your client's requirements are, so keep your conversations **jargon free** and speak clearly at all times.

To help identify whether your client has any contra-indicating factors that might affect the service, you will need to ask the right questions and listen carefully to their responses. Make sure you record all questions and answers on the client record card in case of litigation. Use open questions to gather all the relevant information, and closed questions to confirm the requirements. To gain confirmation of their requirements, repeat back to your client what you think to be an accurate account of their needs.

Jargon free
Avoiding hairdressing terminology or slang

ACTIVITY

List the open and closed questions you could ask for a scalp massage service to help identify the service requirements.

RECORD CARDS

Before you start the scalp massage you should refer to the clients' previous record cards and during and after the service make sure they are updated.

MASSAGING PRODUCTS

During a scalp massage service, you might use products that you are not as familiar with as you are with the day-to-day shampoo and conditioner range in the salon. If you are unsure of any products, you must seek advice or training from your salon supervisors or senior stylists. Always read and follow the instructions set out by the manufacturer.

MASSAGE MEDIA

During this service, you will use:

- shampoo
- conditioner
- spirit-based products
- pre-blended oils.

Shampoos

If you are completing a shampoo and conditioning treatment for scalp conditions, such as dry, oily, dandruff-affected or sensitive scalps, use a shampoo to suit the scalp condition. Equally, if you are shampooing hair that needs to be cleansed prior to the service, shampoo the hair in the normal manner. For either situation you will need to be familiar with your product range for the following scalp conditions:

- dry
- dandruff-affected
- oily
- normal
- sensitive.

Conditioners

If you are completing a treatment for the hair or scalp condition, you will need to be familiar with your conditioner product range for the following hair and scalp conditions:

- dry hair
- dry scalp
- damaged hair
- sensitive scalp
- oily scalp.

You also need to be familiar with the following treatments:

- penetrating conditioners
- scalp treatments.

ACTIVITY

List your salon or college range of shampoos and conditioners for the following hair and scalp conditions: dry, sensitive, oily, damaged and dandruff-affected.

> **HANDY HINTS**
>
> Always follow your client's instructions (where possible) and any instructions from your salon supervisors.

Spirit-based products

Spirit-based products contain alcohol. Because of this they are mostly used on oily scalps. They can be sprayed or sprinkled directly onto the scalp from the bottle or applicator. They are generally scented and contain ingredients for either soothing a scalp, or preventing/slowing down the production of sebum – the hair's natural oils. The ingredients could be rosewood or sandalwood – popular scents in barbering products.

Pre-blended oils

These oils are similar to aromatherapy oils, but rather than mixing carrier oils such as grape seed oil, with essential oils such as tea-tree, lavender or ylang ylang, they are already mixed together and ready for use. These oils are most suitable for dry and sensitive scalps and can help scalp conditions such as dandruff.

ACTIVITY

List your salon's or college's range of spirit-based products and pre-blended oils. Note the ingredients in case your clients suffer with allergies.

HANDY HINTS

Always check with your client if they have any allergies, such as a nut allergy, as these pre-blended oils might be mixed with almond oil. If clients have allergies, record this information on the client record card.

Mineral and vegetable oils

Mineral oils which are petroleum or paraffin based, such as baby oil, or vegetable oils, are made from vegetable or fruit oils, such as olives, coconut or almonds, for example. These can also be used to massage the scalp. Due to the ingredients in these oils, they are mostly suited for massaging dry and sensitive scalps.

MASSAGING EQUIPMENT

For your scalp massage assessments you will use manual massage – your hands – but you will also need to understand how and when to use high-frequency and vibro-massage machines.

HIGH-FREQUENCY MASSAGE MACHINES (H/F)

High-frequency massage provides electrical currents to stimulate the nerve endings, and tiny vibrations which increase blood circulation. They are also used in some beauty treatments, in fact you are more likely to see this machine in a beauty salon than a hairdressing salon, as they are not a popular service in the hair salon.

VIBRO-MASSAGE MACHINE

Vibro-massage machines are hand-held massagers that can vary in size, from very small, battery-operated vibrating scalp massagers, to large, heavy massagers which are used all over the body and are good for sports massage. Large massage machines would be too heavy for the head and would cause discomfort but, generally, any vibrating massage machine can be used for scalp massage. These are pulsating machines that come with varying attachments and increase blood circulation.

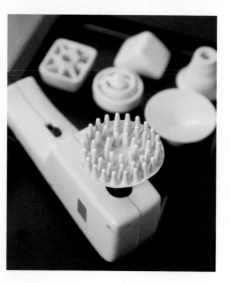

ACTIVITY

Research what type of high-frequency and vibro-massagers are available on the market and how much they cost.

FACTORS AND CONTRA-INDICATIONS

As part of your consultation you will need to consider whether certain factors or contra-indications will affect or prohibit the service. Factors such as scalp/hair condition and length, and contra-indications such as skin and scalp abnormalities, infections and infestations, can affect not only the service, but the products or equipment you are able to use.

FACTORS

The following chart shows how factors can affect the service:

Factors	Effect on service	Manual massage	H/F	Vibro-massage
Scalp condition	You might carry out massage treatments on the following scalp conditions: dandruff-affected, dry, sensitive or oily.			
	Dandruff-affected – you will need to use products that will help the scalp condition. If you are using pre-blended oils, then oils such as tea-tree or lavender might help the condition.	✓	✓	✓
	Dry – you will need to use moisturising products, such as coconut and almond, and increase blood circulation to stimulate the sebaceous glands and promote the production of sebum.	✓	✓	✓
	Sensitive – you will need to be careful with your choice of products; avoid heavily scented products and use a gentle massage.	✓	✓*	✓*
	Oily – you will need to use products with ingredients such as lemon or lime, and avoid over-stimulating the sebaceous glands and causing more sebum to be produced.	✓**	✗	✗
Hair condition	For hair which is fragile, dry or damaged, you must consider using products that will aid improvement of the condition.	✓	✓	✓
	If you are using the vibro machine, remove the machine from the head at regular intervals, taking care not to tangle the hair.			
Hair length	For longer hair lengths, you will need to ensure that the hair is brushed through thoroughly to untangle the hair prior to and during the service.	✓	✓	✓
	Avoid tangling the hair and causing discomfort to your client.			
	Make sure you use a sufficient amount of product for the hair length.			
	When you are using manual massage or vibro, regularly remove your hands/machine to untangle the hair.			
Hair density	Abundant hair – make sure you use enough product and adapt the amount of pressure you use during the massage to ensure you reach the scalp sufficiently.	✓	✓	✓
	Fine/sparse hair – use less product and less pressure during the massage.	✓	✓	✓
Unusual features	Psoriasis or cuts – avoid spirit-based products on the scalp, as this will cause great discomfort to your client.	✓	✓	✓
	Swellings or cysts – use less pressure during the massage and avoid certain areas if necessary.	✓	✗	✓
	Cuts, scars or recent injuries – avoid massaging these areas.	✓***	✓***	✓***

*Depending on how sensitive the scalp is.
**Use gentle effleurage.
***Avoid certain areas.

CONTRA-INDICATIONS

 SmartScreen 215 worksheet 2

Some of the following contra-indications will prevent you from carrying out the service and others might require an adaptation to the massage service you provide.

Contra-indication	Do they restrict the service?	Do they prevent service?	Manual massage	H/F	Vibro-massage
Broken skin – cuts and abrasions		If the skin is broken and open, there is a risk of cross-contamination.	✗	✗	✗
Swelling/inflammation	Vibro or H/F could cause discomfort – all massage movements should be gentle. Avoid the swollen area.		✓	✗	✗
Disease – infection and infestation		Risk of cross-contamination.	✗	✗	✗
Pregnancy		H/F might cause distress to the expectant mother.	✓	✗	✓
Circulation conditions and heart conditions		Risk of heart attack, condition might worsen.	✓	✗	✓
High blood pressure		Condition might worsen due to increased blood flow.	✓	✗	✓
Epilepsy		Risk of seizure.	✓	✗	✓
Chemotherapy and radio therapy	Client might feel unwell.		✓	✗	✓

HANDY HINTS

Do not use the H/F machine on clients with an excessive amount of metal fillings, as they will feel the electrical current through their teeth.

 SmartScreen 215 handouts 3 and 4

ACTIVITY

Complete a record card for the following client, who you have just completed a service on:

Fatima Keondra – she had a dry scalp with mild psoriasis. You carried out a dry scalp treatment with a manual massage.

Using your salon product range, what products could you have used?

What details should you record?

List some example questions that you should have asked the client.

215 PROVIDE SCALP MASSAGE SERVICES

During this part of the unit you will learn:

- the structure of the skin
- the bones and muscles of the head and neck
- the benefits of massage
- massage techniques
- step-by-step-instructions
- aftercare advice that should be given to clients.

STRUCTURE OF THE SKIN

Your skin is the body's largest organ. The two main layers are the epidermis and the dermis; the outer layer is the epidermis, consisting of five layers.

THE EPIDERMIS LAYER

Covering the surface of the epidermis is a very fine film called the acid mantle. The acid mantle is made up of sweat and sebum and acts as a barrier to bacteria and other contaminants.

The epidermis is made up of five main layers which protect us from bacteria and temperature changes and are regularly replaced. House dust is partly made up of the epidermis that our bodies have shed. Our whole body is covered with the epidermis which varies in thickness; it is thickest on the soles of our feet and thinnest on our eyelids.

The the top three layers of the epidermis contain dead cells, the next layer contains aging cells which are still living, and the bottom layer is constantly producing new cell growth and has a blood supply and nerve endings.

- The cornified layer – the **stratum** corneum is the outer top layer and provides us with a waterproof 'coat'. This 'horny' layer flakes and dries out easily. We remove the dead skin cells from here when we exfoliate.
- The clear/translucent layer – the stratum lucidum is a clear layer present only in thick skin, helping to protect it from the force of friction.
- The granular layer – the stratum granulosum is a granular layer which contains most of the skin's protein, called keratin.
- The spinous layer – the stratum spinosum is the prickle-cell layer. These cells are formed as new cells grow and the old ones are pushed up to create a new layer. The cells interlock and are capable of **mitosis** under friction or pressure, ie on our feet or on the palms of our hands.
- The basal/germinal layer – the stratum basale/germinativum is the base and deepest layer of skin. It is the primary site of mitosis, which produces new cell growth. It can take 28–30 days for cells produced here to move through the five layers of the epidermis before they are shed. This layer contains a pigment called melanin, which gives the skin its natural colour.

Every minute, our bodies shed 30,000 cells, taking dead skin cells and bacteria away from the body. Over a period of 1 month, we replace all of our skin from the epidermis.

HANDY HINTS

The function of the epidermis is to protect the dermis.

Stratum

Layer

Mitosis

Cell division

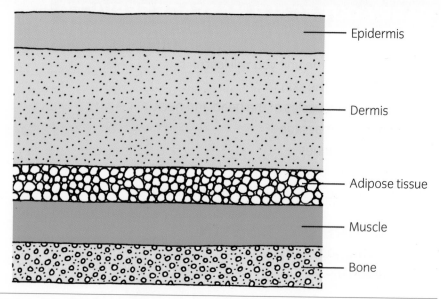

Epidermis

Dermis

Adipose tissue

Muscle

Bone

Cross-section of the body's tissues

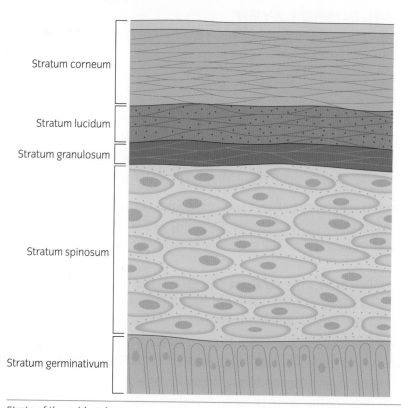

Stratum corneum

Stratum lucidum

Stratum granulosum

Stratum spinosum

Stratum germinativum

Strata of the epidermis

HANDY HINTS

To help you remember which layer is on the top – use the 'E' from epidermis to remind you it is the 'exiting' layer – exiting from the skin and becoming house dust!

 SmartScreen 215 wordsearch 1

THE DERMIS LAYER

The dermis has four main functions:

- Protection – by secretion of sebum, which protects and lubricates the skin; the lubrication prevents absorption of water into the skin. The skin also protects the body against friction and injury to the bones and muscles.

- Excretion and secretion – elimination and removal of waste, such as sweat, and secreting the sebum for protection against the sun's radiation.

- Sensation – we can feel pressure and pain from the nerve endings.

- Temperature control – keeps us warm, and cools us down by the excretion and evaporation of sweat.

The dermis is attached to the epidermis on one side and the subcutaneous layer of the skin (the fatty tissue) on the other side, and passes nutrients between the two layers.

Between the epidermis and the subcutaneous layer are the:

- blood capillaries, which provide oxygen and nutrients to the skin
- arrector pili muscles, which contract to raise the hairs and gives us 'goose-bumps' when we are cold (in mammals with fur or hair on their bodies this traps an insulating layer of warm air between the hairs)
- sebaceous glands, which secret sebum to lubricate the hair and skin
- suderoforous (sweat) glands, which produce sweat to cool us down
- nerve endings, which make the skin sensitive to sensations.

HANDY HINTS

Remember PEST – protection, excretion/ secretion, sensation and temperature.

HANDY HINTS

Our skin secretes sebum. This can make our hair oily, but we need it to waterproof our skin (and form the acid mantle), which also stops bodily fluids evaporating in the heat.

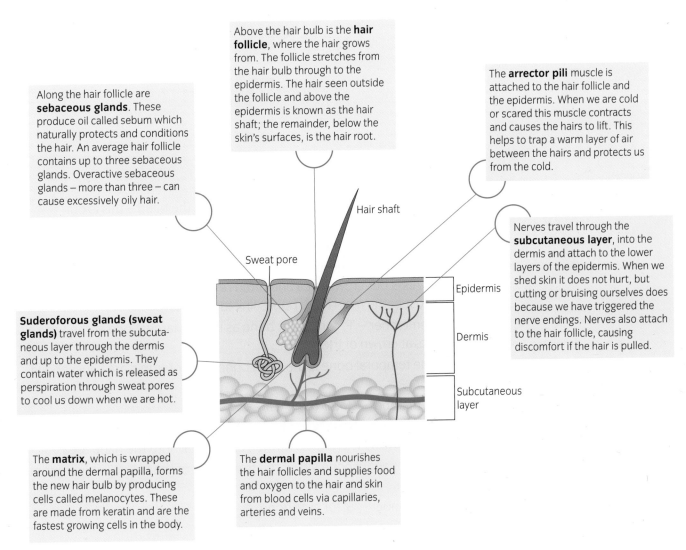

Along the hair follicle are **sebaceous glands**. These produce oil called sebum which naturally protects and conditions the hair. An average hair follicle contains up to three sebaceous glands. Overactive sebaceous glands – more than three – can cause excessively oily hair.

Above the hair bulb is the **hair follicle**, where the hair grows from. The follicle stretches from the hair bulb through to the epidermis. The hair seen outside the follicle and above the epidermis is known as the hair shaft; the remainder, below the skin's surfaces, is the hair root.

The **arrector pili** muscle is attached to the hair follicle and the epidermis. When we are cold or scared this muscle contracts and causes the hairs to lift. This helps to trap a warm layer of air between the hairs and protects us from the cold.

Hair shaft

Sweat pore

Suderoforous glands (sweat glands) travel from the subcutaneous layer through the dermis and up to the epidermis. They contain water which is released as perspiration through sweat pores to cool us down when we are hot.

Nerves travel through the **subcutaneous layer**, into the dermis and attach to the lower layers of the epidermis. When we shed skin it does not hurt, but cutting or bruising ourselves does because we have triggered the nerve endings. Nerves also attach to the hair follicle, causing discomfort if the hair is pulled.

Epidermis

Dermis

Subcutaneous layer

The **matrix**, which is wrapped around the dermal papilla, forms the new hair bulb by producing cells called melanocytes. These are made from keratin and are the fastest growing cells in the body.

The **dermal papilla** nourishes the hair follicles and supplies food and oxygen to the hair and skin from blood cells via capillaries, arteries and veins.

SmartScreen 215 worksheet 3 and wordsearch 2

BONES AND MUSCLES OF THE HEAD AND NECK

When we carry out scalp massage services, we stimulate and tone the underlying tissues and increase blood flow to the muscles in the head and neck.

BONES IN THE HEAD AND NECK

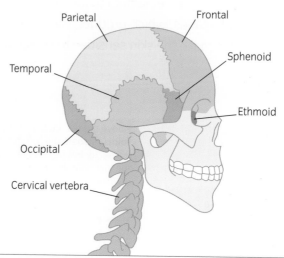

Bones in the head and neck

- The frontal bone sits right at the front of the head – this is our forehead.

  Remember – 'F' for forehead or front.

- The parietal bone is the largest bone and sits behind the frontal bone – this is our crown area and often referred to as the 'roof' of our head. Most of the main head bones link to this one.

  Remember – 'P' for parent bone as it is the largest one at the top and sits at crown of the head.

- The temporal bone is the main bone by our temple area, just above our ears.

  Remember – 'T' for temple area.

- The occipital bone is just below the crown. We are more familiar with this bone as we refer to it when cutting hair into the nape area.

- The sphenoid bone sits at the front sides of the head, just in front of the ear.

  Remember – 'S' for side bone.

- The ethnoid bones are our eye sockets.

  Remember – 'E' for eye bone or eye socket.

- The cervical vertebrae is at the top of the spine – our neck bone.

  Remember – 'V' for vertebrae.

WHAT IS LYMPH?

Lymph is a colourless fluid, like plasma, that has been filtered through the walls of the capillaries in the tissues. Lymph distributes nutrients and oxygen to the tissues, and takes away carbon dioxide and other wastes via the vessels of the lymphatic system.

We have lymph nodes in the armpits, neck and groin. In the lymph nodes, harmful bacteria are destroyed by the lymphocytes, helping to fight infection. It is these nodes that swell when we have a cold or an infection.

Like veins, lymph vessels have valves that keep the lymph flowing in the right direction. Movements of our larger muscles in the body force the lymph towards a vein near the heart. This allows the lymphatic system to help remove waste from the body.

Massaging the scalp increases the flow of lymph, bringing oxygen and nutrients to the tissues and removing waste and carbon dioxide. Other benefits of massaging the scalp include:

- Stimulating the nerves increases the supply of sweat.
- Stimulating the scalp increases the breakdown of fatty tissue/cells.
- Stimulating the scalp increases sebum – good for dry scalps, but not for oily scalps.
- Stimulating blood supply aids the healing process.
- Stimulating blood supply means extra oxygen travels to the papilla (hair bulb) and increases hair cell growth.
- Massage can help to decrease tension and pain and relax your client.

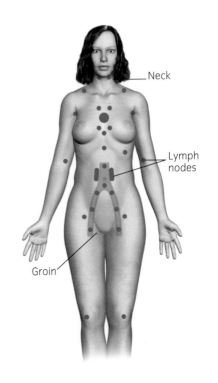

Where the lymph nodes are in the body

MASSAGE TECHNIQUES

When you carry out a scalp massage service, you will need to select the most suitable products, choose the correct equipment and adapt your massage techniques to suit the identified factors and contra-indications, as well as the needs of the service.

MANUAL MASSAGE

Carrying out a manual massage can take place at the shampoo area or at your workstation. You will need to shampoo the hair in the normal manner, with a suitable shampoo product, and prepare the hair for the massage.

Your two practical assessments will include a manual massage for conditioning purposes and a manual massage to relax your client.

Manual massage techniques

As with normal shampoo and conditioning treatments, apply any products using the effleurage massage technique, followed by other massage techniques and finishing with effleurage.

- Effleurage – a gentle stroking, relaxing movement used at the start and end of the service, as well as in between any change of massage movement. Effleurage is used to distribute the massage media through the hair and is a flowing, linking movement.

- Petrissage – positioning your hands in a claw-like manner and using your finger pads only, massage the scalp in a deep, firm, slow, circular kneading movement, moving around the head and neck of the nerves. Start at the front hairline, move through to the sides, to the ears and then down to the nape, and finally back up to the crown and forehead again. This stimulates blood supply and the movement of lymph. It also stimulates the sebaceous glands and improves muscle tone.
- Tapotement – a tapping movement. Use the pads of your fingers and work around the head and neck area. Take care with this massage movement, as the scalp has little skin and tissue for protection and firm taps could cause client discomfort. This movement stimulates the blood supply to the smaller capillaries, producing antiseptic effects on the skin, and gives the head and neck an invigorating, stimulating massage.
- Friction – a pinching, squeezing and kneading massage movement which stimulates blood supply and nerve endings. Do not be too firm; you must consider your client's comfort.

The diagram below shows that these massage movements should follow a sequence and flow into each other.

Start with effleurage

Move on to petrissage

Return to effleurage

Move on to tapotement

Return to effleurage

Move on to friction

Finish with effleurage to relax the client and the scalp

HANDY HINTS

Adapt your rate and rhythm of massage to suit the factors and the needs of the service/client.

Follow this massage routine all over the head and the top of the neck area if you are working at a workstation. You should work from the temple area to the forehead, across the crown and down into the neck; repeating the process in reverse order and ending with your finger pads paused at the temple area for a few seconds at the end.

You can use the above-mentioned massage techniques for the following scalp conditions:

Scalp condition	Effleurage	Petrissage	Tapotement	Friction
Dandruff-affected	✓	✓	✓	✓
Dry	✓	✓	✓	✓
Sensitive	✓	✓ but gently	✗	✗
Oily	✓	✓ but gently	✗	✗

STEP-BY-STEP INSTRUCTIONS
Step-by-step guide to manual massage techniques

STEP 1 – Gown and protect your client.

STEP 2 – Consult with your client to identify the service objective.

STEP 3 – Shampoo and rinse the hair.

STEP 4 – At the workstation or shampoo area, apply the chosen massage media.

STEP 5 – After effleurage massage, use petrissage massage to stimulate blood supply.

STEP 6 – Work methodically around the head and finish with effleurage massage to relax your client.

VIBRO-MASSAGE

Carry out a vibro scalp massage service at your workstation on clean dry hair. The machine vibrates and simulates friction and tapotement massage movements. There are a variety of attachments that you can add – for the scalp, a rubber spiky attachment is generally used.

Gently move the machine around the head and neck area, massaging the muscles in the head and upper neck. It is important that you bear the weight of the massage machine in your hands, rather than resting its whole weight on your client's head and neck.

Step-by-step demonstration of vibro-massage

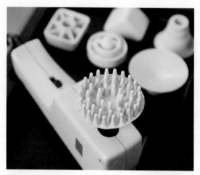

STEP 1 – Ensure your tools are clean and sterilised.

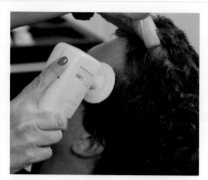

STEP 2 – Start the vibro massage at the temple area.

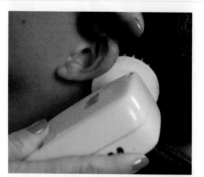

STEP 3 – Work progressively around the hairline, and over the whole head.

STEP 4 – Ensure you massage the nape area to stimulate blood supply.

HIGH-FREQUENCY MASSAGE

When using an H/F machine, it is important that you make a contact circuit between yourself and your client – placing your hand on your client's shoulder or head will make a contact circuit. If the H/F machine is switched on and you place the electrode straight onto your client, without making a contact circuit, your client might feel discomfort. The machine delivers electrical currents and therefore a mild electrical shock sensation might be felt.

High-frequency massaging can be carried out in two ways – direct or indirect application. In both instances, the glass electrodes are used but in different ways. The following glass electrodes are available for use with H/F:

- Glass bulb – used for direct applications and moved around the head and neck. It can be used to focus on specific areas, such as bald spots – alopecia.

- Glass comb – used for direct applications. This is literally used like a comb and moved through the hair. Take care not to catch the comb in the hair, breaking contact with the electrode and the head.

- Glass rod – used for indirect applications and held by your client; your hands are used for the scalp massage. The current passes through the glass rod and your client, while your hands stimulate the blood supply.

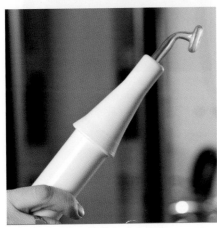

Glass electrode – bulb

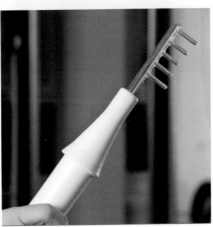

Glass electrode – comb

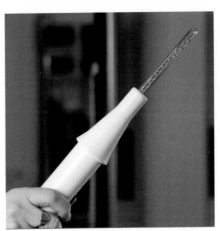

Glass electrode – rod

Direct application

Apply the glass electrodes directly onto your client's scalp following the steps below.

STEP 1 – Remove all jewellery and prepare the H/F machine.

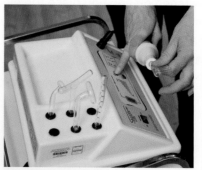

STEP 2 – Adjust the H/F machine settings to the lowest level and make a circuit with the glass electrode.

STEP 3 – Ensuring a circuit is maintained throughout, place the glass bulb electrode on to your client's head and adjust the settings.

STEP 4 – Work the bulb around the top of the head and then change to the glass comb and rake through the hair.

STEP 5 – Ensure you always maintain contact. If you remove the electrode from the head, your other hand must complete the circuit.

STEP 6 – When you place the electrode back on the head, do not remove your second hand until the glass bulb has made contact with your client's head to complete the circuit.

Indirect application

STEP 1 – Carry out a thorough consultation with your client.

STEP 2 – Check the hair and scalp for any contra-indications.

STEP 3 – Ask your client to hold the glass electrode with both hands to create a circuit. Place your hand on the head, prior to switching on the H/F machine.

STEP 4 – With your client creating the circuit, massage the scalp, keeping one hand on the head at all times.

STEP 5 – After carrying out indirect massage, you can carry out direct H/F massage.

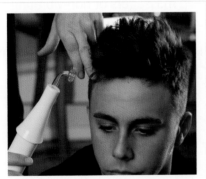

STEP 6 – Ensure you create a circuit before you place the electrode onto your client's head.

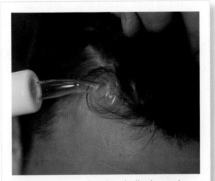

STEP 7 – Using the glass bulb electrode, work around the hairline area of the head.

HANDY HINTS

It is very important that all metal accessories and jewellery are removed from both your client and yourself, otherwise the electrical current might travel through the metals and cause discomfort/shock pulses.

 SmartScreen 215 handout 2

AFTERCARE ADVICE

Although it is very unlikely that your client will have access to high-frequency machines and hand-held vibro-massagers at home, you are still able to provide some valuable aftercare advice and recommend products and equipment that can be used at home in between salon visits.

PRODUCTS

The shampoos and conditioners that have been used for the scalp massage treatment can be purchased by your client and used at home. Explain to your client the features and benefits of using the massage media in between salon visits. Make sure you advise them on how much to use and how often to use them.

If you used a spirit-based product, could your client sprinkle this onto their scalps and manually massage their scalp themselves? Probably yes! Talk them through the sequence of a basic massage and explain the healing benefits and how the blood supply can be increased.

For clients with dry, sensitive or dandruff-affected scalp conditions, recommend any pre-blended oils that your client can use at home. Make sure you give suitable advice on how to remove the oils from the hair, as well as how and when to use them.

If your client has damaged or fragile hair, recommend penetrating conditioning products to help increase the strength and condition of the hair.

EQUIPMENT

For home maintenance you could recommend manual massaging to stimulate blood supply, but your clients could also purchase small vibrating hair brushes, mini vibrating scalp massagers or non-vibrating massagers, such as a manual head massager.

These might be sold by the salon or you could recommend to your client where they can buy them or search for them on the Internet.

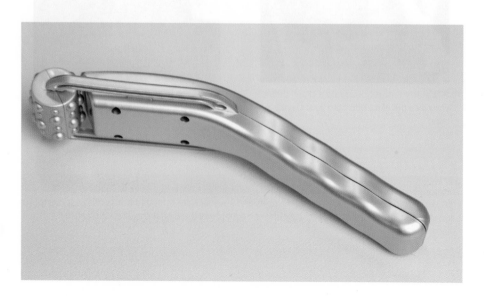

WHEN TO RETURN TO THE SALON

If your client is having H/F, then he/she would benefit from a series of treatments. You should recommend how often they should book for their appointments and explain the benefits of a series of treatments carried out in succession.

FUTURE SERVICES

If your client is having scalp massage services for scalp disorders, relaxation or to treat the hair, there is no reason why they could not have other services too. If they are having H/F for hair-loss reasons, then it would be wise to steer clear of chemical services.

During the scalp massage service and at the end, recommend to your client suitable services that would help them to achieve a great look – promoting the salon's services, such as cutting and colouring, and making your client feel great.

 SmartScreen 215 revision cards

Turn to page 485 for the answers.

1 Which **one** of the following is **not** a preparation method required for scalp massage?

   a Removing the client's jewellery.

   b Checking electrical equipment.

   c Completing a consultation.

   d Checking all medical records.

2 Which **one** of the following products is used to treat an oily scalp?

   a Pre-blended oils.

   b Spirit-based lotion.

   c Mineral oil.

   d Penetrating conditioner.

3 Which **one** of the following describes a high frequency massage?

   a Provides electrical currents to stimulate the nerve endings, and tiny vibrations which increase blood circulation.

   b Hand-held massagers which are used all over the body and are good for sports massage.

   c Pulsating machines that come with varying attachments and increase blood circulation.

   d Friction hand movements that are mostly suited for massaging dry and sensitive scalps.

4 When you are using a vibro machine, it is important to remove the machine from the head at regular intervals to:

   a Avoid scalp oiliness.

   b Minimise scalp irritation.

   c Avoid tangling the hair.

   d Minimise over-stimulation.

5 **Statement 1:**
Avoid the use of spirit-based products on clients with psoriasis or cuts as they will cause great discomfort to open skin.

Statement 2:
If a client has a scar from a recent injury it is important to avoid this area when massaging to minimise discomfort and avoid aggravating the wound.

Which **one** of the following is correct for the above statements?

	Statement 1	Statement 2
a	True	True
b	True	False
c	False	True
d	False	False

6 Which **one** of the following is a contra-indication to all massage services?

   a Pregnancy.

   b Oily scalp.

   c Infestation.

   d Skin inflammation.

7 Massaging the scalp increases the flow of lymph, bringing oxygen and nutrients to body tissues and removing:

   a Waste and carbon dioxide.

   b Red and white blood cells.

   c Platelets and disease.

   d Bacteria and haemoglobin.

8 **Statement 1:**
High-frequency massage can be carried out by the indirect method, which uses a glass comb that is gently moved through the hair.

Statement 2:
A glass bulb is used for direct applications of high-frequency massage and is an effective method of treating specific areas such as bald patches.

Which **one** of the following is correct for the above statements?

	Statement 1	Statement 2
a	True	True
b	True	False
c	False	True
d	False	False

CASE STUDY: DANIEL CACERES

Daniel is an Artistic Team member and long hair/hair up/bridal hair aficionado. Born to Spanish parents and raised in France, Daniel started hairdressing in 1994, and has been at Trevor Sorbie since October 2001. He boasts an impressive celebrity client list, including Lesley Ash, Kim Cattrall, Lesley Garrett, Olivia Harrison, Lorraine Kelly, Bridget Neilson, Bonnie Langford, Zandra Rhodes, Jayne Torvill, Denise Van Outen, Natasha Kaplinski, Bonnie Wright, John Barrowman, Glenn Carter, Julian Clary, Christopher Dean, Danny Harrison, Trevor Nunn, Olivia Harrison, Tamara Beckwith and Chris Tarrant.

Experienced in fashion shoots, high-profile fashion shows, video and television, he has worked all around the world. Here are his six scalp massage tips for you:

1 Do not let your client cross their legs or arms, and do not cross your own legs – it restricts the circulation. It is better for your posture to stand straight, while the client will get more benefit from the relaxing massage if their body is relaxed.

2 Do not wear any dangling jewellery as this can disturb the client.

3 Always keep hands in contact with the client, so always keep a hand on the head even if you are reaching for a product. This is more relaxing than your hands moving on and off.

4 Avoid water temperature changes.

5 Do not talk over the client's head while they are having their treatment.

6 Move the scalp gently, not too vigorously. Work in a pattern and move the hands systematically.

The reception area is the heart of the salon. When a client walks into the salon for the first time, make sure he/she has the 'wow' factor. The reception area of any salon must be in pristine condition and advertise the salon's image, and the receptionist must be smartly dressed, attentive and responsive at all times. First impressions last, so make sure they are positive, but equally remember that the client's last impression of the salon will also take place at reception.

There are three learning outcomes in this unit. The learner will be able to:

- carry out reception duties
- book appointments
- deal with payments.

During this part of the unit you will learn how to:

- maintain the reception area
- communicate and behave at reception
- attend to clients and enquiries
- take messages correctly.

MAINTAIN THE RECEPTION AREA

At the start of each day, the receptionist must deal with any answer-phone messages that have been left overnight and ensure that the reception area is prepared for the day ahead.

The daily activities of a receptionist might include:

- maintaining a clean, tidy and well-stocked reception area
- maintaining the levels of retail products
- meeting and greeting clients
- maintaining the salon's hospitality and offering refreshments to clients
- dealing with enquiries and bookings
- solving problems at reception, such as services running late or clients arriving late
- providing information about salon services and retail products
- answering the telephone
- checking emails and any other electronic methods of communication
- organising the salon's post and distributing it to the relevant people
- taking messages and passing them on to the relevant people
- maintaining communication between clients and stylists
- handling payments and promoting the sale of retail products
- preparing client record cards
- maintaining confidentiality of clients' records
- maintaining salon security at the reception area
- maintaining the level of change in the till
- balancing the till at the end of the day.

 SmartScreen 216 handout 1

Salon reception – answer the phone promptly

KEEP THE RECEPTION AREA CLEAN AND TIDY

As a receptionist you must ensure that the salon is always well-presented and portrays a professional image. You must always make sure that the seating area is clean, tidy and welcoming.

Neaten any magazines and clear away any used refreshment crockery. You must ensure that the reception area's surfaces and floor are free from dust and hair.

Retail stand and tidy reception area

MAINTAIN STATIONERY STOCKS

As the receptionist you are responsible for maintaining the stationery levels. This will help the salon run smoothly and effectively. You should:

- maintain the appointment systems
- ensure a notepad and pen is to hand for taking messages
- maintain an appropriate level of appointment cards and notify the salon manager when these are running low
- know your salon price structures and display the salon price list for services and retail products
- clearly display any special offers. Check with your salon manager what offers are available, and know which days and stylists they apply to, eg a new stylist promotion. Some salons advertise discounts and special offers for certain services only. This could be to promote new business or encourage the sale of services that are not as popular as others
- keep records of the stylist job sheets – this is particularly important if the salon does not have an electronic computer system and the stylists are on a **commission basis** for the sale of services and products.

Commission basis
When stylists receive a percentage of the sale value that they create

Well-maintained reception desk

MAINTAIN THE SALON'S SECURITY

Each salon will have a different policy for maintaining security of the premises and stock, and the safety of staff and clients. Some salons might have a shutter that covers the salon doors and windows when it is closed for the day; others might have a 'buzz' entry or video entry system, which allows entry to authorised clients and salon visitors only. Most salons will have a front door which allows access and entry to all; this is often best kept closed, for your personal safety and those around you.

To prevent breaches in security you must follow your salon policy for the reception area. This could include:

- storing minimal cash in the till
- never leaving cash in the till overnight
- keeping the till drawer locked at all times and the key removed when the receptionist leaves the reception area
- rarely (ideally never) leaving the reception area unattended
- keeping staff personal belongings in a locker or secured in the 'staff only' areas
- ensuring clients keep their personal belongings with them at all times
- displaying retail stands either behind the reception desk, away from the entrance door or in a lockable glass display cabinet.

You must also ensure that client records and/or credit/debit card payment slips are kept securely at the reception area to keep clients' details confidential. If clients pay by card using a chip and PIN machine, you should discreetly look away as they enter their PIN (personal identification number).

Client keeping her handbag with her

Buzz entry systems on salon entrance

Lockable cabinet

Staff lockers

COMMUNICATION AND BEHAVIOUR

Effective salon communication starts with the receptionist, who should help to enhance the salon image and improve business. This will ensure the salon runs smoothly and the stylists work efficiently.

You should always greet your clients promptly and warmly. Offer to hang up their coats, show them to the seating area and offer refreshments and magazines to read. Some salons offer TVs and computer games to entertain clients while they wait for their service and during development times. When you have informed the stylist that their client has arrived, keep the client informed as to how long they might have to wait. You must maintain a friendly yet professional approach at all times.

HANDY HINTS

Remember to promote positive body language at all times.

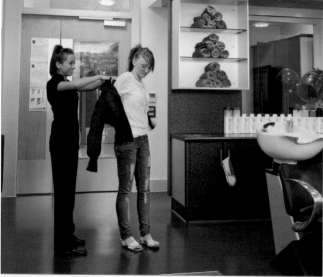

Helping a client with her coat

Client sitting comfortably

ACCURATELY IDENTIFY THE CLIENT'S REQUIREMENTS

For you to be able to identify what your client's requirements are, you will need to ask a series of open questions. These types of question start with 'what', 'when', 'where', 'why', 'who' and 'how', and enable you to obtain full answers from your clients. Some examples of these types of question are:

- What service would you like?
- When would be a suitable date and time?
- Which stylist normally looks after you?
- What other times and dates can you make?
- If Suzie is not available on this day, who could look after you?

ACTIVITY

Can you think of some more open questions that might be asked at reception? Make a list.

To clarify the booking of the appointment, you should switch to closed questions, which require 'yes' or 'no' responses. Some examples of these types of question could be:

- Is 3 pm on Tuesday suitable for you?
- Can you confirm that you would like a cut and finish after your colour service?

ACTIVITY

Can you think of some more closed questions that might be asked at reception? Make a list.

DEALING WITH THE PUBLIC

The reception area can be very busy at times and you will have to balance people's needs. Clients visiting the salon in person can see how busy you are, but people telephoning the salon cannot, so try not to let the telephone ring more than three times before you answer it. You will need to identify who needs your attention first and avoid upsetting those who are still waiting to be seen.

When you are rushed off your feet, apologise to clients for keeping them waiting, suggest they take a seat, offer them refreshments, keep them informed about the situation and reassure them that you will not keep them waiting for longer than necessary. If you are really busy, ask for help from the salon team.

As a stylist, and indeed a receptionist, you will meet a variety of people with different needs and expectations. You might encounter:

- an unexpected client who has, or at least thinks they have, booked an appointment
- double-booked appointments or late arrivals
- children who need to be treated suitably and might need reassuring
- a client who wishes to change their appointment service
- a client who is unsure of what service to book and when to book it

- a confused client
- an angry client
- clients with different cultures or those whose first language is not English
- a client who wants to complain
- a client with mobility needs/disabilities.

Confused client

Angry client

Client with mobility needs

Complaining client

SmartScreen 216 handout 6 and worksheet 2

When communicating with clients, you must do so politely at all times.

Always speak clearly and pronounce your words distinctly. If your client is confused or English is not their first language, you should avoid technical jargon and adapt your language style to suit their needs and the situation. Always show your client that you are listening carefully by maintaining eye contact and nodding, even if your client does not pause for breath, and use positive body language and suitable verbal responses. If you need to encourage a client to move a conversation forward, keep to the subject matter and the purpose of the discussion and summarise any agreed points.

ACTIVITY

What would you do and say if a client enquired about the whereabouts of a stylist who had recently left your salon?

ATTENDING TO CLIENTS AND ENQUIRIES

You will need to attend to clients and deal with enquiries, both via the telephone and face to face. In some salons you will also deal with electronic enquiries, which might be via text message or email. Whichever way your enquiries arrive, you must always deal with them and respond to clients promptly and politely.

Client booking in at reception

Professional waiting area

CLIENT ARRIVALS

As clients arrive, always confirm their appointment details to ensure the booking is correct, and then promptly inform the relevant stylist of their client's arrival. Checking that the appointment has been correctly booked in enables you to know in advance if there are likely to be any unforeseen problems, such as delays in the service or double bookings, and enables you to adapt to any service changes that the client might request.

Receptionist taking the client to the stylist

Receptionist with poor posture and lack of interest

Stylist introducing herself to the client

Lost client, wondering where to go

SALON ENQUIRIES

For all salon enquiries it is important that you clearly identify the purpose of the enquiry. As a receptionist, you might deal with the following types of enquiry, either on the telephone, face to face or electronically:

- appointment enquiries
- salon opening and closing times
- costs for services and products
- product representatives selling or promoting their stock
- wholesale deliveries.

It is important that you can answer and deal with these enquiries professionally and **adeptly**, and give accurate information to any visitor to the salon.

Adeptly
Expertly

Client being gowned for service by stylist

Receptionist referring an enquiry to the manager

Client with coat on at workstation

Stylist recommending a retail product

Receptionist showing client the price list

TAKING MESSAGES CORRECTLY

If the relevant person is not available to deal with a telephone call themselves, you must take a message and clearly record the details of the conversation. When that person is free, make sure you pass on the message promptly, to ensure that the salon runs smoothly.

When you are taking a message for someone, always record the following details:

- who the message is for
- the date and time the message was left
- a brief but accurate description of the message
- who the message is from
- the contact details of the caller/visitor, such as email address or telephone number
- the action to be taken, such as to return their call, the best time to call and preferred number
- whether the message is urgent or a general enquiry
- who has taken the message.

When you are taking messages, follow the salon's procedures for recording the message details, and when to pass them on to the relevant person. Make sure the details are written in neat handwriting with all the relevant details accurately recorded. If you take a person's phone number down incorrectly, the message becomes useless and the person expecting the return call could be annoyed. If this is a client, they might choose to book their appointments elsewhere, costing the salon business and revenue! Equally, if you fail to pass the message on to the relevant person, it could cost the salon business and the salon could get a reputation for being unreliable.

HANDY HINTS

Always deal with enquiries within the limits of your own authority and refer other enquiries to the relevant person.

WHY DON'T YOU...

Identify who you would refer enquiries to if they are outside the limits of your authority.

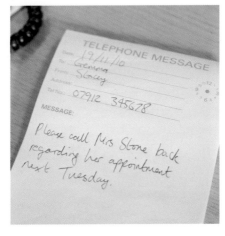

SmartScreen 216 handout 7, worksheet 1 and wordsearch 1

During this part of the unit you will learn how to:

- make and record appointment bookings
- follow legislation.

MAKE AND RECORD APPOINTMENT BOOKINGS

When you make appointments for the salon's clients, you need to ensure they are booked carefully, to suit the needs of the business as well as the client. Your role will involve dealing with client requests and accurately identifying their requirements.

A typical conversation between a receptionist (Natasha) and a client (Sarah) might be similar to this:

Receptionist Hi Sarah, how are you? How can I help you?

Sarah I'm fine, thank you, Natasha. I'd like to book an appointment for a colour and cut please.

Receptionist Which stylist do you normally see for your cut and colour?

Sarah Amraf does my cut and Tina usually does my colour.

Receptionist When would you like to come in for your appointment?

Sarah Any chance you can fit me in on Saturday?

Receptionist Amraf is free and can cut your hair at 2 pm, but Tina is on holiday. Would you mind if Julia coloured your hair?

Sarah Yes, that's fine, thank you.

Receptionist Great, are you having your usual colour or do you fancy a change?

Sarah No, thank you, I would like my usual highlights, but just the top section this time please.

Receptionist OK Sarah, is 12.15 a suitable time for your colour?

Sarah Yes, perfect, thank you.

Receptionist Just to confirm then, Sarah, I have booked you in with Julia at 12.15 for your half head of highlights and then Amraf will cut your hair at 2 pm. Is that ok?

Sarah Perfect, thank you, see you on Saturday. Bye.

Receptionist Goodbye – have a lovely day!

SCHEDULING APPOINTMENTS

When you have confirmed with the client the type of service required, the preferred time and date, and which stylist will service the client's hair, you must record the appointment either in the appointment book or on a computer.

Paper-based appointment booking system

Client being booked in for her next appointment

Electronic booking systems vary greatly and you must be trained by your salon manager before using such a system. Written appointment systems tend to follow a set format from salon to salon.

As a guide, the abbreviations that salons tend to use in written appointment books are shown in the table below.

Appointment	Abbreviation
Wet cut	W/C
Cut and blow dry	CBD
Restyle	Restyle
Blow dry	B/D
Shampoo and set	S/S
Dry set	D/S
Regrowth tint	REG or roots
Woven highlights	WHL
Half-head woven highlights	½ WHL
Lowlights	L/L
Full-head colour or whole-head colour	FHC or WHC
Cap highlights	CAP
Pulled-through highlights	P H/L
Semi-permanent colour	Semi
Quasi-permanent colour	Quasi
Permanent wave (perm)	P/W
Top perm	Top P/W

WHY DON'T YOU...
Find out if these abbreviations differ from your salon's system.

How would your salon abbreviate the following?

1 Half-head foil highlights and cut and blow dry.
2 Full-head highlights and blow dry.
3 Wedding hair.
4 Perm, and cut and blow dry.
5 Cut, shampoo and set.
6 Cut, blow dry and straighten.
7 Blow dry and tongs.
8 Hair up.
9 Two-tone full-head colour and blow dry.
10 Regrowth tint with woven highlights.

APPOINTMENT TIMES

Most salons will have slightly varying appointment times and scheduling procedures. You must always check your salon policy before booking in any clients. However, most appointment systems have booking spaces for every 15-minute interval, such as 10.00, 10.15, 10.30 and so on.

Many salons will allow about 15 minutes for a consultation for technical services, and then the salon assistant will prepare or shampoo the client's hair ready for the service. These times might not be seen in the appointment book. Below is a timing guide for a variety of services.

Service	Time allocated
Wet cut	30 minutes
Cut and blow dry	45 minutes
Blow dry	30 minutes
Regrowth tint	30 minutes
Full-head colour	45 minutes
Full-head woven highlights	60–90 minutes
Half-head highlights	45 minutes
Perm	45 minutes

When booking appointments, not only must you know the abbreviations and the timings, but you must understand how long services take to develop. For example, if you booked Mrs Rossi for a full head of woven highlights followed by a cut and blow dry at 10.00 am on Wednesday with Melanie, the appointment might be recorded as:

Time	Melanie	
10.00	Mrs Rossi	
10.15	WHL	
10.30		
10.45		
11.00		
11.15		
11.30	Mrs Rossi	
11.45	CBD	
12.00		
12.15		

From this example, Melanie would be free to take another service at 12.15, but what the receptionist has not thought of is the development time of the colour and the colour removal process. As a guide, if we say that Mrs Rossi's woven highlights would take 60 minutes to be developed and removed, Melanie could complete another service (Linda for a long haircut and blow dry and straightening) in this 60-minute gap.

The appointment page should look like this:

Time	Melanie	
10.00	Mrs Rossi	
10.15	WHL	
10.30		
10.45		
11.00		
11.15		
11.30	Linda	
11.45	L/hair CBD	
12.00	straighten	
12.15		
12.30	Mrs Rossi	
12.45	CBD	
1.00		
1.15		

Melanie would now be free for her next service at 1.15, or she might be scheduled for a lunch break.

If, after Melanie's 1-hour lunch break, she has Siobhan in for a cut, followed by a long-hair perm service and a diffuser dry, the appointment book would now look like this:

Time	Melanie	
10.00	Mrs Rossi	
10.15	WHL	
10.30		
10.45		
11.00		
11.15		
11.30	Linda	
11.45	L/hair CBD	
12.00	straighten	
12.15		

12.30	Mrs Rossi	
12.45	CBD	
1.00		
1.15		
1.30	**Melanie**	
1.45	**LUNCH**	
2.00		
2.15	Siobhan	
2.30	C & P/W	
2.45	Long hair	
3.00		

3.15		
3.30	Aimee	
3.45	CBD	
4.00		
4.15	Siobhan	
4.30	Diff-dry	
4.45		

SmartScreen 216 worksheets 3, 4 and 5

As you can see, this would allow Melanie to complete Aimee's cut-and-blow-dry service while Siobhan's perm was being developed and neutralised, and Melanie would now be available for the next service at 4.45 pm. It is extremely important that you book the services accurately, as incorrect timings can mean that:

- services do not run to time
- clients might be irritated by the inconvenience, which might lead to client losses
- the stylist's time is not used effectively, which can lead to a loss of revenue for the salon and the stylist.

ACTIVITY

Practise booking some appointments. Using the time guides above, book in the following clients with stylists Nathan and Donna:

Nathan works 10.00 am until 7.00 pm and his lunch break is usually 1.30–2.30 pm. His clients for the day are:

- Angela, who would like a half head of highlights and a cut and blow dry at 4.00 pm
- Nina, who would like a cut and blow dry at 10.30 am
- Chelsea, who would like a regrowth tint and blow dry and straighten in her lunch break, and can be flexible with the times from 12.30–2.30 pm
- Kristian, who would like a wet cut in the morning
- Abagebe, who would like a restyle any time after 3.00 pm
- Scott, who would like a wet cut after work, from 5.30 pm onwards.

Donna works from 8.30 am until 5.30 pm and her lunch break is around 1 pm for an hour. Her clients for the day are:

- Louise, who would like a cut and blow dry after she has collected the children from school, from 3.30 pm onwards
- Gemma, who would like a full head of woven highlights and a cut and blow dry at 11.00 am
- Parneet, who would like a cut and blow dry late morning
- Sue, who would like a perm and a trim and blow dry, any time from midday onwards
- Becky, who would like a restyle as early as possible in the morning and must be finished by 11.00 am to go to work.

When you have booked a client appointment, you should ensure that you have entered their name correctly and have taken a contact number. You must then complete an appointment card for the client, clearly stating the date and time. You must always confirm the stylist's name, the service that has been booked and the approximate cost of the service. The appointment card must show the salon name and contact details in case the client needs to change their appointment.

For telephone bookings, try to answer the phone promptly, use a pleasant and friendly tone of voice and speak clearly. Smile while you talk on the phone and you will have a happier sounding voice. As you answer, state the salon name, as per your salon policy, and say something along the lines of: 'Good morning/afternoon, Grateful Heads salon, Usman speaking. How can I help you?'

Face-to-face enquiry

Always smile on the phone – you sound happier

The impression the client gets from the receptionist is very important, so make it a positive one!

You would book the service in exactly the same way as a face-to-face booking, but as you cannot see the client's hair length you might need to ask a few extra questions to allow sufficient time for the stylist. Some salons send text message reminders to their clients instead of an appointment card, so always ensure their contact details are up to date. You must verbally confirm the booking details with the client prior to completing the call.

 SmartScreen 216 handout 8

Some salons receive booking enquiries via email or text message. You must always send a reply to the client, confirming the details in the same way you would face to face or on the telephone. If the client's request cannot be met, then a further few emails/text messages might be required to offer alternative times and confirm the appointment. You might need to contact them by telephone to clarify any complications.

HANDY HINTS

When you send electronic responses, always check your spelling and punctuation are correct and the message reads well, before you press the send button.

Email appointments

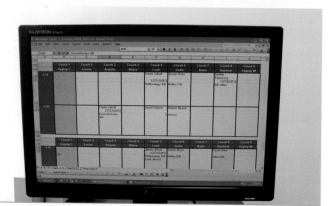

Computer appointment booking system

FOLLOW LEGISLATION

When selling retail products, you must follow your salon's procedures and the legal requirements. Always follow:

- **The Sale of Goods Act** – goods must be as described and of satisfactory quality.
- **The Consumer Protection Act** – goods must comply with certain safety standards and clients can sue for damages if they do not.
- **The Prices Act** – the prices of products must be displayed and clients must be given accurate information.
- **The Trade Descriptions Act** – the description of any goods must be accurate and not misleading.

CONFIDENTIALITY

As the receptionist, you will need to take client contact details when making appointments or recording messages. Make sure you write down the contact details accurately and read back the telephone number to the client to double check. Never leave client contact details lying around for unauthorised people to see. Always keep these details confidential and secure.

Part of your role could mean that you access client service records and prepare record cards for the stylists. Salon staff must comply with the Data Protection Act (DPA), and if staff or client information is kept on a computer, your salon manager must register the salon with the Data Protection Registry.

The other rules of the DPA state that all records must:

- be kept up to date
- hold accurate information
- be kept in a secure location
- be used only for professional purposes which relate to salon services
- not be shared with unauthorised personnel or a third party
- be kept only for as long as the client remains a client
- be disposed of securely, such as by shredding
- be available for clients to see if they wish.

 SmartScreen 216 handouts 3 and 9, wordsearches 3 and 4, revision cards and sample questions

DEAL WITH PAYMENTS

During this part of the unit you will learn how to:

- handle salon payments.

HANDLING SALON PAYMENTS

It is very important that as the receptionist, you are competent at accurately totalling the client's bill at the end of the service. Incorrectly itemised bills can lead to discomfort and embarrassment to you and the client.

Clients will be unhappy if they are overcharged, and the salon will lose money for any uncharged items.

CALCULATING COSTS

You must be knowledgeable on the pricing structure for the salon services and retail products. Services and retail products are subject to value added tax (VAT), and prices should be displayed inclusive of VAT. If the prices shown exclude VAT, you will need to be able to calculate this with a calculator or electronic till. VAT is currently charged at 20% in addition to the basic cost. If the Government changes the VAT amount, you, as the receptionist, would need to be able to revise the prices to reflect this.

The majority of salons have a pricing structure that varies between stylists, depending on their experience. It would not be unusual to see a price list that varies by 30% or more for a director or artistic designer, compared with a newly qualified stylist. There might be occasions when you have to calculate a varied bill. For example, a colour service by a stylist and a cut and blow dry by a director. If you are then adding a retail product to the bill, you can see that it can start to get complicated.

ACTIVITY

Using the price list below, which includes VAT, calculate the following costs, including retail products.

Service	Stylist – Andy	Director – Melanie
Cut and blow dry	£25.00	£42.50
Woven highlights	£75.00	£99.00
Regrowth colour	£38.00	£45.00
Blow dry	£17.50	£25.00

- Chris had a set of woven highlights with Andy and a cut and blow dry with Melanie.
- Elaine had a regrowth colour with Melanie and a blow dry with Andy.
- Jill had a set of woven highlights and a cut and blow dry with Melanie.
- Jean had a regrowth colour and cut and blow dry with Andy.

Three of your clients bought retail products. Using the retail price list below, add the retail costs to their service bills.

Product	Cost
Volumising shampoo	£7.99
Smoothing conditioner	£7.49
Colour stay shampoo	£7.49
Colour stay conditioner	£6.99
Funk sticks	£5.49
Funk paste	£5.99
Funk gel	£4.99
Naturally Moved mousse	£7.49
Naturally Moved root lift enhancer	£6.99
Naturally Moved hairspray	£7.99
Flat-iron heat protector spray	£8.99
Heat protector oil	£7.99

- Elaine purchased funk paste.
- Jill purchased colour stay shampoo and conditioner.
- Jean purchased Naturally Moved root lift enhancer, flat-iron heat protector spray and Naturally Moved hairspray.

Although working through these tasks and calculating the bills with a calculator is good practice, it is likely that your salon will have an automated computer system that works out the cost for you. To calculate a client's bill you could use:

- a calculator
- a pricing scanner
- a till
- an electronic point of sale device
- a pen and paper.

Informing the clients of costs

When you are confirming the total bill to your client, you should do so politely and courteously. Explain the service cost first, then any retail products, and then give them the overall cost. This will give your client the opportunity to cancel the retail products if the costs are higher than expected. However, with clearly displayed retail product prices and by previously informing clients of the likely charge for the service, you should be able to avoid any embarrassment or surprises regarding the bill.

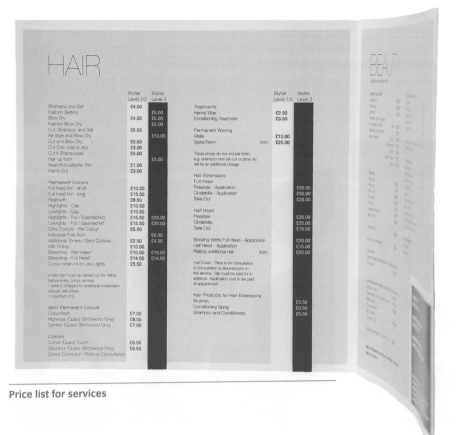

Price list for services

Price list for products

TYPES OF PAYMENT

When you have calculated the cost of the services and any retail goods to be purchased, you will need to establish your client's preferred method of payment and record the sales correctly, following your salon policy.

Payment by cash

If your client chooses to pay with cash, check all notes and coins to verify they are not forged or defaced in any way. There are several ways in which you can check that the notes and coins are genuine:

- The type of paper – does it feel 'normal'?
- Distinct markings on the notes – is the watermark visible? Is the colour accurate? Is the silver strip present throughout the note?
- Is the note still in circulation? Notes are updated and there is a period of time where old notes can be used but, after this period, these notes are no longer **legal tender**.
- The weight of a coin – is it heavy enough?
- The markings on the coins – are the correct markings present?

If you are happy that the cash is acceptable, take your client's money and count it, but do not place it in the till until your client has received their change: leave it in sight of both you and the client. Cash payment

Legal tender
Money that is legal in a given country

WHY DON'T YOU...
Visit **www.bankofengland.co.uk/ banknotes/current** for more information about banknotes.

discrepancies are easier to solve if the money has not been placed in the till, and you can confirm exactly how much money the client gave you.

If you think you have been given a forged note, check the note with your salon manager and inform the client. Politely ask them for an alternative method of payment. Always follow your salon policy and ensure you know what to do if you encounter unacceptable cash or non-legal tender.

When you have calculated the required change, count this out as you hand it to your client, so that you both agree that you have given the right change. Ask your client to check the change and then issue a receipt.

Client buying retail products

Client paying cash

Cash at the till

Payment by voucher

Your client might wish to pay with a cash equivalent. These might be:

- gift vouchers
- discount vouchers
- special offer promotions – 'three for two' or 'buy one get one free'
- introductory offers
- loyalty card points
- travellers' cheques.

Cash equivalents are used instead of cash payments, but work in the same way. Some salons might give cash or vouchers as change if the total bill does not match the gift voucher's value, but you must check this against your salon policy. Salons rarely give cash as change when accepting discount offers or loyalty points as payments.

Clients might need to add payment to a voucher to cover the outstanding bill. Be careful to calculate this correctly, making sure that the client is not over- or under-charged, and that the till is balanced at the end of the day.

When taking these types of payment, you must record what the value is, the bill total and check that the voucher is in date and valid. Often, the receptionist signs the vouchers to state they have been used. They should be dated and recorded on the takings sheet, for cashing up purposes and till balancing. Vouchers are often numbered and this should also be checked off against the salon records.

Payment by cheque

Cheque payments are becoming less popular and are gradually being phased out as a payment option. Previously, cheques were guaranteed with a 'cheque guarantee card', which meant the banks honoured the payment to the retailer, even if the account holder had insufficient funds in their account. Since the **demise** of cheque guarantee cards, many salons will no longer accept cheques as a method of payment.

If your salon still accepts cheques from regular clients, you must carry out several checks to ensure that they are completed accurately. Incorrectly completed cheques will cost the salon money as the bank will not cash them.

When you inform the client of the total bill, your client will need to complete the front of the cheque with the following information:

- the salon/business name
- the amount in words
- the amount in figures
- the date
- their signature.

When you have carried out all of these checks, place the cheque in the till and update the salon takings sheet.

HANDY HINTS

If your salon accepts travellers' cheques, these must be treated differently to all other cash equivalents. Travellers' cheques must be signed in front of you and a passport or photo ID must be produced as identification. Always check that the signature on the identification matches the signature you witness.

HANDY HINTS

You might need to obtain authorisation from the relevant person when accepting non-cash payments at reception.

Demise
Termination or end

Paying by voucher

Cheque payment

Payment by card

Cards have become very popular and are an easy payment method for clients to use. However, credit cards are costly to the salon and not all salons accept card payments.

If your salon takes card payments and this is your client's chosen payment method, then you need to identify whether your client is using a debit or credit card.

With debit cards the payment is taken immediately from the client's bank account and issued to the salon's bank account when the payment system is processed at the end of the day. Credit card companies request payment from the client on a monthly basis, but pay the salon when the payment system is processed at the end of the day. Therefore banks often charge salons for this service. Your salon will have a floor/salon limit, which states the amount of money the salon can take in one transaction. To accept payments above this, your salon will require authorisation from the card company. You will need to know what the salon's limits are before you process any credit card payments.

The procedure for paying with a debit or credit card is the same, and you will use a chip and PIN machine called a merchant machine, or a card reader or a chip and PIN terminal.

When you have agreed the cost with the client:

1 Key in the amount and press 'enter'.

2 Hand the merchant terminal to the client to insert their card.

3 Ask the client to check the amount, then type in their PIN and press 'enter'.

4 When the card has been authorised, ask the client to remove their card.

5 Issue the client with the customer copy of the receipt and place the salon/merchant copy in the till.

SmartScreen 216 handout 10

Debit card

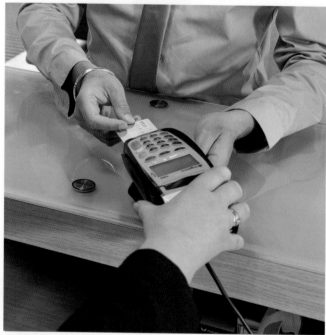

Pin machine/terminal

Paying by card

PAYMENT DISCREPANCIES AND DISPUTES

As the receptionist, it might be part of your role to identify and resolve payment discrepancies or disputes, and you must do so within the limits of your own authority. Any payment discrepancies or disputes that are outside your authority must be referred to the relevant person. Payment disputes could be disagreements over the total bill, over- or under-charges, insufficient funds, suspect tender or invalid payments.

Invalid currency

Invalid currencies could be notes that have expired, those with incorrect markings or even foreign currency. Some salons in the UK accept Euros, particularly those in tourist areas. Check your salon policy about receiving payment in Euros.

Invalid cards

Invalid cards might be unsigned, out of date, look or feel counterfeit, have an unclear hologram, the cardholder's name might not match the client's name, or a warning might appear on your card machine.

Incorrect completion of cheques

Cheques that have been incorrectly completed might have the incorrect amount in figures or words, an incorrect date or an incorrect signature.

An unsigned card is an invalid card

Suspected fraud

Suspected fraud does not mean you are accusing your client of fraud, it might simply be that the card is declined by the merchant terminal, the card cannot be authorised or the card company suspects fraudulent spending on the card. If you suspect fraud is taking place, excuse yourself from your client, take the card with you and inform your salon manager.

If the merchant terminal informs you that the card is stolen or counterfeit, you must follow the step-by-step instructions on the merchant terminal. This might tell you that you must retain the card and, in some cases, call the police.

For all of the above, you would need to inform the client tactfully that their payment has been declined or cannot be accepted and ask for an alternative payment method. If the client does not have an alternative payment method, then ask your salon manager what you should do.

WHY DON'T YOU...
Ask your salon manager how you should deal with the following discrepancies:
- invalid currency
- invalid card
- incorrect completion of cheque
- suspected fraud.

SmartScreen 216 wordsearch 2

HANDY HINTS

Always try to solve payment discrepancies or disputes as simply and discreetly as possible, to avoid embarrassment to clients and staff, to avoid loss of profit and to ensure that the till balances at the end of the day.

Turn to page 485 for the answers.

1 Which **one** of the following identifies types of stationery required at a salon reception?

   a Pens, appointment cards, paper and stock sheets.

   b Paper, price lists, appointment cards and message pads.

   c Staff rotas, stock sheets and receipts from the wholesaler.

   d Receipts, message pads and details of stylists' commissions.

2 Which **one** of the following is the **best** way to maintain security at reception?

   a Keeping the till key under reception.

   b Keeping the daily takings in a locked till overnight.

   c Ensuring that staff only leave the reception area at lunch times.

   d Ensuring that retail displays are locked and away from the door.

3 Which **one** of the following is considered 'best practice' for a receptionist?

   a Immediately greeting the client with a smile and dealing with their enquiry.

   b Waiting until the phone conversation has finished before taking their coat.

   c Maintaining eye contact throughout the transaction.

   d Only using open questions when communicating.

4 **Statement 1:**
When you are taking a message, ensure that the recipient is present so it can be handed over straight away.

Statement 2:
Name, date, time and a brief description should all be recorded on a message.

Which **one** of the following is correct for the above statements?

	Statement 1	Statement 2
a	True	True
b	True	False
c	False	True
d	False	False

5 Which **one** of the following correctly identifies the abbreviations used in a hairdressing appointment system?

   a S/S, W/T, FHY.

   b CBB, W/C, DSW.

   c W/C, CBD, S/S.

   d CBD, TFL, W/C.

6 Which **one** of the following is the typical time allocated to complete a full head of woven highlights?

   a 10–30 minutes.

   b 30–40 minutes.

   c 50–60 minutes.

   d 60–90 minutes.

7 **Statement 1:**
Smiling on the phone is important, as the voice sounds happier.

Statement 2:
When you are sending appointments via text, it is very important to spell correctly and use punctuation.

Which **one** of the following is correct for the above statements?

	Statement 1	Statement 2
a	True	True
b	True	False
c	False	True
d	False	False

8 Which **one** of the following is required under the Data Protection Act?

a All client details should be shredded after 1 year.

b All client details should be kept securely.

c Clients might not see any notes kept by the salon.

d Clients are allowed to ask for details of staff.

9 **Statement 1:**
With debit cards the payment is taken immediately from the client's bank account.

Statement 2:
Clients using a credit card will be billed at the end of the month by the credit card company.

Which **one** of the following is correct for the above statements?

	Statement 1	Statement 2
a	True	True
b	True	False
c	False	True
d	False	False

I trained as a hairdresser with Richard Ward in the mid-1980s, working my way up to senior stylist level. After a few years, I had a change in direction by heading to university to gain a 2:1 degree in Sociology with Applied Women's Studies. My love of the industry led to me eventually returning to work at the salon on reception in the late 1990s. I discovered my talents as a 'people person' – this led to the creation of a new role, and an industry first – as 'Maître D' of the Richard Ward salon.

I love the reception – it gives the crucial first and last impression. I can make someone's day by remembering the smallest detail, I can get a client fitted in when at first it seems impossible. There is no right or wrong way to run your desk – just be sincere, honest and never contrived. Answer the phone with a smile: the client will hear it. Do not sound rushed, especially at busy times. Never say no! Appointments must flow. Take ownership of appointment times – what we sell is people's time. Most importantly, just love what you do. A professional, well-run desk will equate to a professional well-run salon: excellent service is key.

201 Working in the hair industry

1 a and d, **2** b, **3** b, **4** c, **5** a, **6** a, **7** d, **8** d

202 Follow health and safety practice in the salon

1 b, **2** d, **3** c, **4** c, **5** a, **6** d, **7** a, **8** a

203 Client consultation for hair services

1 a, **2** a, **3** d, **4** d, **5** c, **6** b, **7** a, **8** a

204 Shampoo and condition the hair and scalp

1 a, **2** b, **3** a, **4** a, **5** d, **6** a, **7** b, **8** c

205 Promote products and services to clients in the salon

1 a, **2** a, **3** d, **4** d, **5** b, **6** c, **7** c, **8** d

206 Cut women's hair

1 b, **2** d, **3** b, **4** a, **5** d, **6** c, **7** a, **8** b

207 Colour and lighten hair

1 a, **2** a, **3** b, **4** c, **5** a, **6** a, **7** b

208 Perm and neutralise hair

1 a, **2** a, **3** a, **4** d, **5** b, **6** b, **7** c, **8** a

209 The art of dressing hair

1 a, **2** b, **3** a, **4** a, **5** a, **6** d, **7** b, **8** a

210 Cut men's hair

1 b, **2** b, **3** a, **4** d, **5** c, **6** b, **7** b, **8** a

211 Cut facial hair

1 a, **2** a, **3** d, **4** b, **5** c, **6** a, **7** b, **8** a

212 Create an image based on a theme within the hair and beauty sector

1 a, **2** c, **3** c, **4** b, **5** d, **6** a, **7** a, **8** a

213 Display stock to promote sales in the salon

1 d, **2** c, **3** a, **4** b, **5** b, **6** a, **7** b, **8** d

215 Provide scalp massage services

1 d, **2** b, **3** a, **4** c, **5** a, **6** c, **7** a, **8** c

216 Salon reception duties

1 b, **2** d, **3** a, **4** c, **5** c, **6** d, **7** a, **8** b, **9** a

INDEX

A

abroad, working 15
abscesses 369
accelerators 114, 237, 301
accident books 56, 57, 142, 327
accidents, reporting and recording 42, 56–7
acid perms 233
acne 73
activators 277
advertising
    and image creation 386–7
    and product displays 422
African-type hair 11, 83, 85
aftercare advice
    colouring and lightening hair 223–4
    cutting facial hair 380–1
    cutting men's hair 356–7
    cutting women's hair 168–9
    dressing hair 320–1
    perming and neutralising hair 262–3
    scalp massage 454
    shampoo and conditioning 114–16
age
    and cutting men's hair 335
Age Discrimination Act 28
alkaline perms 233–4
allergies 70
    remedial action for 46, 174
    to colouring products 195
    to perming products 243
alopecia 72
alpha keratin 273, 274
ammonia 185, 211
anagen 85
angles, cutting
    men's hair 345–7
    women's hair 157–8
anti-frizz lotion 277
anti-oxidant conditioners 188–9, 214
appearance see personal presentation
appointment cards 473
appointments 468–74
    by email/texts 474
    electronic booking systems 469
    scheduling 468–70
    telephone bookings 473–4
    times 470–4
    written appointment systems 469
aprons 20, 40, 46, 94, 174, 235
armed forces 15
arrector pili muscle 81, 82, 443
Asian hair 83, 85
asthma 46, 174, 176
autoclaves 21, 51, 52, 53

B

back-brushing 316
back-combing 316
baldness 72
    and cutting men's hair 334
band protectors 236
barber's itch (sycosis barbea) 369, 380
Barbicide 21, 51, 52
barrel curls 312, 313
barrier cream 236
beards see cutting facial hair
beehive 317
behaviour 144, 177, 270, 330, 365
bendy rods 237, 312
beta keratin 273, 274
bleach gel/creams 184
bleach powders 184, 189
blood, composition of 446
blot drying 251
blow drying 294–300
    airflow 294
    angles 295
    and brushes 294
    finger drying 299
    one length, above shoulders 297
    one length, below shoulders 296
    sectioning the hair 294
    short, layered hair 298
    and tension 294
blow-dry lotion 277
blunt cutting 153, 340
body language 62–3, 98–9
    positive and negative signals 125
body positioning
    colouring hair 175–6
    cutting facial hair 362–3
    cutting hair 143–4, 329
    dressing hair 268
    shampoo and conditioning 94
body shape
    and dressing hair 291
boils 74, 369
bones, in the head and neck 444
bouffant style 317
Brazilian Blow-dries 3
brick winding 257, 306, 308
bridal/prom styles 9, 316–18
brushes
    and blow drying 294
    denman 281
    dressing-out 281
    radial 281–2
    washing and sterilising of 52, 53
bullying, in the workplace 29
buying signals 133

C

Caceres, Daniel 457
Cameron, Patrick 324
cap highlights 217
card payments 480
cards, invalid 481
career paths 11–12
career patterns 14–16
    armed forces 15
    cruise-liners 15
    fashion, media or photography 14
    freelance hairdresser 14
    hospitals and clinics 15
    hotel and healthclub salons 15
    manufacturer technicians/
        demonstrators 16
    owning your own salon 14
    training and assessing 16
    transferring to other sectors 18
    tv, film and theatre work 14
    working abroad 15
cash payments 477–8
catagen 85
chemical spray 51, 52
chemical wipes 51, 52
chemicals 45
    safety and disposal considerations
        20–1, 41, 53, 176, 229
chemotherapy 15, 440
cheques 136, 479
    incorrect completion of 481
chignons 283, 316–17
children, communicating with 62
chin curtains 374
chin puff 374
chlorine 223
City & Guilds 8–9
clay 356
client arrivals 465
client enquiries
    attending to in reception area 465–6
client record cards 65, 69, 78, 79
    colouring and lightening hair 178
    perming and neutralising hair 231
    scalp massage 435
client requirements 77
    colouring hair 191
    cutting facial hair 367
    dressing hair 286
    identifying of in reception area 463
    perming and neutralising hair 239
climazone 114, 176, 250
clipper grade attachments 372, 373
clipper grades 341–3
clipper over comb 343, 373